THE CLIMATES
OF THE CONTINENTS

THE CLIMATES
OF THE CONTINENTS

By
W. G. KENDREW, M.A.

Third Edition

OXFORD
AT THE CLARENDON PRESS
1937

OXFORD UNIVERSITY PRESS
AMEN HOUSE, E.C. 4
LONDON EDINBURGH GLASGOW NEW YORK
TORONTO MELBOURNE CAPETOWN BOMBAY
CALCUTTA MADRAS
HUMPHREY MILFORD
PUBLISHER TO THE UNIVERSITY

First published 1922
Second edition 1927
Reprinted 1930
Third edition 1937

PRINTED IN GREAT BRITAIN

PREFACE TO THE THIRD EDITION

'THIS book aims at filling a gap in the sources available for the study of the Earth. For some time there has been no lack of treatises on meteorology; excellent works exist also on the general principles of climatology, describing the features of the main types of climate; but there is no adequate description of the actual climates of the countries of the Earth, considered regionally, available in English. It is necessary to refer to foreign sources, most of them German, for more information than the short sketches contained in general works.' (*From Preface to the first edition,* 1922.)

Though in the fourteen years which have elapsed more than one effort has been made to fill the gap referred to, a new edition of this work is now called for. Revision was certainly desirable in view of the great spread of interest in climatology since the Great War, largely as a result of the advance of aviation. New meteorological stations have been established, and many old ones have now collected long enough series of records to provide an adequate picture of their climatic conditions.

In this edition all statistics have been revised, and very many of them replaced by new ones based on longer or more reliable observations, though in some cases the latest means differ so little from the old that change seemed unnecessary. Many records from new stations have been incorporated. In nearly all cases the means now given may be relied on as approximately accurate.

In the text of the book no very serious alterations have been made for most of the world, though every page has been altered to some extent to secure greater accuracy or improved presentation, and most of the maps and diagrams have been redrawn. But some chapters have been almost entirely rewritten, where the previous edition necessarily depended on inadequate data, and new material is now available. Most of these large alterations concern parts of Africa and South America.

The many shortcomings of mere statements of the mean values of the notoriously variable atmospheric elements, which are the basis of such a work as this, are by none more clearly recognized than by those who deal constantly with such statistics. But in spite of many attempts to devise improved and more elaborate systems of presentation, none which is at once theoretically satisfying and practically convenient seems yet to have appeared.

I have pleasure in repeating the following words from the preface to the first edition:

'The fullest acknowledgement is tendered to the authors of the works, and to the persons responsible for the other sources, which are the foundation of this book. Without such sources a compilation of this kind would have been impossible; and it will be obvious to the reader that in many chapters little has been attempted beyond setting them out in a form suitable to the plan of the book.'

I am grateful to the Clarendon Press for allowing me such extensive revision that complete re-setting of the book was necessary, and to all its staff for the care and interest they have shown.   W. G. K.

OXFORD
December 1936.

CONTENTS

LIST OF ILLUSTRATIONS

PART I. INTRODUCTORY

PART II. AFRICA

PART III. ASIA

PART IV. EUROPE

PART V. NORTH AMERICA

PART I

INTRODUCTORY

CHAPTER I

ON CLIMATIC STATISTICS

THE most important of the elements which combine to form climate are temperature and rainfall. These have been more carefully and frequently observed than the other factors such as sunshine, cloudiness, and humidity, which are subsidiary though by no means unimportant. Hence it seems well to make some general remarks here concerning temperature and rainfall, to which such constant reference will be made in the following pages.

Temperature. The air temperature at any place is constantly changing, and it is clearly impossible to give a complete statement of such a varying element. In climatic descriptions it is usual to state the average temperature, and also to indicate, if possible, in some way how far the temperature from day to day may be expected to vary from that average. 'Average temperature' is an abstraction, and if it is to be of real significance the extremes of the individual figures from which it is derived must not be very far apart. Hence for most parts of the world the mean temperature for the year is the least satisfactory statement of that element; Peking and the Scilly Islands have almost the same mean annual temperature, while the monthly means range from 79° to 23° at Peking, from 61° to 43° at the Scilly Islands. In the neighbourhood of the Equator, it is true, the annual mean is a useful figure since the temperature varies little from month to month, but in general it is necessary to supplement it with the mean monthly temperatures. Means for a shorter period than a month would be still more valuable, but they entail overburdensome statistics.

The mean temperature for any day is in most cases taken to be the mean of the highest and lowest temperatures of that day, recorded in the shade under certain recognized conditions

B

to ensure uniformity of observation. The mean for a month is the mean of the daily means, and the mean for a year the mean of the twelve monthly means. True means are obtained arithmetically from the figures for the day, month, or year for a long period, if possible 35 years. By subtracting the mean temperatures of the warmest and coldest months we obtain the 'annual range', a most important element. At Peking the mean annual range is seen from the figures given above to be 56°, at the Scilly Islands 18°; in the neighbourhood of the Panama Canal it is only 1°. The 'mean diurnal range' for any period is the mean difference between the highest and lowest temperatures for each day in that period, usually a month being taken, for a series of years, and it also is a valuable figure. For example, London has a mean diurnal range of 20° in July, the mean daily maximum for that month being 74°, the mean daily minimum 54°; the Scilly Islands enjoy a more equable climate, having a mean diurnal range in July of only 9°. The limits within which the mean diurnal range varies in different parts of the earth are not so wide as those for the annual range. Both the diurnal and the annual range depend largely on the position of the station, on or near the sea or inland, and on the humidity of the atmosphere, the highest range being found in the heart of an arid desert far removed from sea-influence. The annual range is controlled very much by latitude also, since the seasonal change of insolation depends on the latitude.

It must be noted that the diurnal range is considerably greater than the annual range in many parts of the world, especially near the Equator. Thus at Bolobo (Congo) the mean diurnal range is 16°, the mean annual range only 2°. It may at first seem surprising that the range of temperature from day to night should exceed that for the year, which includes 365 days and nights, but in reality there is no inconsistency involved, since the annual range is calculated from the mean monthly temperatures, in which the daily extremes are combined so that they neutralize each other.

All the world over the mean temperature becomes less with increase of altitude, and the rate of decrease is approximately the same everywhere, about 1° for 300 feet of elevation. Fort William is 15° warmer on the average than Ben

Nevis, some 4,400 feet higher. Hence for some purposes of comparison it is possible and convenient to 'correct' the actual temperature to its 'sea-level value' by adding 1° for every 300 feet of elevation. In drawing isotherms these corrected temperatures are used, and where isotherms are referred to in this book they must be understood to be the usual sea-level isotherms. But with this exception temperatures mentioned are actual observed temperatures not corrected to sea-level, unless the contrary is stated.

A glance at any map of isotherms shows that the temperature varies greatly along any parallel of latitude. The mean temperature for the parallel may be obtained by taking the mean of the temperatures at a large number of points spaced evenly along it. The difference between this mean and the temperature at any place on the parallel is called the 'anomaly of temperature' for that place, a positive anomaly if the place is warmer than the mean, a negative anomaly if it is colder. 'Isanomalous lines' for any month or for the year are lines drawn through places with the same anomaly. The greatest temperature anomaly on the earth is over the north-east of the Atlantic Ocean in January, where a large area has a positive anomaly of more than 20°; the British Isles belong to this favoured region (Fig. 80, p. 236). Anomalies are calculated from temperatures which have been reduced to sea-level. They assist us in analysing the complex influences to which the temperature of any place is due. In calculating them we really eliminate the effect of latitude; the effect of altitude has already been eliminated, and thus the map of isanomalous lines presents a simpler picture, showing chiefly the influence of land and sea, ocean currents and prevailing winds.

Among temperature statistics it is useful to indicate the highest and lowest temperatures that normally occur in each month, or, to use the technical terms, the mean maximum and mean minimum for each month; and also the mean daily maximum and the mean daily minimum for each month, these being the means of the 30 daily maxima and the 30 daily minima recorded in the month for a series of years. These figures can only occasionally be given in this book owing to limitation of space. The extreme temperatures that have ever been recorded, called technically the 'absolute maximum' and 'absolute minimum', are also interesting and useful, provided that the records have been kept for a sufficiently long time. Short records are even less valuable in this connexion than for establishing average values. The longer the observations are continued the higher the absolute maximum and the lower the absolute minimum may be expected to prove themselves. Records of less than 35 years especially for periods of less than a year are not trustworthy, but in 35 years samples of the greatest heat and the greatest cold to which a place is liable will probably have been experienced. Unfortunately, in lieu of better, some figures are included in the following pages which depend on much shorter records. The length of the record is not stated, but the statistics given are believed to be the best available.

Rainfall. A mere statement of the mean amount of rainfall for the whole year at any place is not sufficient. It must be supplemented by some indication of the seasonal distribution, and the mean rainfall for each month ought to be given. The significance of the seasonal distribution is well known to the botanist and the zoologist, for it is a matter of fundamental importance to the plant world whether the rain falls during the warmest or the coldest season. Hence frequent reference will be made to this aspect of rainfall, since it is not only a feature of interest to the meteorologist, but an important factor in the life of plants and therefore of animals and men.

The seasonal distribution or 'régime' is independent of the total rainfall amount. Two stations may each have twice as much rain in summer as in winter, or in other words they may have the same régime, but the total annual rainfall at one may be many times greater than at the other. Or again, two stations may have the same mean annual rainfall, but the régimes may be different, one station having most of its rain in summer, the other, perhaps, having equal amounts in all seasons. In order to compare more conveniently the distribution of the rainfall over the year at stations with different annual totals, we may express the rainfall for each month or for each season as a percentage of the total for the year. The main rainfall régimes are the following:

(i) equatorial; two seasons of heaviest rain in the course of the year, at or about the time of the overhead sun; intervening months much less rainy but there is no pronounced dry season. It occurs only within a few degrees of latitude on each side of the Equator, e.g. at Yaundé, Kamerun, but by no means everywhere in that belt.

(ii) tropical, between the zone of (i) and the tropics of Cancer and Capricorn; most rain during the hottest months when the sun is highest; winter a pronounced dry season. We may subdivide into:

(a) with two maxima of monthly rainfall, found in some regions between the equatorial zone and the neighbourhood of lat. 15° N. and S., approximates to the equatorial régime, but the two maxima following the overhead sun are closer together, and there is a long dry season during winter, e.g. Mongalla (R. Nile).

(b) with a single maximum, on the poleward side of (a); the two maxima of (a) coalesce, and the dry season is longer, e.g. Khartoum.

(iii) monsoon, with a pronounced maximum in summer, and a long dry season, much like ii (b); occurs both inside and outside the tropics especially on the east coasts of continents, e.g. Peking.

(iv) Mediterranean; most rain in the winter six months, with either a single maximum in November or December or with two maxima in autumn and spring respectively; summer is almost, or quite, rainless, e.g. Athens.

(v) continental interiors of temperate latitudes have most rain in summer (late spring and early summer in the steppes) and winters much less rainy but not rainless; the periodicity is not so marked as in the monsoon and Mediterranean types.

(vi) west coasts of continents in temperate latitudes have abundant rain in all seasons, with the maximum in autumn or winter. Mountains cause a local modification of the rainfall régime as well as an increase in the amount of rain.

The nature of the rainfall is an important element. The rain may be of the thunderstorm type, falling in heavy showers during the hottest part of the day; or cyclonic, falling irrespective of the time of day, less heavy but often lasting longer than thunderstorm rain; most of the rain of the British Isles is cyclonic. Or again the precipitation may be mainly drizzle, or even dew. Snow, too, is included in rainfall statistics unless specially excepted, a foot of snow being considered equivalent to an inch of rain. It is useful to know the average number of days on which there is appreciable precipitation, that is to say 0·01 inch or 0·1 mm. according to the usage of most meteorological services. It must be remembered that the months are of unequal length, and therefore their rainfall totals are not directly comparable as an exact expression of the monthly distribution.

In this book nearly all the statistics are means, a necessary result of the limitation of space. The abnormal weather conditions however are very important, for the possibility of an abnormally long or severe frost, or of a prolonged drought in a region which is usually well watered, is the final consideration which may override for the practical affairs of life the value of the mean conditions. Moreover, there are innumerable very local differences of climate depending on such topographical features as slope and exposure, mountain shadow or shelter, basin or summit, the nature of the soil and its plant cover if any; though these effects are in a sense minor they may be the dominant factor, for example at health resorts. This book aims at indicating the main features of the climates described but in only a few cases attempts to refer to the local modifications.

The convention is adhered to, in most cases, of expressing temperatures to 0·1° F. and rainfalls to 0·1 inch. Such refinement suggests an accuracy which is not present in view of the variation in the types of instruments used at meteorological stations and their exposure, and in the skill and care of observers; moreover, the actual means for different series of the same number of years at the same station are not exactly the same, even though the series may cover more than 30 years.

CHAPTER II

PRESSURE AND WIND SYSTEMS

IT is not intended to give an introductory account of the distribution of the climatic elements over the globe as a whole as such an account may be found elsewhere, and this book attempts rather to describe the climates of individual countries. But it may be useful to sketch here the main features of the distribution of atmospheric pressure and the prevailing winds. Generally speaking pressure is not an element of climate, for its fluctuations, even in regions where they are greatest, are not perceptible to us except with the help of delicate instruments. It is only where the pressure is reduced to two-thirds or a half of the normal at sea-level that we can consider it an element of climate, as for instance on high mountains where a direct physiological effect is produced, the rarefaction of the air causing mountain sickness. But indirectly pressure, as controlling the wind systems, may be truly said to be a fundamental element in climate everywhere, for climate probably depends more on the prevailing winds than on any other single factor.

Fig. 1 shows the distribution of atmospheric pressure and the resulting wind systems which would probably exist on a planet in other respects like the Earth, but having a homogeneous surface, all land or all water.

But the surface of the Earth is far from homogeneous. The arrangement of land and water causes irregularities in the distribution of temperature, and these in turn produce pressure irregularities. Allowance must be made, moreover, in dealing with the actual Earth for the changing temperature differences between continents and oceans from season to season. On a homogeneous Earth the only important effect of the seasonal changes would be a swing of the whole system of belts of temperature, pressure, and winds. But the conditions on the Earth are much more complicated.

Fig. 2, based on Hettner (*Die Klimate der Erde*), shows in diagrammatic form the distribution actually found. The land masses are represented by a triangle with its base in the northern and its apex in the southern hemisphere, to suggest the main land masses of the Earth. In the first diagram it is summer in the northern hemisphere and the pressure belts have swung north. The land masses in the summer hemisphere have heated rapidly and low pressures tend to spread and deepen over them. The low-pressure systems so formed are extensions of the equatorial low pressures, and they break

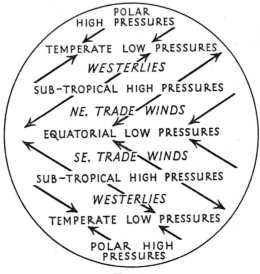

POLAR HIGH PRESSURES
TEMPERATE LOW PRESSURES
WESTERLIES
SUB-TROPICAL HIGH PRESSURES
NE. TRADE WINDS
EQUATORIAL LOW PRESSURES
SE. TRADE WINDS
SUB-TROPICAL HIGH PRESSURES
WESTERLIES
TEMPERATE LOW PRESSURES
POLAR HIGH PRESSURES

FIG. 1.

the continuity of the subtropical high pressures. The air which is thrown off from the heated continents finds a place partly in the winter hemisphere and partly over the relatively cool oceans of the summer hemisphere. The subtropical high pressures of the summer hemisphere are represented by detached anticyclones over the oceans, where pressure is higher in summer than in winter, and the low pressures of temperate latitudes coalesce with the continental low pressures. In the southern hemisphere the land is cool but its area is small, and there is no very great disturbance of the planetary belts.

The planetary winds are of course profoundly modified, in parts almost beyond recognition, by these modifications in the distribution of pressure. The south-east trades are drawn across the Equator into the northern hemisphere, and coming under the influence of right-handed rotational deflection may appear as south-west winds, generally light in force, which will be referred to in later chapters as 'deflected trades'. But on the east coast of the continent the winds that start as south-east trades are drawn far into the northern hemisphere as the summer monsoon, a most important current. This monsoon is a reversal of the trade winds which formed a belt round the whole of the homogeneous globe. In reality in

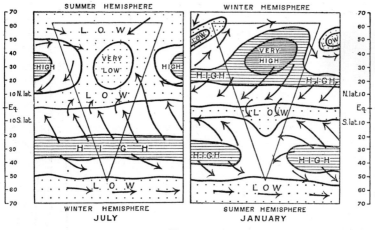

FIG. 2.

summer the trades blow only in the eastern and central parts of the oceans in their appropriate latitudes. They are the winds on the east and south sides of the subtropical anti-cyclones over the oceans, and blow from the north on the east side of the centre of high pressure, from the north-east on the south-east, and from the east on the south of this centre. Over the ocean north of the subtropical anticyclones the wind is westerly in summer as in winter, but it is lighter in force in summer. It is drawn in somewhat towards the continent and becomes in places north-west. Along the north coast of the continent the wind is north-east.

In January (second diagram of Fig. 2) the land in the northern hemisphere is very much colder than the sea, and the subtropical high pressures are greatly intensified over it. Indeed the most prominent features of the isobars of the earth for January are the great anticyclones over Asia and North America. The oceans have relatively low pressures, but the subtropical high-pressure belts can be clearly traced, though they are much less pronounced than in July. The temperate low pressures are deepened, forming the so-called 'permanent cyclones' over the northern parts of the oceans, vast depressions representing the temperate low-pressure belt which is interrupted in winter by the continents, where high pressures extend far north. The continental anticyclone affects the winds profoundly. The winter monsoon blows out from it on the east coast and continues across the Equator, blowing from the north-west at first, becoming north, then north-east, and finally, after crossing the Equator, north-west; generically it is a modified and strengthened trade wind, and thus the trade winds extend in a belt right round the globe in the winter hemisphere. The stormy westerlies sweep with great violence over the northern oceans; their direction is variable from day to day, under the control of the numerous depressions which travel generally from west to east, but the resultant air movement is from the west and south-west on the equatorial side of the most frequented cyclone tracks. On the north coast of the continent the wind is west, and thus the westerlies form a continuous belt round the globe in winter but are thrust poleward by the continental anticyclones, so that in temperate latitudes the wind is south-west on the west side of the continent, west on the north, and north-west on the east, the interior being a region of comparatively calm air.

The land mass in the southern hemisphere is hotter than the sea in January and the equatorial belt of low pressures spreads south, not so much, however, as was the case in July in the northern hemisphere, since the land area is smaller. The north-east trade is drawn south over the Equator and becomes a north-west wind. The south-east trade is deflected towards the heated land and becomes an east wind, in places north-east, so that the trade winds are interrupted as in the northern hemisphere in July, though to a less extent.

The terms 'winter', 'spring', 'summer', and 'autumn' denote particularly the seasons of temperate latitudes, but it is convenient to use them also for low latitudes in an astronomical sense, referring to the position of the sun in relation to the hemisphere concerned.

PART II

AFRICA

CHAPTER III

GENERAL FEATURES

AFRICA, alone of the continents, extends to almost equal distances north and south of the Equator. The southern part projects far into the ocean remote from other land masses, but in the north-east Africa joins Asia, and the climate of a large portion of Africa is controlled to a great extent from Asia. Yet in spite of this external control the same series of climates can be traced northward from the equatorial belt of heat and moisture to the shores of the Mediterranean Sea, and southward to the Cape of Good Hope. The Sudan has its counterpart in Rhodesia, the Sahara in the arid tracts of the Kalahari and South-west Africa, the Mediterranean coast in the district round Cape Town.

The continent lacks extensive mountain ranges such as are effective elsewhere as climate barriers. Gradual transitions take the place of the sudden changes of climate to which the Andes, for example, give rise. Africa, however, has vast areas of plateau, especially in the south and east where much of the surface is more than 3,000 feet above the sea, and here the climate is dry and invigorating, and well suited for European settlement even in latitudes which are usually very unhealthy near sea-level.

Oceanic conditions. The west coast of North Africa is washed by the Canaries current. This is a cool current, partly owing to the direction of its flow from north to south to feed the north equatorial current, partly owing to the upwelling of cool water along the coast under the influence of prevailing offshore winds; the surface of the sea at Mogador has been observed to be at 60° F., while 20 miles from shore the surface temperature was 70°. The effects of the Canaries current can be distinctly recognized from the Strait of Gibraltar as far south as 12° N. lat. in February and 17° N. lat. in August in the low temperatures, frequent fogs and scant rainfall of the coast. The conditions on the coast and in the interior are very

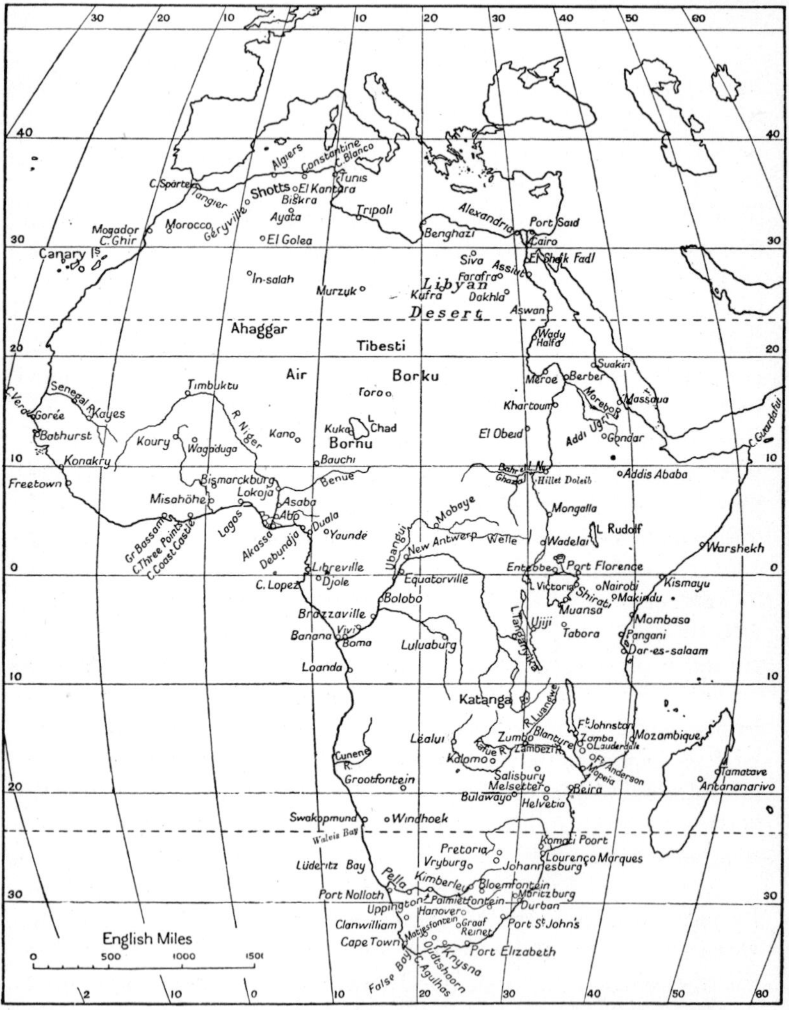

FIG. 3. Africa. Key map, showing the position of places mentioned in the text. For East Africa see Fig. 19.

different, especially in summer, for in August the mean temperature of the sea does not exceed 65°, while the arid sands inland may reach 160° about midday under the blazing overhead sun.

The Benguela current south of the Equator corresponds to the Canaries current in the north, and it is still more important in its climatic effects, which are in evidence from the Cape of Good Hope almost to the Equator. The coolest water is found off the south of South-west Africa, where the mean sea-surface temperature is below 55° in August, 57° in February. A cool foggy seaboard, much of it an almost rainless desert, is, in part at least, the result of these oceanic conditions. Between the Canaries and the Benguela currents the warm waters of the Guinea current, with a temperature of over 80°, bring excessive heat and moisture to the coast between Cape Verde and Cape Lopez in summer, Freetown and Cape Lopez in winter.

The ocean currents on the east of Africa are in striking contrast, and have a surface temperature much higher than those on the west coast. For the present purpose the circulations of the Indian Ocean south and north of the Equator may conveniently be considered apart. South of the Equator the general features remain similar all the year. A massive and wide equatorial current flows from east to west, centred along 15° S. lat. to meet the African coast about Cape Delgado, and thence spreads north and south, north to about the Equator all the year, and much farther in summer, south all the year as far as Cape Agulhas where it meets the cool Benguela current; part of it washes eastern Madagascar. This equatorial water is warm, the temperature ranging in July from about 64° off the south of the Cape Province to 78° at the Equator, in January from about 70° to 82°. Thus the main body of sea-water is about 10° warmer on the east than on the west of southern Africa.

North of the Equator the currents are in part controlled by the monsoons of south Asia. In summer the equatorial current which starts north from Cape Delgado is helped forward by the south-west monsoon, and forms the very strong and well-marked East African coast current, which sweeps along in an almost direct line past Arabia to the head of the Arabian Sea, its velocity frequently attaining 4 knots near the Equator. The coasts of the Arabian Sea and the Bay of Bengal have a clockwise circulation; and a distinct 'south-west monsoon current' flows eastward across the Indian Ocean between Ceylon and the Equator to strike Sumatra. The body of equatorial water which is driven north-east along East Africa and south Asia might be expected to be very warm, and such is the case in general, the sea surface temperature being about 82° or higher in most of the ocean north of the Equator, and as high as 85° over large areas in April and May. But the conditions off the East African coast are abnormal, for the sea temperature is lower there than out in the open ocean throughout the year, and as much as about 5° lower during June to September. Along the south-east coast of Arabia also the water in these months is about 5° cooler than off the Malabar coast. This cool water is due to upwelling from the lower strata of the ocean, which results not from any offshore winds but from the tendency of the East African coast current to edge away from the coast, a movement which is very pronounced about lat. 10° N. during the south-west monsoon, when part of the coast current diverges east and south-east with a velocity of sometimes as much as 7 knots to form the 'south-west monsoon current'. This cooler coastal water must be an important factor in the aridity of Somaliland and south Arabia.

By November the winter monsoon of the north Indian Ocean is established, and the surface water is blown towards the south-west by the north-east winds. In the Bay of Bengal and in the Arabian Sea the water moves anticlockwise along the shores; along East Africa the current is north-east as far as the Equator. The coolness of the winter season is added to the equatorward movement of the water to lower the temperature, and the coastal water is about 3° cooler than the main ocean.

In February, although the north-east monsoon is still blowing strongly the current begins to set north-east along the African coast, and a clockwise circulation is re-established in the Arabian Sea and in the Bay of Bengal; this new circulation continues in a strengthened form when the south-west monsoon begins. During the months February to April the water is only slightly cooler off East Africa than out in the open ocean.

In both the Arabian Sea and the Bay of Bengal the sea is appreciably warmer on the east side than on the west during the months December to March, owing to the counter-clockwise circulation which brings warm equatorial water to the east sides. In April and May there is little difference between the two sides and from June to November this continues true of the Bay of Bengal, but in the Arabian Sea the water off the Malabar coast is much warmer than the water off Somaliland and Arabia, owing to the upwelling of cool water along the latter coasts as already described. Speaking generally the surface water is about 2° warmer in the Bay of Bengal as a whole than in the Arabian Sea, and as much as 5° warmer in August and September.

The Red Sea is very hot at all seasons, with a surface temperature in January of 72° in the north and 78° in the south, and in July of 80° and 89°, but the effect on the climate of the coasts is greatest in winter. On summer days the water, hot though it is, even exerts a cooling influence on the still hotter sun-baked desert coasts. The Red Sea is too narrow to have more than a very limited local influence. The Mediterranean on the other hand is very important in its effect on the meteorology and climate of all the north of Africa. In winter the warm moist air over the sea engenders low atmospheric pressure, and the weather of the surrounding coasts is mild and rainy. In summer the sea does not become so hot as the land and the high pressures normal to the subtropical latitudes in which the Mediterranean is situated spread over it; the great extent of the Sahara is largely due to this fact. The annual range of temperature of the sea surface is considerable both in the Mediterranean, where it is 25°, and in the Red Sea, where it is 15°. In autumn the Mediterranean retains much of its summer heat, but by spring it has cooled considerably, and hence autumn is notably warmer than spring in the Mediterranean lands.

The oceanography in this section is based on articles incorporating the available information, in the *Marine Observer*, 1928 and 1935.

Pressure. January (Fig. 4 a). In the winter of the northern hemisphere the great difference in temperature between land and sea north of the tropic of Cancer causes the high pressures normal in subtropical latitudes to be profoundly modified, since vast high-pressure systems are developed on their northern side over the cold land masses of Asia and America, and these continental anticyclones are the most prominent features of the pressure distribution. Over the North Atlantic and Europe we find what may be considered as a 'bridge' of moderately high pressures connecting the continental anticyclones. The continuation of this bridge north of Africa is of the highest importance in the meteorology of the continent. The high pressures over the North Atlantic are centred about 30° N. lat., those over Asia about 45° N., and between them lies the Mediterranean region, an area of warm and moist air in winter, with a tendency to low pressures. The high-pressure bridge therefore takes up its position not over, but to the north and to the south of the Mediterranean, that is to say over Europe where it is most marked, and over the north of Africa, with a centre of highest pressure over the snow-covered Atlas and plateau of Algeria; and between the two bands of high pressure is the

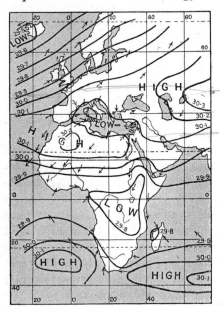

January

FIG. 4 a. Mean isobars and prevailing winds.

Mediterranean 'lake' of low pressure, the path of numerous depressions. These depressions are closely connected with those of the westerlies of North-west Europe; some enter the Mediterranean as fully developed systems, others form or deepen over the warm sea. It is more accurate to regard the Mediterranean in winter as an independent meteorological area than as merely an extension of the region of the oceanic westerlies.

As over the Mediterranean, so in the neighbourhood of the Red Sea there is a break in the high-pressure belt, a result of the warmth and humidity and the lesser friction over water than over land.

Along the north coast of Africa all the way from Morocco to Egypt the prevailing winds in winter are westerly, controlled by the low pressures over the Mediterranean (Fig. 5). The high-pressure region over the north of the Sahara has calms and variable winds, and south of it extends the arid region where the north-east trades hold undisputed sway.

Sweeping across the Sahara and the Sudan, they blow almost to the shores of the Gulf of Guinea in the west, beyond the Equator in the centre of the continent, and as far as about 15° S. lat. in the east. Their goal is the low-pressure system, the modified doldrums, which now covers Africa south of the Equator and extends westward in a long trough over the Upper Guinea coast about 5° N. lat. The northerly position of this trough is explained by the fact that even in January the southern Sahara and the Guinea lands are warmer than

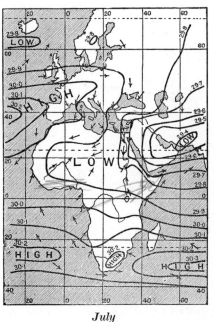

July

Fig. 4 b. Mean isobars and prevailing winds.

the South Atlantic Ocean. On the Guinea coast, therefore, south-west winds, 'deflected trades', are still frequent in winter, bringing with them the hot steamy weather of the 'white man's grave'. The trades are found on approaching Sierra Leone, and north of this point white men find life bearable for at least part of the year.

Over South Africa low pressures replace the normal subtropical high pressures in January owing to the heat of the overhead sun. The south hemisphere high pressures appear in the form of well-marked anticyclones over the South Atlantic and South Indian Oceans about 30–40° S. lat., connected by a 'bridge' over the extreme south of Cape Province, which enjoys fine weather and sunny skies in the southern summer. The south-east trades, strengthened by a monsoonal in-draught, blow as a steady current from the anticyclone over the Indian Ocean on to the east coast of Africa as far north as Mozambique. Having crossed a wide expanse of warm sea, they give copious rain where they are forced to ascend the

lofty eastern edge of the African plateau. Onshore winds blow on the west coast of Africa also, but they are merely coastal sea breezes and, having come from a cold sea, they bring no rain. Some little distance off this coast the south-east trades start on their long journey to the doldrums, which, over the Atlantic Ocean, are north of the Equator.

July. (Fig. 4b). During the northern summer the sub-tropical high pressures of the northern hemisphere form very

Fig. 5. Prevailing winds.

well-marked anticyclones over the oceans. The continents are relatively hot, the air over them expands, and low-pressure systems result. Africa is influenced especially by two of these systems. The first, the North Atlantic anticyclone, lies mainly west of the Strait of Gibraltar, but has an eastward extension over much of Western Europe and the Mediterranean Sea. Africa north of the Equator, especially the Sahara, is strongly heated by the blazing sun, and hence the high pressures of the Mediterranean are limited by the north coast of the continent. The second, the low-pressure system over the south of Asia, centres in Baluchistan and Sind; North Africa forms with Asia a vast hot land area, and a great westward extension of the Asiatic low pressures develops over the Sahara. If the latest isobar maps give a true picture of the conditions, a notable change in the pressure gradient occurs at the Nile Valley; east of the Nile the isobars are close, circling round the low-pressure centre, while over the Sahara there is an extensive region of slight gradient. This continental low-pressure system represents the doldrums drawn far north and extended over the hot land. The trough of lowest pressure crosses Africa from Suakin on the Red Sea through Berber to the mouth of

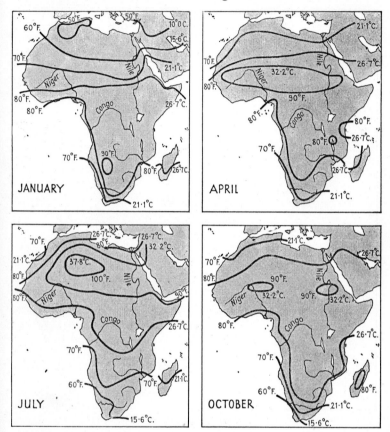

FIG. 6. Mean temperature.

the Senegal River, and forms a most important divide between the dry north-east and north winds which blow from the Atlantic and Mediterranean high pressures on the north, and the rainy south and south-west winds, the monsoon which is drawn in from the south. All Africa north of this line is arid in summer except for a little rain in the mountains and occasional violent cloud-bursts in the plains; it is largely the influence of the Mediterranean Sea in maintaining high pressures immediately north of Africa that produces the great extent of the Sahara. But for the high pressures which spread east over the Mediterranean Sea, the trade winds would have less

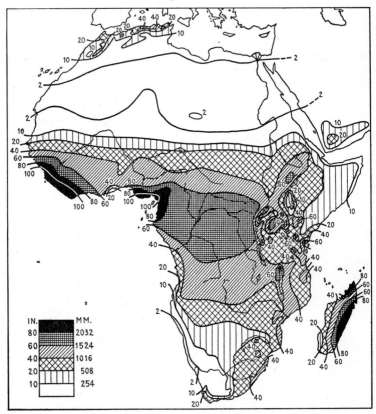

FIG. 7. Mean annual rainfall.

force, and the monsoon which produces the heavy rainfall and luxuriant vegetation of the Guinea lands would make its way much farther into the continent and fertilize the southern part of the Sahara.

The equatorial low-pressure system swings from its extreme southern position in January to its extreme northern position in July, lagging in general about one month behind the overhead sun. It migrates through about 13° of lat. in the west of the continent, and about 40° in the east.

The southern hemisphere is under winter conditions in July, when the land is cooler than the surrounding oceans and a high-pressure system is developed over South Africa, forming part of the subtropical belt of high pressure and giving fine dry

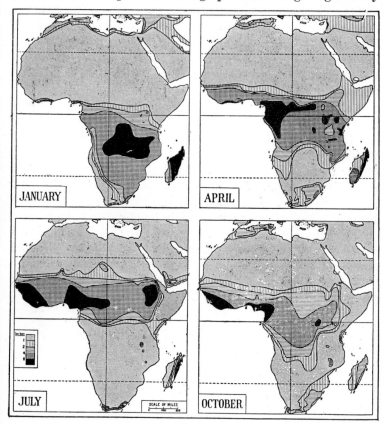

FIG. 8. Mean Rainfall.

weather. At this season too the oceanic high pressures have moved somewhat north of their January position, and leave Cape Town and the southern tip of the Cape Province exposed to the stormy westerlies and a considerable winter rainfall. Natal has calms and weak onshore winds, but between the tropic of Capricorn and Cape Guardafui the wind blows parallel to the shore, towards the Asiatic low pressures. The west coast of South Africa is under the influence of the south-east trades which are now at their greatest strength, but sea breezes mask them on the immediate littoral.

Temperature. Africa may be truly described as the hottest of the continents in respect of the mean annual, the summer, and the winter temperature (Fig. 6). Especially is this so in the northern summer when vast expanses of the Sahara have the highest temperature on the Earth. Africa is the only continent in which the 50° isotherm never appears. The greater part of the continent has more than nine months with a mean temperature above 70°.

A distinction which will be frequently referred to, especially in dealing with East and South Africa, is that between the low coastal plain and the interior plateau. In general, the coasts within the tropics are rainy, enervating, and unhealthy owing to the monotonous moist heat (but the west coast of South Africa is exceptional in being so arid as to be almost deserted for that reason). The plateau is less rainy and much more healthy since, although very high temperatures may occur by day, the air is dry, and moreover the cool fresh nights afford a welcome relief for European residents; the seasonal change of temperature also is much greater on the plateau.

Rainfall. The mean rainfall for the year is shown in Fig. 7, for January, April, July, and October in Fig. 8.

CHAPTER IV

MEDITERRANEAN AFRICA

THIS region comprises the northern parts of Morocco, Algeria, and Tunisia where the rainfall exceeds 8 inches a year. Lands of very varied physiography are included: 1. the coastal strip with a pure Mediterranean climate (p. 269); 2. the plateau of the Shotts at an altitude of some 3,000–4,000 feet, with a steppe climate and vegetation; 3. the ranges of the Atlas which bound the plateau on the north and the south, generally exceeding 5,000 feet, and in Morocco attaining over 12,000 feet; snow lies most of the year in the higher parts on the seaward side; 4. the Sahara south of the Saharan Atlas, but Saharan conditions prevail in parts of the plateau of the Shotts also. Divisions are also necessary from west to east: (1) the Atlantic coast of Morocco, (2) the Mediterranean from the Strait of Gibraltar to Tunisia.

The Atlantic coast of Morocco is washed by the cool Canaries current which keeps the summer temperature low for the latitude (Fig. 9, Mogador); the coolest water is off Cape Ghir, the surface temperature showing the anomaly of decreasing southward from Cape Spartel; the mean air temperature in July is below 70° along much of this coast. The north-east trades blow strong in summer, but in winter westerly and south-westerly winds are frequent, since the westerlies often dominate the weather. Cool summers, small range of temperature, scanty rainfall but high humidity of the air, with heavy dews and frequent fogs, are results of the cold current. Between the coast and the Atlas Mountains the summers are hotter, the winters colder, and the rainfall less. The Atlas Mountains have rain in summer as well as in winter, but elsewhere there is drought during the summer months, and the south of Morocco has hardly a drop of rain from April to September, but the drought is to some extent alleviated near the sea by the heavy dews and the low temperature. The land is sometimes swept, especially in spring, by the sirocco from the south-east, bringing hot and extremely dry air from the Sahara, with clouds of dust which is sometimes carried as far as the Canary Islands.

Eastward from the Strait of Gibraltar the summers become much warmer, the sky being almost cloudless (mean cloudiness at Algiers $\frac{3}{10}$) and the sunshine powerful. On the coast of Algeria the mean temperature in August, the hottest month, is about 75° and 100° is recorded in most years; but the prevailing north-east winds blowing from the sea prevent excessive heat. In winter the weather is controlled by depressions passing along the Mediterranean, which give south-west winds, with much cloud (mean cloudiness at Algiers $\frac{5}{10}$), moist air, and abundant rain; 80 per cent. of the rain falls in the winter half-year. The mean January temperature is 55°; frost is very rare. The sheltered valleys of the Tell such as the Mitidja have the best type of Mediterranean climate for agriculture and are famous for orange groves and vines. The annual precipitation exceeds 20 inches everywhere, being least in the west in the lee of Spain, and exceeding 60 inches in Khroumirie on the north slopes of the mountains, which have much snow in winter; here there are extensive forests of cork-oak, and above them cedars. The ranges of the Djurjura often rise snow-clad behind Algiers in winter.

The steppe climate of the plateau of the Shotts is the result of the altitude and the distance from the sea, whose influence is shut off by the Atlas ranges; the Saharan Atlas forms a bounding wall towards the Sahara on the south. In winter it is often bitterly cold, when dry north winds sweep across the open plains at a temperature well below freezing-point, sometimes with severe snowstorms; Géryville has 84 days a year with frost, and has recorded a minimum of 16°. On summer days on the other hand it is as hot as at sea-level, often hotter (Fig. 9), for the clear air gives free passage to the rays of the unclouded sun; the land is parched and the mirage mocks the traveller. Cool nights follow the hot days, the daily range of temperature being as much as 35°. The mean annual precipitation is about 12 inches, with a strong maximum in spring due partly to the cyclonic activity of that season, partly to local convection; the low temperature in winter, and the steady northerly winds in summer, do not favour heavy precipitation, but there are thunderstorms in summer and a certain amount of rain and snow in winter (Fig. 10). The region has the scanty rainfall and the extreme temperatures characteristic of steppe countries; alfa grass is a typical vegetation, and the drier parts are very poor steppe.

The Saharan Atlas has more precipitation than the plateau owing to the greater altitude, and there are even forests in places as in the massif of the Aurès. The rain is the source of much of the underground water which supplies the oases of the neighbouring Sahara, and the possibility of using it for

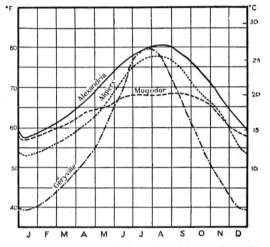

Fig. 9. Mean temperature. The cool summer at Mogador is due to the Canaries Current. The hot summer but cold winter at Géryville (4,280 feet) as compared with Algiers shows the plateau influence.

direct irrigation of parts of the desert has been considered. The ranges form a sharp climatic divide; looking north in spring we see the green steppes of the plateau, but at our feet on the south the sands of the Sahara stretch away to the horizon. Biskra has the Mediterranean winter rainfall maximum, but the scantiness of the rainfall, 8 inches, and the high range of temperature from day to night, and from winter to summer, show that it must be classed with the Sahara and not with the Mediterranean.

The remainder of the Mediterranean seaboard, north Libya and north Egypt, differs from Algeria and Tunisia in having a more southerly position, and in lacking a mountain system to bound the Sahara behind it. Though the midday heat is mitigated by the strong sea breeze the summers are very

hot, 105° being recorded in most years. The rainfall is scanty
—at Tripoli 16 inches, Benghazi 11 inches, Port Said 3 inches.
The rain falls in winter but reaches only a narrow coastal
strip—Alexandria has 8 inches, Cairo only 1 inch. The prevailing summer winds are north-west and north, those of

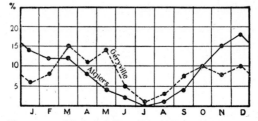

Fig. 10. Mean monthly rainfall at Géryville and Algiers, expressed
as percentages of the yearly total.

winter west and south as in the rest of this region. The sea
tempers the summer heat for a short distance inland (compare
the curves of temperature for Alexandria and Cairo, Fig. 16),
but otherwise desert conditions reach the coast in many parts.
Autumn is considerably warmer than spring, as everywhere
on the Mediterranean.

Further information is given in pages 269 *et seq.*, where
the climate and meteorology of the Mediterranean region as
a whole is more fully considered.

CHAPTER V

THE SAHARA

THE meteorology of the Sahara depends essentially on the fact that the barometric gradient over the region is from north to south throughout the year, giving winds from a northerly point, generally north-east. In summer Saharan conditions extend northward to cover the Mediterranean Sea, in winter southward almost to the Gulf of Guinea. The true Sahara covers some 13° of latitude. The prevailing winds are shown in Fig. 5.

During the winter months the north-east wind blows with great regularity over the middle and south of the Sahara. On the northern edge the direction of the wind shows itself more variable, and calms are frequent, this being the seat of the high pressures which separate the Sahara from the Mediterranean region. The prevailing winds are between north and west on the plateau of the Shotts.

The mean frequencies in mid-winter are:

	N.	NE.	E.	SE.	S.	SW.	W.	NW.	Calm.
Géryville . .	14	2	7	10	11	5	25	18	7
Touggourt . .	8	14	14	7	2	19	24	11	2
In Salah . .	12	44	13	3	3	6	3	3	13
Cairo . . .	10	2	1	3	28	6	3	3	44

At Asyut 80 per cent. of the winter winds blow from northwest, north, or north-east.

In summer winds from a northerly or easterly point show a decided predominance in the northern as well as the central parts of the Sahara:

PERCENTAGE WIND FREQUENCY IN MID-SUMMER

	N.	NE.	E.	SE.	S.	SW	W.	NW.	Calm.
Géryville . .	13	2	6	16	19	7	17	10	11
Touggourt . .	4	11	37	19	12	10	3	5	0
In Salah . .	6	41	30	7	2	6	3	1	4
Cairo . . .	43	8	3	0	1	1	12	15	17
Aswan . . .	83	3	0	0	1	2	1	5	5

But in the south, south-west winds begin to make their appearance and the southern limit of the desert is found about 18° N. lat. where these rain-bringing winds become predominant in summer. On the Atlantic coast the winds are north to north-west, the deviation from the normal direction of the trades being due to the strong daily sea-breeze effect between the cool water off the coast and the intensely hot interior.

The northerly winds of the Sahara have the usual trade wind characteristics but naturally they are much drier and dustier and less constant in speed and direction than the trades over the oceans; they have even been given the distinctive name of Harmattan, but this seems undesirable. There is very little cloud, and the sun's rays beating down from the deep blue sky scorch the naked land. The summer temperatures include the highest known on the Earth. During the midday hours it is a veritable furnace, but the clear dry air also favours rapid loss of heat from the bare ground after sunset, and the night minimum temperature is 30° or even 40° below the day maximum, but even so the temperature does not fall below 70° or 80° and the nights are cool only by comparison with the days.

'Suddenly, after hardly any twilight, the sun rises into the clear sky. In this dry atmosphere its rays are already scorching in the early morning, and under the influence of the reflection from stone and sand the layer of air next the ground is warmed rapidly. There is no active evaporation to moderate the rising temperature. After 9 o'clock the heat is great and goes on increasing till 3 or 4 in the afternoon, when the quivering mirage is sometimes seen, produced by the vibration of the air, heated as in an oven. It gets slowly cooler towards evening, and the sun, just before it sets, suffuses the cloudless sky with a glow of colour. In the transparent night the rocks and sand lose their heat almost as rapidly as they acquired it, and the calmness of the atmosphere, which is so still that a flame burns without a tremor, also favours the cooling of the air. We shiver with cold and it is no uncommon thing in winter to find water on the surface of the ground frozen in the morning' (SCHIRMER, *Le Sahara*).

The Sahara, then, is a region of very great diurnal range of temperature. The mean daily range (°F.) at Dakhla Oasis is:

Jan.	Feb.	Mar.	Apr.	May	June	July	Aug.	Sept.	Oct.	Nov.	Dec.	Year.
30	33	34	36	36	33	31	31	29	29	29	29	32

The daily range in the heart of the desert in August is often 55°.

In Borku, in May 1871, the mean daily maximum tempera-

ture was 112°, the mean daily minimum 67°, mean daily range
45°. Far higher figures than the mean of course occur. On
15 May 1871, at Toro, south Borku, the temperature at sunrise was 59°, at 2 p.m. 116°, range 57°. On Christmas day,
1879, Rohlfs and Stecker observed a minimum of 31° and a
maximum of 99°, giving a range of 68° for the day.

On winter nights the temperature may fall below freezing-
point: 23° has been recorded at many stations in the Libyan
desert and also in the Algerian Sahara; Touggourt has on
the average six nights with frost in the year; occasionally
the irrigation channels in the oases have a thin covering of
ice on winter mornings. The day temperatures in summer
are the highest known on the Earth for a large area. The
highest reading ever recorded under standard conditions (but
not admitted as reliable by some meteorologists) is 136·4°
on 13 September 1922, at Azizia, 25 miles south of Tripoli,
and here 110° is attained in each month from May to September every year. The surface of the sand is sometimes
baked to a temperature of 170° or more. Schirmer truly
remarks 'the desert is a country with extreme temperatures,
where in spite of latitude it is by turns colder than on the
Mediterranean and warmer than on the Equator'. The annual
range of temperature also is very large for the latitude; at
Aswan the mean temperature is 61° in January and 95° in
July, range 34°.

The Sahara has the hottest summers on the globe. The
mean July temperature (reduced to sea-level) somewhat exceeds 100° over a considerable tract between Tunisia and the
Ahaggar; all the central Sahara has a mean above 95°, and
temperatures above 120° are recorded in most years. Perret
mentions the case of In Salah where for a period of 45 days in
1931 the mean daily maximum was 118°, the absolute maximum 127°, and the absolute minimum 70°. On the other
hand the Saharan winter is comfortably cool with a mean
January temperature of 50° in the north and 70° in the south.

To sum up the main reasons for the dryness of the air in the
Sahara, the north-east trades which sweep the desert originate
in part as currents of air settling downwards from the upper
atmosphere in the subtropical high pressures, and in descending the air tends to be warmed by compression as it reaches

denser strata. Thus in their origin the trades are dry winds, and as they blow towards the south over a great land mass they become warmer and warmer and hence the relative humidity is still further decreased. In lands which have a plant covering much vapour is transpired into the air by the leaves, but this source is lacking in the Sahara for there is no vegetation. The climate is too dry to support plant life, and owing to the lack of vegetation the air remains dry. The almost total absence, or feebleness, of such irregularities of pressure as are the immediate cause of most of the rainfall of the westerlies is another very important factor. At In Salah the mean relative humidity is 56 per cent. in winter, 36 per cent. in spring, 25 per cent. in summer, 39 per cent. in autumn. The air may be so dry that plant life is impossible; wood splits and leather dries as hard as a board. Man can live only so long as he drinks about 10 pints of liquid a day. But the vigorous evaporation has the great advantage of cooling the body very appreciably and so making human life possible; the wet-bulb thermometer may be as much as 40° lower than the dry bulb on summer days, and the maximum wet-bulb reading is rarely above 85°.

There is very little cloud; the mean annual amount of cloudiness is less than $\frac{1}{10}$ of the whole sky in the eastern Sahara including the Nile Valley, which indicates that even small clouds are rare. The amount increases westward, but even the Atlantic coast has only about $\frac{4}{10}$, and this comparatively high figure is due to the cool ocean water off the coast. In the almost complete absence of cloud there is hardly a break in the sunshine throughout the day, and the insolation is particularly rich in radiation of short wave length in this dry climate.

The mean annual rainfall is less than 5 inches everywhere, and practically nil in the Libyan desert and Egypt. Cairo has 1·3 inches and in the Nile Valley to the south even the smallest shower is rare. The mean annual rainfall of a vast belt lying roughly between 20° and 25° N. lat. but interrupted by mountain groups is probably less than 1 inch, but there are few good series of records; the belt includes the Nile Valley between Cairo and Meroe. The Atlantic coast probably has slightly over 1 inch. In the northern Sahara the little rain that does fall comes in the winter half year, most in spring and autumn, and is mainly associated with the Mediterranean depressions of that period. In the south such rain as there is falls in summer, and is an extension of the monsoon rain of the Sudan; as in the Sudan it is generally thunderstorm rain, sometimes very heavy while it lasts. Much of the Sahara receives no rain at all for years at a time. In Salah has an appreciable shower of rain, and it may be a very heavy one, about once in 10 years; in such a land as the Sahara 'mean annual rainfall' is a term of little practical significance. Black clouds sometimes pass over, but the trails of rain that can be seen descending from them are evaporated by the thirsty desert air before they can reach the ground. If the air is sufficiently cooled by ascent up mountains, or by cyclonic or convectional influences, there may be violent downpours of rain—as much as 2 inches in a single storm in regions which are quite rainless for years. The wadis rush along brim-full, and much damage may be done, but the underground water-supplies on which life depends are renewed. A letter by Capt. Aymard, quoted by Lasserre (*Les Territoires du Sud de l'Algérie*, i, p. 254), illustrates this:

'On Jan. 15, 1922, at 8 p.m. a hurricane, followed by torrential rain, descended on the Tamanrasset district. The roofs of nearly all the houses fell in, and the natives took refuge in the Laperrine and Le Père de Foucauld forts. The flood swept away the huts and the gardens by the side of the wadi. The rain continued on Jan. 16, the wadi had overflowed and was rushing along with the speed of a galloping horse. At 5 p.m. the outer wall of the Père de Foucauld fort collapsed and buried 22 people, who were dug out in the icy rain; 8 were found to be dead and 8 wounded. On Jan. 17 the rain was less heavy, the wadi went down and the weather cleared. Snow could be seen on the neighbouring mountains.'

The mountains in the Sahara are much more favoured than the plains. The southern groups of Aïr and Tibesti get a considerable rainfall every summer, often in thunderstorms of great violence which cause sudden floods in the neighbouring wadis. The unwary, both animals and men, who happen to be in their path, even far away from the storm area, may easily be swept away. The Ahaggar, farther north, is fortunate in getting a share both of the summer rains from the south

and the winter rains from the north, and there are many
running streams in its deep valleys. Brooks deduces from
various indications a mean annual rainfall of about 10 inches
in the Ahaggar and Aïr, only 2 inches in Tibesti which though
high is in the heart of the desert. Many summits are snow-
capped in winter, and snow sometimes falls heavily even on
the lowlands of the northern fringe of the Sahara, but it does
not lie long.

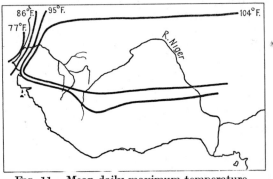

Fig. 11.   Mean daily maximum temperature,
May 1923.   (Hubert.)

Dust is one of the worries of life in the Sahara as in all
arid lands. Even a light breeze blowing from sand dunes
carries its load of fine particles, and travel is often rendered
unpleasant, and even entirely stopped by clouds of dust swept
along by the strong winds which blow by day. Sometimes a
real dust-storm, known as a Simoon, is experienced, and the
hot air is filled and darkened with the whirling dust-clouds.
Many Egyptian proverbs are suggestive of the terrible preva-
lence of eye diseases which are largely due to the ubiquitous
dust—'dimness of sight is better than blindness', 'the desire
of the blind man is a basketful of eyes'. Strong southerly
winds are specially hot and unpleasant, and they are distinguished everywhere by local names such as sirocco, chili,
khamsin.

The Atlantic coast of the Sahara between Morocco and
Senegal is washed by the cool Canaries current. The heat is
much less than in the interior, especially in summer, the July
mean being as much as 20° less than in the Libyan desert

(Fig. 11). Fogs are fairly frequent, as on all coasts washed by a cool current.

The Red Sea coast is distinguished by its great humidity and small range of temperature as compared with the rest of the Sahara. At Suakin the mean temperature in August is 95°, in January 72°; the daily range of temperature averages 24° in summer and only 12° in winter; the mean relative humidity is 49 per cent. in summer and 72 per cent. in winter. There is a mean annual rainfall of 9 inches, most of which falls during the winter months, when the hot moist wind from the Red Sea meets the cooler hills inland. There is copious dew at night caused by the cooling of the warm moisture-laden air, the water deposited often equalling a heavy shower of rain.

The Saharan climate is not unhealthy. The summer days are hot indeed, but the air is very dry, cool, and invigorating at night except in the hottest months. It presents a great contrast to the belt which is to be described next, where the heat is oppressive by night as well as by day, and is associated with high humidity, an exceedingly unhealthy combination for white settlers.

CHAPTER VI

THE SUDAN WEST OF LAKE CHAD;
THE GUINEA LANDS

THE antithesis of the Sahara is the region of the Congo and the Guinea coast where the abundant rainfall throughout the year and the constant moist heat produce the rank luxuriance of the almost impenetrable rain forest.

Separating these opposites there is a transition region, a belt of country stretching right across the greatest width of Africa, which has rain in summer and a well-marked drought in winter, the length of the rainy and dry seasons varying according to the latitude. This is the Sudan, a region probably of great potential agricultural value, as yet only very partially developed and not entirely explored.

Pressure and Winds. In January the equatorial low-pressure system is south of the Equator over the continent, but in the Gulf of Guinea the trough is still north of the Equator since the Guinea lands are warmer than the sea. The axis of the tongue of low pressure lies along or just south of the Guinea coast. The north-east trade winds which dominate the Sahara now sweep as far south as this line, and bring Saharan conditions almost to the coast; they are named the Harmattan (Fig. 5). Their aridity, however, is somewhat tempered by the vegetation and the numerous rivers. South of the trough of low pressure south-west winds prevail, an extension of the south-east trades of the southern hemisphere which are deflected when they cross the Equator. On the coast itself the prevailing winds are south-west even in January, but they are then weaker than during the rest of the year and are much interrupted by calms. They are rain-bringing winds and are responsible for the moist heat which is so enervating for Europeans.

In March the sun is overhead at the Equator, but already the hottest zone is 600 or 700 miles farther north, where the clear dry air permits a more rapid rise of temperature than can occur in the moist forested equatorial zone, and the equatorial low pressures have migrated far into the northern hemisphere. By July they have reached their highest latitude, the north-east trades have their least extension southward, and the damp south-west winds, 'the monsoon' from the Gulf of Guinea, their greatest extension northward, bringing steamy heat and heavy rain far inland; the northern limit of the south-west winds in summer is the southern boundary of the Sahara. About the end of August the trough of low pressure begins its return journey towards the south. Hence the central parts of the region over which the low-pressure belt swings experience a double pressure wave in the course of the year, the extreme north and the extreme south a single wave. The extreme north has dry north-east winds during the greater portion of the year, broken by a short spell of south-west winds in late summer, and the land is too arid for agriculture. The extreme south of the Guinea lands on the other hand is under the influence of the south-westerlies during almost the whole year, and the climate is equatorial and the rain forest as luxuriant as in the Congo. Travelling southward in July along the west coast of the Sahara we first meet south-west winds some distance north of the Senegal River. The mouth of the Senegal itself has south-west winds during the four summer months and north-east trades during the rest of the year; the duration of the south-west winds increases rapidly to the south. At Bathurst they blow for eight months, and in the south of Portuguese Guinea and right along the Guinea coast they are the prevailing winds throughout the year. These south-west winds on the coast are in part merely sea breezes rather than a true monsoon, for the interior, beyond the reach of the sea breezes, seems to have longer spells of north-east wind in the winter months than the coast in the same latitude. In the middle of summer south-west breezes extend as far as about lat. 20° N. in the interior, north of the Niger bend. Four hundred miles out to sea, in the Cape Verde Islands, the north-east trades blow for nine almost rainless months; August to October is the 'Tempo das Aguas', when south-west breezes bring sultry weather and rain, and justify the name of the group. Fig. 12 shows the swing of the boundary between the Harmattan (or north-east trade) and the monsoon during the year along the meridian of 7° 30′ W.

Rainfall. In the Guinea lands the rainfall is by far the most prominent climatic factor. The year is divided into two seasons, the rainy and the dry. The heaviest rainfall occurs just on the south of the trough of low pressure, so there tends to be a well-marked double rainfall maximum in the course of the summer, one as the low-pressure trough passes north, the other as it returns south. However, during the whole season of south-west winds there is considerable rainfall.

The rains are a time of intense life for the plant world, which

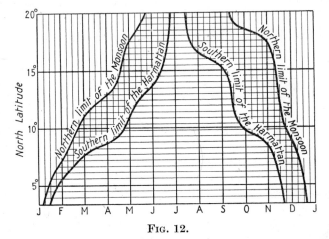

F<small>IG</small>. 12.

Migration of wind systems, in 1935, on long. 7° 30′ W. (Hubert.)

wakes from its annual sleep with their advent. For the European it is the most unhealthy part of the year. Fever is rife, and activity is very laborious in the sweltering steamy heat. The rivers are in high flood and much of the low ground is under water. Unfortunately the district most visited by Europeans is the coast, precisely the region with the longest and heaviest rains, the pernicious effects of which are increased by the foul odours that arise from the rotting vegetation and slimy ooze of the mangrove swamps. Sierra Leone and the Niger delta have earned the reputation of having one of the most unhealthy climates in the world. Sierra Leone is known as the 'white man's grave', but the interior of that colony, especially the higher parts (and much of the interior is elevated), is far less unhealthy than the coast, where the wide expanses of mangrove swamp and the insanitary settlements provide ideal breeding-places for mosquitoes. The application of hygienic measures has already done much to diminish the unhealthiness, and still greater success is to be expected in the future. But a country with a mean annual temperature of 80°, with only 4° difference between the temperatures of the warmest and the coolest months, and an annual rainfall of over 175 inches, can never be an ideal residence for Europeans.

The following description given by Borius of a day during the rainy season in Senegambia presents a vivid picture of the conditions that prevail over the whole of the Guinea lands:

'The sun rises out of clouds which soon melt away under its rays; the air is fresh and pleasant, with a few puffs of wind from the south-west, and light white clouds spread fanwise from the horizon and cross the valley, slowly changing form. Soon after sunrise the shade temperature is 80°. The calm air gets hotter and hotter, and by 9 a.m. it is unpleasant to walk abroad, even with a sunshade. The wet ground reflects the bright sunshine, and this fact combines with the high temperature, the moisture-laden air, and the fever germs to make the sunshine at this season so dangerous.

'About 10 a.m. in spite of an increase in temperature of perhaps 3°, the heat is still bearable and admits of a little activity. The south-west breeze is beginning but is irregular and seems to be on the point of dying away at any moment. At midday the thermometer is still rising, and by 1 p.m. it stands at 86°; the sun is hidden at times as a few cumulus clouds cross the sky from south to north, and the surface wind oscillates between west and south-west, but is still very weak. By 4 p.m. the temperature is 88°, the sky is three-fourths clouded, and masses of cloud are piling up on the horizon; the wind often drops altogether. The heat is very oppressive, and though after 4 p.m. the thermometer hardly rises a degree yet the heat seems to be increasing considerably, and we are astonished that the thermometer does not show a greater rise. We perspire profusely on the slightest exertion.

'At 6 p.m. the sun disappears in thick clouds, which it colours a brilliant copper. It falls calm except for a few puffs from the south and south-west which bring no life and fail to reach the inside of the house, and we have to go out on the roof to try to get a breath of cool air. A little black cloud passes overhead from the south-west, and a few drops of rain fall from it but not enough to wet the ground. We go in again, but the heat indoors is overwhelming and we long desperately for a breeze. The water, which is kept in porous vessels, and which seemed cool in the morning, is now lukewarm. There is no need for a hygrometer to show that the air is saturated with moisture. The vapour pressure is 23 mm., and it is this high humidity that makes the heat so overpowering, although the actual temperature is not excessive.

'Nothing can be compared with the feeling of utter prostration that overcomes a European. Though he sits motionless in an arm-chair he perspires as after violent toil; his fatigue is not like what is felt after work, but rather a weakness in the limbs, and especially in the bones—an indescribable feeling of discomfort, which precludes all movement, all bodily or mental work, but yet forbids sleep. Clouds of mosquitoes swarm round him and he feels suffocated.

'At 10 p.m. it has fallen dead calm. The temperature still continues high and our discomfort becomes greater than ever. We can neither read nor work, for that would require an effort of the will which we are incapable of making; our mental energy is sapped even more than our physical strength. Night drags on in this painful way unless a thunder-storm bursts, with heavy rain, in which case the temperature falls and we feel a welcome freshness in the air. We may form some idea of the painful conditions of life on the Senegal during the rains if we think of the discomfort sometimes felt in Europe just before a summer thunder-storm and imagine that discomfort increased tenfold.'

The rainfall diminishes from south to north; much of the south-west and south coast has over 100 inches per annum, Timbuktu only 9 inches, and at 17° N. lat. the average amount is probably inappreciable. It is impossible to lay down as a definite line on a map the exact limit of appreciable rainfall, since the conditions are very variable from year to year. There are few rain gauges, and conclusions have to be drawn from the vegetation. Districts which travellers have reported to be quite arid and apparently rainless have been found by later visitors to have an abundant plant covering. Thus the Sahara is bounded to the south by a debatable belt, which is far too arid for any cultivation, but in wet years may receive enough rainfall to produce good vegetation.

The 10-inch isohyet (Fig. 13) is an almost straight east–west line which runs from the mouth of the Senegal to Lake Chad; and not far south, and roughly parallel to it, are the isohyets of 20 and 30 inches. North of about 10° N. lat. there is only a single short rainfall season. Timbuktu has only two

months, July and August, with more than 2 inches of rain,
and the rain is very variable in amount from year to year, as
in most arid countries. South of 10° N. lat. the double maximum is clearly marked except on the south-west coast (Fig.
14). In the interior November to February is the dry season.
Heavy rains begin in April, and the early summer maximum
is in June. In July and August the rainfall is somewhat less,
though still heavy, and in September the second maximum

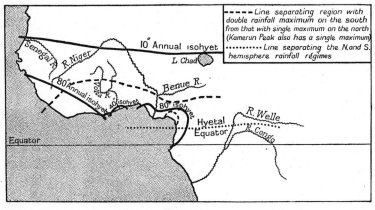

FIG. 13.

occurs, higher than that of June (Bismarckburg, Fig. 14).
On the coast the rainfall régime is similar, but the early
summer maximum is far higher than the later one; almost
two-thirds of the year's rain falls in April, May, and June.
The August minimum is very pronounced, that month being
practically rainless (Cape Coast Castle, Fig. 14). Sierra Leone
and most of the Liberian coast have only one maximum, the
rainfall increasing steadily till August and then diminishing
(Freetown, Fig. 14). This difference from the régime up
country in the same latitude is doubtless due to the strong
summer monsoon from the south-west meeting the elevated
coast, the precipitation being greatest when the inflow is
strongest, during the months when the interior is hottest
(compare Kamerun Peak, p. 55). The rainfall is not so much
convectional, with a maximum following each passage of the
overhead sun, as orographical.

The total rainfall is very heavy, over 175 inches, in much of

Sierra Leone; most of it falls in the months April to November. It increases very rapidly on the coast southward from the Sahara. Cape Verde has about 20 inches, Bathurst 50 inches, Konakry almost 200 inches. The other specially rainy part of Upper Guinea, the Niger delta, has two maxima, in June and October, but every month of the year has a considerable rainfall. At Akassa the driest month, January, has an average of 3 inches, and all other months have over

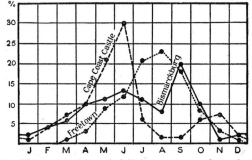

Fɪɢ. 14. Mean monthly rainfall (percentage of yearly total) in the Guinea Lands.

6 inches; the wettest month is October, with 25 inches, and the yearly total is 144 inches.

Separating these two very rainy areas there is a narrow coastal strip between Cape Three Points and Nigeria with the remarkably small rainfall of about 30 inches (Fig. 13). Hereabouts the interior has more rain than the coast; fifty miles inland there is over 50 inches. The prevailing winds are the same on this drier strip as on each side, and the probable cause of the low rainfall is the existence in summer of an area of upwelling cool water off the coast, caused not by an offshore wind, for the prevailing winds blow from the southwest, but by the pull of the Guinea current; the tendency to fog supports this view. But all Dahomey seems to have less rain than the country on the west and east, the mean annual total ranging from 40 inches in the south to 20 inches in the north on the River Niger. The trend of the coast parallel to the prevailing winds is another possible factor.

The rain of the Guinea lands is of the equatorial type, much of it falling in very heavy showers between noon and midnight, generally accompanied by thunder and sometimes by tornadoes (see p. 43). During the whole rainy season the air is damp, often quite saturated, and there is much cloud.

The dry season presents a striking contrast. The prevailing north-east winds bring pronounced drought especially when the Harmattan blows strong. The sky is almost cloudless, but yet far from clear, for the air is often full of a fine dust from the Sahara, producing a dismal dull grey which the sun can hardly pierce. Lake Chad is being slowly filled up by the dust blown into it from the north-east. The smoke from the bush fires started by the natives to burn the dead savanna vegetation is another source of dull skies in the dry season.

The Harmattan is the east or north-east wind, really the trade wind, which blows direct from the desert and is very dry and dusty. It is almost constant in the northern part of the area during the dry season, less and less frequent farther south, but it is known even on the Guinea Coast, though its drying influence is much less on the seaward side of the Yoruba uplands. Dryness is its most prominent feature, humidities below 10 per cent. being observed. The leaves of the trees turn yellow and fall, and wood splits. The change from the rains is often so sudden that the land dries up and hardens before the ground nuts can be harvested. Man suffers great discomfort from the dry dusty air, but even this is a relief from the steamy heat and on parts of the littoral the Harmattan has acquired the name of 'the doctor'. It is usually described as a cold wind, especially at night, but in reality the sensation of cold is due to rapid evaporation from the observer's skin rather than to any specially low temperature of the wind. Fogs are frequent in the dry season on the Guinea coast.

The mean monthly vapour pressure is about 0·8 inch along the Guinea coast eastward from Monrovia all the year, a degree of humidity far above what is healthy or comfortable for white men. In January there is a rapid decrease northward and inland to less than 0·2 inch north of 12° N. lat.; the mean is about 0·2 inch along the north frontier of Nigeria. In July and August the humidity is rather higher in the interior and west than on the south coast, and it is probably highest, exceeding 0·9 inch, between Dakar and Konakry, but the whole region from the coast to 12° N. lat. has about 0·8 inch. The seasonal range in the interior, and the marked contrast in winter between the interior and the coast are usefully shown by the figures given above, which express a climatic feature of great biological significance.

Temperature. In the hot season temperature is highest not in the south, where the sea reduces it though it provides the humidity which makes it uncomfortable, but inland, where the mean for the warmest month exceeds 90°. In the dry season

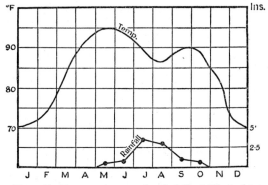

Fig. 15. Temperature and rainfall at Timbuktu.

the interior is coolest, but even at Timbuktu the mean for January is over 70°. However ground-frost is not uncommon in the clear nights of the dry season, even as far south as Koury. The mean annual range of temperature is greatest inland, being 23° at Timbuktu, and only 6° at Cape Coast Castle. The mean daily range is also greatest inland, at Timbuktu 31° in the dry season and 24° during the rains; at Grand Bassam it is 17° in January, 9° in July.

As in most monsoon countries the highest temperatures occur just before the rains begin, for when the rains are at their height the thick clouds cut off the sun's rays and the falling drops cool the air. A second maximum may occur when the rains cease. This is well seen at Timbuktu (Fig. 15), where May is the hottest month; the temperature falls decidedly till August and rises again after the rains—but not to the May figure. This town and the belt of country it represents in the north of this area, e.g. Senegal, may be said to have three seasons (1) November to January, dry and cool, (2) February to May, dry and hot, and (3) June to October, the rains.

Along the coast, and indeed everywhere south of lat. 10° N., the drop in temperature in July and August is very marked, the means for these months being actually lower than those for December and January. But the mean annual range is small, considerably smaller than the daily range. The natives, enervated by the hothouse atmosphere, are very sensitive to temperature changes and light great fires to keep themselves warm at night.

It should be noted that very much higher temperatures are recorded in the Sahara than in the Guinea lands, where the clouds and moist air screen the fierce rays of the sun. The highest shade temperatures observed on the Guinea coast do not exceed 100° and the usual maximum for the year is about 95°. Away from the sea, where the rains are shorter, higher maxima are recorded, and Timbuktu, with summer readings exceeding 118°, approaches very near to the furnace heats that prevail farther north. But the nights are less cool near the coast than inland; thus the mean minimum temperature for the year at Freetown is 72° (abs. min. 65°), at Timbuktu 44° (abs. min. 42°). The sultry nights are one of the main discomforts on the coast. The unhealthiness of the Guinea coast is due to the combination of excessive humidity with considerable heat, not to excessive heat; at Freetown the wet bulb has recorded 100°, an extremely high reading.

Tornadoes. The most violent storms of the Guinea lands are called Tornadoes. They are thunder squalls which often start very suddenly, last but a short time, sometimes only a quarter of an hour, and may do considerable damage on land and sea. They almost always travel from east to west, and are especially frequent at the beginning and end of the rains. They are generally accompanied by exceedingly heavy rain and blinding lightning, but dry tornadoes also occur. They result from the meeting of the shallow monsoon of warm damp air, probably not more than 4,000 feet thick, with the dry north-east winds from the Sahara which blow, for at any rate a considerable distance, above the surface monsoon, and

hence they are most frequent in March–May and October–
November near the coast, in July–September in the far interior. The violent convectional overturnings are most liable
to occur in the daytime when the surface air is strongly
heated. A tornado has a linear front of perhaps 10 miles
which may grow to 200 miles, and it may advance for even
500 miles.

The tornadoes of the Guinea lands must not be confused
with the storms of the same name in the U.S.A. These latter
have, in general, less rain, and far more violent winds revolving rapidly with a short radius.

Nigeria. The climate of this large and important British
possession merits special description. Long series of meteorological observations are unfortunately few, except from the
coast.

Three belts may be recognized. The northern includes all
the country north of the central hilly region about 11° N. lat.
It is the driest belt, and has a very clearly marked monsoonal
change of wind and weather. The seasons may be compared
with those of the plains of India. December, January, and
February are the cool season, but the mean temperature is
as high as 70° in January. There is no rain. The usual wind
is the Harmattan from the north-east, and since the desert
is not far distant it is very dry and brings much dust, so that
clear air and bright skies are rare. Trees shed their leaves,
and various other devices to check loss of water characterize
the vegetation.

In March the temperature rises fast and April, May, and
early June are the hot season. The sun is overhead, and in
May, as few clouds have yet appeared to screen it, the heat
is intense, the mean temperature for the month being over
90°. But the wind still blows from the north-east and the air
is dry; night gives some relief from the excessive heat of
the daytime, so that the conditions are not unhealthy. June
brings a decided change; south-west winds set in with abundant cloud, and the rains begin. Violent dust-storms, ʻdry
tornadoesʼ, mark the change of season. Temperature falls
owing to the cloud canopy, and the range from day to night
is less than in the previous months. The air is almost saturated with moisture, and rain falls daily. Just as in the cool

season Saharan conditions were in evidence, so now the weather is that of the Guinea coast, with thunderstorms, tornadoes, and violent hailstorms. The rivers, many of which had quite dried up, roll along in heavy flood and much of Bornu becomes a great lake.

The rains last till September. The rainfall is least in the north, but even the northern frontier of Nigeria probably gets about 20 inches, and the Kano district about 30 inches. At the end of the rains the temperature rises again as the sky clears, and this is the most unhealthy part of the year, worse even than the rains, but the rise in temperature is soon checked by the retreat of the sun to the southern hemisphere. By December the north-east winds are well established, and Europeans find life less burdensome.

The central belt comprises the country between the division just described and an arbitrary line which may be drawn at about 7° N. lat. The rainfall is everywhere abundant, increasing from 40 inches in the north to 60 inches in the south. There are considerable differences in the altitude of the country. The valleys of the Niger and Benue, being only a few hundred feet above the sea, have less rain but higher temperatures than the uplands; they are heavily forested in many parts, and unhealthy. The Bauchi plateau, 4,000 feet above sea-level, is much cooler and has a healthy climate; the mean annual rainfall at Bauchi is about 40 inches. In this central belt the rains last longer than in the north, at Bauchi from May to September, at Lokoja from April to October, and the temperature is lower during the rains and higher in the dry season.

The third belt includes the rest of Nigeria. It is chiefly characterized by a very heavy rainfall, the rainy season extending over nearly the whole year, and by the small range of temperature. Most of the region is low-lying, the Niger delta forming a large part of it, and here is the 'West Coast' climate in its worst form. The usual tropical mangrove swamp fringes the innumerable creeks and streams, the trees growing out of fetid and pestilential ooze which reeks with rotting vegetation. The climate is probably the most unhealthy in the whole world, an enervating moist heat day and night throughout the year. The prevailing winds are south-west, the Harmattan reaching the coast only occasionally in January and February. The temperature never falls below 60° at night, and usually remains between 70° and 90° throughout the twenty-four hours. The air is almost always saturated with moisture, and the constant damp heat weakens the strongest European constitution and leaves it a prey to malaria and other diseases fostered by the climate and the insanitary native villages. Very violent thunderstorms are frequent, thunder being heard on about 75 days in the year. The mean annual rainfall exceeds 120 inches along the seaward edge of the delta, and decreases northward to about 80 inches at Abo and 53 inches at Asaba. July and September are the wettest months, and there is a marked break in the rains in August, which facilitates the harvesting of the early crops and the sowing of the later. The higher land on both sides of the Niger probably has a heavier rainfall. March, April, and December are the hottest months, August the coolest, so that the usual seasons of the northern hemisphere are reversed, owing to the dense cloud screen of the 'summer' months, but the difference between the mean temperatures of the extreme months is only 4°.

CHAPTER VII

THE SUDAN EAST OF LAKE CHAD; EGYPT

No long series of records have been kept in most of this region. The climatic belts of West Africa probably extend right across the continent in similar latitudes, the amount of rainfall becoming somewhat less, and the range of temperature somewhat greater, in the far interior.

The Nile Valley, extending from south to north for more than 33° of latitude, is well equipped with meteorological stations in comparison with the rest of the continent, and as the valley passes through all the climatic belts from the Equator to the Mediterranean the records provide a particularly instructive climatic 'section' of north Africa.

Egypt. The north coast, bordering on the Mediterranean, has a Mediterranean climate of a very arid type—mild winters with a little rain and hot rainless summers (p. 269). The mean annual rainfall at Alexandria is 8 inches, and at Port Said 3 inches. Only a narrow coastal strip is included in this first climatic division, for at Cairo we reach desert conditions with a mean annual rainfall of only 1 inch, all of it falling in winter. In spite of the lower latitude the winters are cooler than on the shores of the Mediterranean, but the summers are far warmer (Alexandria and Cairo, Fig. 16) and the air is much drier; the mean temperature at Cairo in January is 54°, about the same as in England in June. The humidity is least in spring; it rises in summer, and in late summer when the Nile is in flood the atmosphere in the valley is somewhat hazy and the air may feel comparatively sultry. At Helwan the mean relative humidity is only 39 per cent. in May, 55 per cent. in September. Although depressions fail to give much rain, their effect is seen in the Khamsin winds that are a feature of all northern Egypt. These strong south or south-east winds are caused by depressions passing off the delta or moving north-east from the Sahara towards the delta, and owing to the quarter from which they blow they are exceedingly hot and enervating, and readings of 109° have been noted at Cairo; but in winter the south winds may be cooler than the normal.

They carry much dust, so that the air is thick and yellow and the sun obscured. They usually continue for two or three days and are specially frequent in spring and early summer. At Cairo they blow on an average on eleven days in the year. Mention must also be made of the floods of cold air which may sweep south from Anatolia and even eastern Europe in rear of winter depressions. Especially at such times fires are

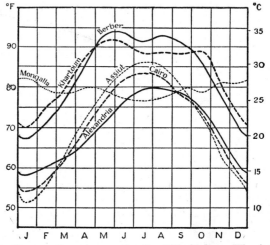

Fig. 16. Temperature curves for the Nile Valley. The influence of the Mediterranean Sea appears at Alexandria which is warmer in winter but cooler in summer than Cairo. The fall in temperature at Berber and Khartoum at midsummer is caused by the monsoon. Mongalla shares the equable conditions of the Equatorial zone.

needed in the homes of Europeans in lower Egypt, and the drop in temperature is sometimes appreciable as far as Khartoum.

South of Cairo the desert conditions already described for the Sahara are more marked. Rain is almost unknown in this land of bright skies and brilliant sunshine. The mean annual rainfall is less than 1 inch; in most years not a drop falls, and then after a series of perhaps 10 or even 20 years a sudden violent storm may give 1 or 2 inches in 24 hours. A case is described by Sutton, L. J. (*Meteorological Magazine*, 1931): Siwa, Lower Egypt, on 28 and 29 December 1930 received 1·5 inches, which did much damage to the houses of the oasis;

the 'mean' rainfall at Siwa in December is probably not more than 0·1 inch. Temperature is very extreme. At Wadi Halfa 126° (in April) is the highest record, 28° the lowest, and the mean daily maximum in June is 106°, the mean daily minimum in January 46°. Berber is situated in the hottest region, and here the average maximum temperature which must be expected on a June day is 112°—the highest in the Nile Valley; the average minimum on a January night is 49°. Naturally, the winter nights are colder farther north, the lowest January minimum recorded being at El Sheikh Fadl (between Cairo and Asyut). Beyond this the warmth of the Mediterranean Sea prevents any further fall. Alexandria is 6° warmer than Asyut in January (Fig. 16).

At Cairo and in the Nile Valley south of it the prevailing winds throughout the year are northerly, and follow almost exactly the course of the river, so strong and constant that Nile boats easily make the journey upstream under sail and float down again with the current. But a change begins at Meroe, which has a short spell of southerly and variable winds in July and August; this is the northern fringe of the summer monsoon of the Sudan, the western part of which has been traced in the Guinea lands. The transition from Sahara to Sudan is rapid, for at Khartoum, only 100 miles south of Meroe, south-west winds are predominant from June to September and give 5 inches of rain, the dry north-east trades holding sway for eight months; the climate is not unlike that of Timbuktu, but drier.

The northern half of the Anglo-Egyptian Sudan experiences very severe dust-storms, 'Haboub', in all months except midwinter and most frequently in summer. The towering masses of sand and dust, rising as a wall to several thousand feet, may have an almost sharp linear front of perhaps 15 miles, which advances at a speed of about 35 miles an hour. The storms seem to be associated with shallow heat depressions in which air masses of different temperatures, though all very warm, come into conflict. Often there is no rain, but sometimes heavy rain falls in their rear at Khartoum in summer (see Sutton, L. J., *Q. J. R. Met. Soc.*, Jan. 1925, April 1931).

South of Khartoum the rains become heavier and last longer, from April to October at the junction of the Bahr-el-Ghazal

4311 E

and the Nile. Mongalla (5° N. lat.) is still in the region of summer rains, but two maxima appear in the rainfall curve. The two maxima become more and more pronounced southward till at Wadelai (3° N. lat.) the climate is equatorial, rain all the year, with maxima in May and October (Fig. 17).

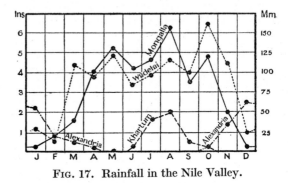

FIG. 17. Rainfall in the Nile Valley.

The change from desert to Sudan is less obvious to the traveller up the Nile Valley, since the Nile forms a continuous oasis. The date palm is cultivated from the Mediterranean coast to Khartoum, but the finest fruit is got between Cairo and Aswan, luscious dates which can be easily dried for export; to the north the air is rather too damp, to the south too hot and dry. South of Khartoum the date palm disappears and the land of the baobab is entered.

CHAPTER VIII

ABYSSINIA, ERITREA, AND SOMALILAND

This region has great diversity of climate owing to its extent in latitude (from the Equator to 18° N.), in longitude and in altitude. There are four main regions:

1. The highlands, a plateau block, the main mass of Abyssinia, with its top level about 9,000 feet, but rising to 15,000 feet in isolated peaks. There is a little snow in winter but none lies throughout the year; most of the precipitation falls as heavy rain in summer. The sides of the plateau rise very steeply and the west and south-west are intricately dissected by long river valleys and gorges, in some places 2–3,000 feet deep.

2. On the north-east of the plateau is the Danakil lowland, below sea-level in the north, and rising in the south to about 2,000 feet. It is bounded on the west and south by the remarkably straight walls of the plateau, and on the east by the Red Sea hills of Eritrea. It is an arid tract, intensely hot and dry in summer, and the streams that enter it from the plateau fail to reach the sea.

3. On the south-east the plateau slopes down comparatively gently through the Ogaden and neighbouring plains to merge in the coastal belt of Italian Somaliland. Most of this region is very poor grazing land with a scanty and uncertain rainfall of 10–20 inches, and a mean temperature at 4,500 feet of about 60° in January, 75° in July. British Somaliland on the north-east is mostly highland of 3–6,000 feet, with a very steep drop to the Gulf of Aden.

4. The shores of the Red Sea and the Gulf of Aden, a very narrow strip, quite arid with a mean rainfall of only 2 or 3 inches falling in winter. Owing to the cloudless skies and the additional heating of the air by descent to the coast after its passage over the sun-baked plateau behind, there is furnace-heat in summer; at Berbera the mean temperature exceeds 90° in June, July, August, and September, and in July the mean temperature is 97°, the mean daily maximum 107°, and the mean daily minimum 88°, remarkably high figures especially for a coastal station. January and February, the

coolest months, have means of 76° (mean daily minimum 69°). Aden, on the opposite shore of the Gulf, faces the sea winds in summer and is 10° cooler in July; in winter the temperature is about the same as at Berbera.

Three main altitude zones are distinguished in Abyssinia:

1. Kolla, up to 6,000 feet, consisting largely of valley bottoms which share the hot summers of the Sudan; May and October are the hottest months. The valleys are sheltered from the main wind currents, and are damp and sultry; they have much dense jungle, and are quite unsuitable for white settlement.

2. Voina Dega ('wine highland'), 6–8,000 feet. This is the most populous part of the country, having much well-cultivated land and excellent pastures. The warmest month is March, mean temperature 60–64°, and the coolest July, 55–57°, so that the temperature is low enough to invite permanent European colonists. The volcanic soil is fertile, and irrigation could be provided for the dry months; disadvantages are the heavy downpours of rain in summer, and the steep slopes of the much dissected land.

3. Dega ('highland'), over 8,000 feet. Cereals are grown up to 12,000 feet, but the higher altitudes are too cold, and the rainfall too heavy, to attract settlers.

At present the most important aspect of the climate of Abyssinia is the rainfall in relation to the Nile flood, since the summer rains are the chief source of the irrigation of the Sudan and Egypt. Unfortunately the meteorological records are quite disproportionate to the economic importance of the climate.

The rain is heaviest on the south-west and west of the plateau, including the upper valleys of the Sobat, Blue Nile, and Atbara, where it exceeds 75 inches over a considerable area and 40 inches over most of the plateau above 6,000 feet; in the north it decreases to 20 inches. The amount falls away very sharply on the north-east, which perhaps explains in part the straight and intact plateau edge where it overlooks the arid Danakil depression, which is in striking contrast to the much dissected south-west and west. In the south-east the rain decreases much more gradually to 10 inches along the coast of Italian Somaliland.

Except on the shores of the Red Sea and the Gulf of Aden where most of the very scanty rain (Massaua 7 inches, Berbera 2 inches) falls in winter, summer being cloudless and rainless, and the Danakil region which has a very little rain both in winter and summer, the rains are restricted to the summer half-year and are brought by the monsoon as in the Sudan, the effect of the plateau being to lengthen the rainy season somewhat and especially to increase the amount of rain, the Nile Valley having only 30 inches and the neighbouring plateau 75 inches.

On the south-west of the plateau appreciable rain begins in the end of March, and continues fairly heavy for a few weeks (the light rains); Addis Ababa has about 3 inches in March and in April: then after a lighter spell in May the heavy rains begin and last till the end of September, being specially heavy in July, August, and September. The rain is of the tropical mountain type, very heavy with much thunder. The water runs off rapidly into the deep gorges which are almost empty in winter, and the thick chocolate-coloured flood reaches the Nile Valley in June and increases in volume till September, so copious that after irrigating the Sudan and Egypt there is some water left over to enter the Mediterranean 1,700 miles away. On the northern plateau, including the Takkaze basin, the rains begin seriously in mid-April and continue throughout the summer, but much less heavily than in the south. The lower slopes of Ogaden have lighter rain, most of it probably in April, May, and June; but Harar (6,500 feet) has good rains from March to September. Winter is dry.

The thick clouds and streaming rain of the monsoon cool the air, so that summer is the coolest season, and the hottest month of the year is March, before the heavy rains set in; the mean annual range of temperature is low, only 7° at Addis Ababa. The plateau is cooler relatively to the Nile Valley (which also is cooled by the summer monsoon) in winter than in summer, and very much cooler in summer than in winter relatively to the arid lowlands on the east—

Difference in Mean Temperature.

	January.	July.
Hillet Doleib—Addis Ababa . . .	21	18
Berbera—Addis Ababa	16	36

The place of origin of the monsoon winds which bring Abyssinia its rain has not yet been established with certainty. The position of the country might suggest that the rain is derived from the Indian Ocean to the south-east, but the July isobars (Fig. 4 b) show a definite gradient for south-west, not south-east, winds, as the Sahara is covered by a great extension of the low-pressure system of South Asia. Moreover, the general winds in Abyssinia at the height of the rains seem to be south-west, though it must be remembered that the records are scanty, and certainly the very broken topography modifies the air currents. In April a closed low-pressure system forms over the upper and middle Nile Valley with the increasing heat of the northern summer, and perhaps this gives south-easterly winds which bring the early rains of Abyssinia. But with the advance of summer this system becomes merged in the great low-pressure system of the Sahara, and after a few weeks of variables a south-westerly current appears in obedience to the new gradient, and gives Abyssinia its heaviest rains from June to September. According to this view the South Atlantic would seem to be the ultimate source of the major Abyssinian rains.

In winter the wind is north and north-east; it gives a little precipitation to the plateau, and also to the coasts of the Red Sea and the Gulf of Aden which have none from the summer monsoon.

The shores of Italian Somaliland have very little rain in any season owing to the winds blowing parallel to the coast, from north-east in winter and south-west in summer. The summer is much cooler than on the Gulf of Aden owing to upwelling cool sea-water (page 14) and frequent fog; fog is noted on 40 per cent. of the observations at sea off this coast from June to August.

CHAPTER IX

KAMERUN

THE climate resembles that of similar latitudes and altitudes in Nigeria. The southern part of Kamerun, however, extends almost to the Equator, and therefore has certain peculiarities. The extraordinarily heavy rainfall is noteworthy, for the west side of Kamerun Peak has 412 inches per annum near sea-level, the second highest record in the world, surpassed only at Cherrapunji (India) which has 458 inches. The rainiest months are June, July, August, and September. The single maximum in the rainfall curve is an interesting variation from the double maximum which is usual along the Guinea Coast, and it is doubtless an orographic effect (compare Sierra Leone, p. 39). The prevailing winds throughout the year are westerly, and the monsoonal inflow is strongest in the late summer of the northern hemisphere when the temperature in the interior is highest, and hence the rainfall, which is largely due to the ascent of the winds up the mountain, is then heaviest. The driest months are January and February, but they also have considerable rainfall.

The parts of tropical Africa described up to this point have shown general agreement in having their rainfall during the summer of the northern hemisphere. In the south of Kamerun at about lat. 3° N. is the rainfall 'Equator' (Fig. 13), where rain falls throughout the year, with two well-marked maxima at the equinoxes, and beyond this the rainfall régime is that of the southern hemisphere, that is to say, the months October to April are the wet season, May to September the dry. At Libreville on the Gabun River, slightly north of the geographical Equator, the rains begin in September and last till May, with maxima in November and March; June, July, and August are practically rainless.

The annual rainfall at Libreville is 96 inches, and every month has heavy rain except June, July, and August. Farther south along the coast the régime remains much the same, but the amount becomes less and the dry season longer from Kamerun to South-west Africa. Banana, at the mouth of the Congo, has only 37 inches, and 5 dry months.

The low rainfall of this coast is due primarily to the prevailing south-east trades, and the resulting upwelling cool water off the shore. The winds actually observed on the coast are generally westerly, but these are merely the local sea breeze, which affects only the coastal strip, and, blowing over a comparatively cool sea, brings little if any rainfall. The rainfall on the coast and islands near the Equator and the estuary of the Congo is very variable in amount from year to year, and the temperature, too, shows considerable variations. The explanation is probably to be found in the oceanic conditions. The sea off this coast is a debatable area, now reached by the Benguela current, now by the Guinea current. When the cold Benguela current is present the temperature is low and the rainfall scanty, but when it is replaced by the warm Guinea current there is higher temperature and more rain.

CHAPTER X

THE CONGO BASIN

THE western part of this region round the mouth of the river has just been mentioned. Its low rainfall especially distinguishes it from the rest of the basin. It enjoys, too, the advantage of a regular sea breeze, a valuable alleviation of equatorial conditions for white settlers, offset, however, by the unhealthy swamps.

The remainder of the state consists of a vast basin generally some 1,000 to 1,600 feet above the sea, enclosed by the higher plateau of the continent. The climate is equatorial. The mean difference in temperature between the warmest and the coolest months is very small, only about 4° F. in the central area. The warmest month is February or March when the rains are at their height, the coolest August in the dry season, the transition from the rains to the dry season being marked everywhere by a fall in temperature (in contrast with the Sudan). The range of temperature from day to night is far greater than from season to season. Thus at Bolobo the mean daily range is 16°, but the difference between the warmest and coolest months is only 2°. The highest temperatures recorded are by no means so high as in the deserts of higher latitudes; at Equatorville no reading above 95° has been known and readings above 90° are unusual, but the minima are far higher than are recorded in the clearer and drier air to the north and south; at Equatorville 63° is the lowest on record. It is not so much excessively high temperatures, as the combination of great humidity and considerable heat, and the monotonous continuation of such hothouse conditions throughout the year, that are so trying to the European in an equatorial climate. However, Sir H. H. Johnston says that the climate of the Congo

'on the whole may be said to be infinitely superior to that of the Niger or the Gold Coast. The great absence of low marshy ground about its banks is doubtless the cause of less virulent fever, and the regular cool breezes from the South Atlantic greatly reduce the tropical heat. The river probably is least healthy between Boma and the sea, owing, no doubt, to the mangrove swamps.

Boma itself is decidedly insalubrious. It is the hottest place on the Congo and surrounded by many marshes. Towards Vivi it becomes decidedly cooler, owing to the greater elevation; and the higher you proceed up the river the healthier the climate becomes.'

The mean annual rainfall varies from about 50 inches in the south to a little over 70 inches in the north. Thus it is notably less than in the same latitudes in the Amazon Basin. South America lies open on the east for the entry of the trade winds, while the Andes close in the basin on the west and force them to ascend and give copious rain. The Congo State, on the other hand, is surrounded by high ground, a considerable barrier especially on the east; and the winds that enter it from the west have come over the cool Benguela current, and hence do not bring very much rain.

There are three rainfall régimes (Fig. 18). In the north, along the Ubangui, where that river runs in an east to west direction, and the Welle, the régime is that of the northern hemisphere (see Fig. 13) with heavy rainfall in every month from March to November inclusive, the rainiest months being June and September; the period December to February is the dry season, January being rainless. Mobaye on the Ubangui with 69 inches illustrates the transition from equatorial to Sudanese conditions. About lat. 2° N., along the northern-most bend of the Congo River, there is an equatorial rainfall régime, every month being rainy, e.g. New Antwerp. South of this the régime is that of the southern hemisphere. At Equatorville, on the Equator, the driest month is July, the rainiest months are November and December, but rain falls throughout the year. Brazzaville on the Congo (lat. 4° S.) has a pronounced dry season from June to September. At Lulua-burg (lat. 5° S.) far in the interior the dry season is shorter, only June and July being rainless. Thus the southern part of the basin receives its rains while the northern part is dry, and vice versa, and in consequence the lower Congo River has two periods of flood in the year, one in December and the other in April and May.

The rain is of the thunderstorm type, and during the rainy season there is a downpour practically every afternoon and evening. The dry season is rendered unpleasant by frequent thick fogs; the sky is often grey, gloomy, and cheerless, and

the air is often thick with smoke from the numerous grass
fires, started by natives in the savannas to clear the ground of
dead vegetation.

'The great fault of the climate lies in the excessive damp.
Even in the dry season there is great moisture in the air, for,
though there is no downright rain, yet the mornings and evenings
are ushered in by dense white mists, like low-lying clouds, which
incessantly filter through the clammy atmosphere a drizzling
vaporous spray that descends over everything like a heavy dew.
This is the "cacimbo" of the Portuguese colonies and the "smokes"

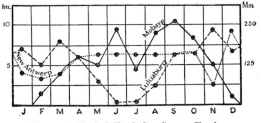

Fig. 18. Rainfall of the Congo Basin.

of the Guinea Coast. These morning and evening mists are
characteristic of the dry season, and during the rainy months they
disappear, and the beginning and closing of the day is generally
bright and clear' (sir h. h. johnston).

In the east of the Congo State the prevailing winds in the
dry season are south-east. During the rains there are calms
and variable winds largely from the west, since a low-pressure
system covers South Africa. In the west the prevailing winds
are west and south-west. The sea breeze is of almost daily
occurrence, setting in at Boma about 1 p.m. and attaining its
greatest force, that of a strong breeze, at sunset. The land
breeze that begins some hours later is much weaker. In the
Congo Valley far above the estuary the sea breeze is still felt,
but a more striking phenomenon is a strong squall which
blows up at or just after sunset from the west or north-west,
and dies down again after about half an hour. Sometimes
the wind increases again from the same direction later in the
evening. These night winds which, contrary to the usual rule
in the tropics, are stronger than the afternoon sea breeze, are
specially characteristic of the dry season. They occur in

Loanda and elsewhere in West Africa. Their origin is not understood.

The storms of the Congo are thunderstorms and tornadoes similar to those of the Guinea lands, most frequent at the beginning and end of the rains. As on the Guinea coast they almost invariably come from the east.

The extreme south of the Congo State, Katanga, is on the South African plateau, much of it at an altitude of 5,000 feet. In climate it resembles Northern Rhodesia (Ch. XIV) rather than the rest of the Congo Basin.

CHAPTER XI

EAST AFRICA (KENYA COLONY, UGANDA, AND TANGANYIKA TERRITORY)

THIS is largely an equatorial region, but owing to the great variation in altitude the conditions range from the sultry heat usual on equatorial coasts to perpetual snow above 15,000 feet. Only small areas, the highest parts of Ruwenzori, Mounts Kenya and Kilimanjaro, are at such an altitude, but there are very large areas of plateau between 3,000 and 8,000 feet.

The climatic belts are the topographical belts which run north and south, roughly parallel with the coast line as indicated in Fig. 19. They are subdivided *a*, *b*, and *c*, *a* denoting northern hemisphere régime of rainfall and temperature, *b* equatorial, and *c* southern hemisphere. The divisions are:

1. The coastal plain.
2. The arid east of the plateau.
3. The middle plateau from 4,000 to 6,000 feet above sealevel.
4. The high plateau, including the Athi, Kapti, and Leikipia plains on the east of the Rift Valley and the corresponding plateau on the west. This is the most suitable area for white occupation.
5. The eastern Rift Valley.
6. The lake and river valleys with small range of temperature, damp though the rainfall is low, malarial, and generally unhealthy for whites.
7. The mountains, with heavy rainfall.
8. The hot and comparatively dry north-east shore of Lake Tanganyika.

In the summer of the northern hemisphere, from May to October, the great low-pressure system over Asia and North Africa gives rise to a southerly air current over East Africa; it is a season of little rain except on the windward slopes of the mountains. As the sun returns south the low-pressure system of Asia fills up and is replaced by the winter high pressures, while a low-pressure system forms over South Africa; the southerly winds over East Africa die away, and after a period of light variable winds in October and November a northerly current, lighter and less constant than the southerly, blows during the summer of the southern hemi-

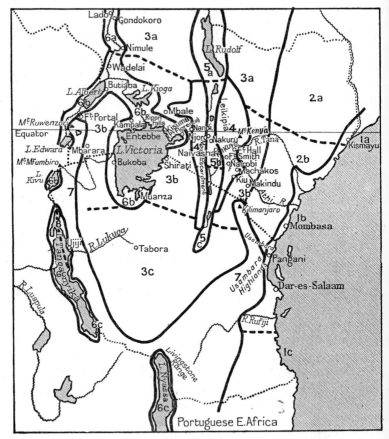

Fig. 19. The major climatic regions of East Africa.

sphere. In March and April there is the transition to the southerly current.

Little rain falls during the seasons of both the northerly and the southerly winds. The northerly winds are dry in their origin, and are of the trade wind character, little interrupted by pressure irregularities. The southerly winds originate as the south-east trades of the Indian Ocean, and they have deposited much rain in Madagascar before reaching East

Africa. The general direction of both the northerly and the southerly winds parallel to the coast is another point which is unfavourable to much rainfall. Nearly all the rain falls in the transition months of light and variable winds just after the passage of the overhead sun. The total amount is small for an equatorial region, much less than, for example, in the Congo basin; both the rainy seasons and the dry seasons share the deficit. The rainfall is liable to vary much from the normal. Wide expanses of the plateau of Tanganyika Territory are poor savanna with a mean annual rainfall of only about 35 inches. But there is much more on the coast, especially between Tanga and the Tana River where there is more than 40 inches, and in the interior above 4,000 feet, including the Highlands of Kenya Colony, where most of the European settlers live (Nairobi 40 inches, Fort Hall 48 inches).

The rain is especially heavy on the south slopes of the mountain masses; the Tukuyu highlands north of Lake Nyassa have more than 50 inches, the seaward end of the Usambara highlands over 100 inches, and Ruanda, a much-dissected elevated plateau north-east of Lake Tanganyika, also seems to have a heavy rainfall in spite of its distance from the sea, and is one of the most densely peopled parts of East Africa. Mounts Kilimanjaro, Meru, Kenya, Elgon, and Ruwenzori have totals of probably nearly 100 inches, and their upper slopes are usually hidden in cloud even in the dry season. They are still densely forested between 5,500 feet and 12,000 feet (except on the north sides which have grass); a zone of pasture and xerophytic bush comes above this, then mosses and lichens, and above 16,000 feet perpetual snow.

Most of Uganda and especially the western shores of Lake Victoria is a much wetter region than East Africa generally, having a mean annual total of about 50 inches; but the tract between Toro and Lake Kioga is comparatively dry, with probably about 35 inches. The higher temperature resulting from the lower altitude, the wide expanses of lake and marsh, and the lake breeze especially on the west and north shores of Lake Victoria, combine to give the heavy rainfall which keeps this land always green and maintains the dense and flourishing native population, but the south and south-east shores of Lake Victoria have not much more than half the rainfall of the north and west. Thunderstorms are far more frequent than on the rest of the plateau, and are notably violent in Kavirondo. As is usual on lands within the tropics they occur especially during the hottest hours of the day, but an interesting exception is the case of the Sese Islands in the north of Lake Victoria where most of the thunderstorms are between midnight and dawn (see G. D. H. Carpenter, *A Naturalist on Lake Victoria*). Thus the lake has the night maximum which is usual on tropical seas. Another maritime characteristic of the lake is its liability to severe, even if short, storms of wind.

Much of the rest of East Africa tends to aridity and is green only during the rains, brown for most of the year. The interior of Tanganyika Territory, including almost a quarter of the whole, seems to have rather less than 30 inches a year. The eastern Rift Valley is an area of rain shadow, sheltered by the high plateaus, and has some 30 inches in the reach extending about 50 miles north and 50 miles south from Naivasha, but northward there is a rapid decrease to probably about 10 inches round Lake Rudolf, and southward a smaller decrease to less than 30 inches at and south of Lake Magadi. Only the central rainier tract provides good arable land, most of the rest being poor pasture or scrub. The western Rift Valley is rainier and wetter than the eastern, but the rainfall of about 40 inches is much less than in the rest of Uganda; the amount decreases north of Nimule down the Nile Valley to the Sudan. The east shore of Lake Tanganyika is a rain shadow with about 30 inches of rain a year. The north-east of Kenya Colony is an arid tract with scanty population, lying comparatively low between the highlands of Kenya and Abyssinia, and even the coast is too dry to be of much agricultural use. The rainfall probably averages about 15 inches, but is very variable from year to year. A tongue with a similarly low rainfall projects south over the forbidding thorn-scrub of the Nyika country. These are arid dusty brown lands most of the year.

The times of the rainy seasons depend chiefly on the latitude. In the extreme north of Uganda there is a long rainy season from April to November, and December to February

is a pronounced dry season; the conditions approach those of
the Sudan. The southern half of Tanganyika Territory has
a long rainless season from May to October like Northern
Rhodesia and Nyasaland (but on the coast no month is rainless). The intervening region, most of the area considered in
this chapter, has a more or less pronounced equatorial type
of rainfall, with two seasons of heavy rain separated by relatively but, especially in Uganda, not quite dry seasons. The
rainy seasons are the transition months between the northerly
and southerly winds, approximately March–May and November–December, the former being the 'long rains', with

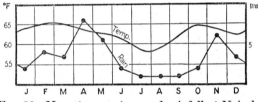

FIG. 20. Mean temperature and rainfall at Nairobi.

almost twice as much precipitation as the 'short rains';
Nairobi (Fig. 20) has 22 inches in February–May, and 8 inches
in November–December, Entebbe 33 inches in February–
June, and 14 inches in October–December. With the approach
of the long rains the trees burst into leaf after the drought,
the brown landscape becomes green, the rivers are soon in
high flood and the earth-roads impassable, so that only the
most necessary transport and travel are undertaken.

The chief dry season is June–September, though a month
without any rain is rare. It is a time of considerable mist and
cloud, and comparatively cool weather on the Highlands; the
mean cloudiness at Nairobi is about $\frac{7}{10}$. There is a shorter
and hotter dry season in January–February, and on the coast
this is the driest as well as the hottest time of the year.

Temperature. The coastal plain and low valleys in the
neighbourhood of the Equator are hot in all seasons, having
monthly means within 3° of the mean annual temperature,
78°, and showing the usual equatorial high, though not
extremely high, temperature, and small range through the
year in respect both of the mean and the abnormal readings.

4311 F

The highest temperature ever recorded at Mombasa was 98°, the lowest 60°. The last figure recalls that very important feature of an equatorial climate, the sultry nights when the warm still air is saturated with vapour. For white residents frequent long leave in a temperate climate is necessary, or at any rate desirable. The range of temperature is rather larger on the coast of Tanganyika Territory south of Dar-es-Salaam, where the dry months June–September are a recognizably cooler season.

On the plateau it is cooler, and on the mountain summits very cold. The temperature varies with the altitude, and on the Highlands, that is the region above about 4,500 feet, it is so much reduced as to be pleasant for white settlers; at 5,000 feet the mean is that of an English July. But the reduction does not much affect the range of temperature from month to month, and the mean annual range at Nairobi, 5,500 feet, is only 7°, about the same as at Mombasa, so that the Highlands have a similarly monotonous temperature, even if a lower one than the coast. But they enjoy the advantage of a greater diurnal range, for the days are warm and the nights decidedly cool always, and especially in the cool season from June to September when heavy dews, fogs, and drizzling rain make fires welcome in the home. Even in the 'hot season', January, February, and March, preceding the long rains, the nights are rather cold, though the days are hot and dry. At Nairobi the mean daily maximum in March is 78° and the mean daily minimum 53°, giving a mean daily range of 25°; in July the corresponding figures are 69°, 49°, and 20°; the highest reading on record is 89°, the lowest 34°. Nairobi is not high enough to have frost, but at 8,000 feet frost is frequent and above 12,000 feet there is much snow. The Aberdares (rising to over 10,000 feet) are too cold and rainy for white settlers.

The conditions are similar at corresponding altitudes on the plateaus on both sides of the east Rift Valley, and part of the bottom of the Rift Valley itself may be included in this connexion with the Highlands, for the floor is about 6,000 feet above sea-level near Naivasha where the Uganda railway crosses it. Here in the depression the air is dry and bracing and the range of temperature greater; at Naivasha in February the mean daily maximum is 82°, the mean daily minimum 47°, the mean diurnal range 35°; the corresponding figures for July are 74°, 46°, and 28°.

The Lake Victoria region, Kavirondo and most of Uganda, lie too low and are too damp to attract white settlers. The mean annual temperature is about 72°, only 6° lower than on the coast, and the range is appreciably less, especially on the northern shore of Lake Victoria where the mean temperature of the warmest month, March, is 71°, of the coolest month, July, 69°, giving an annual range of only 2°. At Entebbe the temperature rarely exceeds 86° or falls below 60°. The high temperature and heavy rainfall, and in many parts the rich soil, make a very suitable land for tropical agriculture, and this is one of the most densely populated parts of East Africa.

On the plateau of Tanganyika Territory, much of it about 4,000 feet above the sea, the hottest months are considerably warmer than in Uganda at the same level owing doubtless largely to the drier air; the mean temperature at Tabora in October, the warmest month, is 78°, at Entebbe 70°. The mean temperature of the coolest months, March to July, is about 70° at both stations.

White Settlement in East Africa. The Highlands of Kenya Colony are notable for being the only area of any extent in the equatorial zone of Africa which is high enough to provide a 'temperate' climate, but not so high that the conditions are too cold for ordinary white settlement. Some of the features which are of significance in respect of the health and comfort of white residents have already been mentioned. The atmospheric pressure is appreciably lower than at sea-level, the average barometer reading being 23 or 24 inches. This reduced air-pressure, and the vigorous evaporation, are in themselves facts of physiological importance, but the physical effect is of greater importance, for the smaller mass of atmosphere offers less obstacle to the passage of the sun's rays, and when the sky is clear the insolation is very much more intense than at sea-level; there is, however, a good deal of cloud during much of the year. This effect of altitude is important on mountains even in middle latitudes, and the insolation at 6,000 feet on the Equator may be powerful enough to be not only uncomfortable but injurious. The glare of the sunshine as well as its high actinic power are certainly unpleasant after a time, and in the opinion of many observers their effect, especially on the nervous system, is so serious that few white men can wisely spend their whole lives on the Highlands, and colonization in the usual sense will never be practicable since the new generations born there will necessarily deteriorate. It is a common opinion that long residence on the Highlands tends to produce a highly strung nervous condition which is specially noticeable in the warmest and driest months. But probably the worst feature of the climate from the point of view of white settlement is the monotony of the temperature. Though very pleasant and healthy for a time the temperature continues nearly the same day after day throughout the year, as if it were a perpetual English July. But north Europeans are adapted to variability, to both a seasonal rhythm and to irregular weather changes, and it seems doubtful if they can flourish permanently in this monotonous temperature. A redeeming feature is the considerable range of temperature from day to night, amounting in March, the month of greatest range, to about 25° at Nairobi, 29° at Fort Hall, 35° at Naivasha, and in July, the month of least range, to 20° at Nairobi, 23° at Fort Hall, and 28° at Naivasha.

But while many people are convinced that white settlement is possible in the restricted sense that the settlers can pass only the prime of life in the colony and should take long leaves in Europe, and others are enthusiastic believers in the possibility of real permanent colonization, most admit that white men cannot engage in ordinary manual labour. Only the experience of generations can provide a satisfactory test of the rival views.

Uganda has only very small areas in the south-west and on the slopes of Elgon at an elevation to correspond with the Highlands of Kenya, and almost the whole country is essentially a black man's land. In Tanganyika Territory there are many white settlers in the north, on the volcanic soils near Mounts Kilimanjaro and Meru at an altitude of about 6,000 feet where the climate resembles that of the Highlands of Kenya Colony, but most of the plateau is not high enough nor well enough watered to be attractive. The Tukuyu district, a large area of highland extending north-east from Lake Nyasa, seems to be excellently suited if it were opened up by road and rail. It lies high enough to have a suitable mean temperature and a good rainfall, and being 8° of latitude from the Equator it has a considerable seasonal change of temperature.

CHAPTER XII

ANGOLA

ANGOLA, lying between 6° and 17° S. lat., may be regarded as a transition region between the rainy Congo State and arid South-west Africa. The rainfall diminishes from north to south and from east to west. The rainy season is October to April, the passages of the overhead sun causing two maxima, which occur in December and March. May to August is an almost rainless period.

The two main divisions of the country are the coastal strip, generally some 60 miles wide, and the interior plateau, as much as 7,000 feet high in the west, and descending gently to 4,000 feet in the east.

The coastal strip is distinguished by its scanty and uncertain rainfall, 20 inches in the north, and less than 14 inches in the south. The aridity is caused partly by the cool Benguela current, from which the prevailing south-west and west sea breezes bring much fog and cloud but little rain, and partly by the position of this coastal strip at the foot of the interior plateau, so that winds reaching it from that direction are descending and therefore dry. The mean annual temperature at Loanda is 74°, lower than that at Luluaburg, 2,000 feet above the sea in the Congo Basin, in about the same latitude, which has 76°. The cool current on the coast more than neutralizes the less altitude of the former station.

The rainfall on the plateau probably exceeds 40 inches everywhere. The mean annual temperature is about 68° where the altitude is 4,000 feet. The rise in temperature in summer is checked by the rain and clouds, so that the warmest months are October and January. The coolest and clearest months are May to September, when, especially in the south, frost is frequent at night owing to the great radiation on the plateau. The air is then often very dry, but at times clouds and heavy mists, 'cacimbo', make their appearance.

CHAPTER XIII

SOUTH-WEST AFRICA

As far north as the Congo mouth a tendency to low rainfall shows itself on the coast. This tendency becomes more and more pronounced southward in South-west Africa.

The prevailing winds are the south-east trades (masked on the coast by the almost constant sea breeze), which, having blown across the continent, and perhaps crossed the Drakensberg, are dry winds. They blow almost constantly in winter, when the subtropical high-pressure belt covers almost all Africa south of Capricorn, and this is the dry season. In the southern summer the high-pressure belt swings south, and is broken by low pressures over the heated continent, which cause the winds of South-west Africa to be variable, though easterlies are still predominant.

The cool Benguela current, which washes the whole west coast of the continent as far as the Congo mouth, intensifies the aridity, since any wind from the sea reaches the continent at so low a temperature that the increase of temperature inland soon makes it as drying an agent as the south-east trades.

South-west Africa and the arid part of British Bechuanaland is the counterpart of the Sahara. The region is far less arid than the Sahara, however, owing chiefly to the less width of the southern land mass, and the Kalahari is by no means a waterless desert. Yet the only perennial streams of South-west Africa are the Cunene and the Orange, its northern and southern boundaries, and the watercourse which reaches the sea in Walvis Bay is said to contribute water to the ocean only once in ten years.

There are three main regions, the coastal strip or the Namib, the highlands, and the Kalahari. The coastal strip has west and south-west winds with hardly a break throughout the year. These are sea breezes, blowing in to the heated continent, in spite of the general tendency to south-east winds in these latitudes. They naturally blow strongest in summer, and during the afternoon and evening hours. The district is an almost waterless tract, the mean rainfall on the coast itself being probably less than 2 inches a year, falling entirely in summer, except at and south of Lüderitz Bay, where there is winter rain. Away from the coast the rainfall is heavier, but even at the foot of the highlands, 50 to 100 miles inland, the total is probably only about 4 inches. Paradoxical though it seems, in a country which is incapable of agricultural development owing to lack of rain the moist air is one of the greatest discomforts of life. The west wind reaches the land from the cool current charged with fog, which at night is dense enough to wet the ground, so that a certain amount of vegetation lives on it. Fog is recorded at the coast stations about once in six observations; Durban on the opposite side of Africa has only one observation of fog in 600. The mean annual relative humidity at Walvis Bay is 84 per cent. The air is generally raw and cheerless; but as the south-west winds make their way inland they become warmer, the fog dissolves, and 70 miles inland it is said to be rare. Temperature is low and uniform, and is in striking contrast to that of the east coast of the continent in the same latitude (page 83).

During winter the almost constant south-west wind is occasionally replaced by an east wind, blowing from the high pressures that form over the land in that season. As the east wind descends from the plateau to the coastal plain, föhn effects are developed, the air is clear, and bright skies replace the usual fog. Remarkably high temperatures and low humidities are experienced. The highest temperatures of the year occur during the winter under these conditions.

On the highlands, part of the South African plateau everywhere more than 3,000 and in parts more than 5,000 feet above the sea, the winds are easterly throughout the year, and the sky is very clear, giving a large range of temperature both annual and diurnal; 109° has been observed by day, followed by frost at night. The mean monthly temperature at Windhoek ranges from 56° to 74°. Frost is frequent in winter. The rainfall is far heavier than on the coast. The southern part receives least, but at Windhoek the yearly total of 15 inches produces very good pasture, and the considerable white community has good conditions for stock-rearing; Grootfontein has 24 inches, and here agriculture is said to be possible without irrigation. In the north the highlands are forested, the annual rainfall being probably 24 to 28 inches. The rain falls in summer, from November to April, almost entirely in thunderstorms. The winter months are rainless.

The rest of South-west Africa is part of the Kalahari Desert, the driest part of the interior of South Africa. It is a low-lying region, the basin of the Molopo River, which, however, rarely contains running water. The rainfall is least in the south, but even here it is estimated at about 10 inches a year. In the north it is probably as much as 25 inches between Lake Ngami and the Zambezi. The rain falls in summer and is very variable from year to year. The Kalahari resembles other arid regions in having a large range of temperature.

CHAPTER XIV

NYASALAND AND NORTHERN RHODESIA

THE distinction to which attention has been so often drawn between lowland and highland climates in Africa is as important here as elsewhere. The lowlands consist of the valleys of the Zambezi and Shiré, and the shores of Lake Nyasa. They have a decidedly tropical and unhealthy climate.

'The heat is frightful just before the rains, the temperature occasionally being as high as 118° in the shade, though at night-time falling to 85°, thus rendering it possible to live. In the height of the rainy season the range of the thermometer is not so great, but the heat is often more unbearable owing to its greater uniformity and the moistness of the air. In the months of January, February, and March, the thermometer may be 100° in the day-time and only fall to 85° or 90° at night' (SIR H. H. JOHNSTON).

The rainy season is very clearly defined, including the months October to April. There is a slight break in the rains at the end of December, when the sun is farthest south, but they soon return with renewed vigour, and January and February are the wettest months. The annual mean in the Zambezi valley between Zumbo and the Shiré–Zambezi confluence is about 35 inches, and in the lower Shiré valley about 45 inches. The amount becomes greater towards the north up the Shiré Valley, and on the north-west shore of Lake Nyasa it is probably between 60 and 80 inches. These lowlands are hotbeds of malaria and other tropical diseases. The highlands, which fortunately are of considerable extent, present a great contrast, and life is not only possible but comfortable for white men.

'Such a place as Zomba (3,000 feet above the sea) may be taken as a fair sample of British Central Africa climate. Here during the cold season from May till September we have a day temperature not exceeding 75° and a night temperature ranging from 40° to 60°. In the months of September, October, and November, the day temperature may rise to 98° and fall at night to 65°. During the height of the rainy season the day temperature ranges from 75° to 95° and the night from 65° to 80°.'

At Blantyre, 3,000 feet above the sea, the mean annual

temperature is only 68°; frost occurs occasionally at night in the dry season. The mean annual range of temperature is about 14°, and the mean daily range varies from about 24° in October to 13° in June. At these altitudes the heat is never oppressive, and still higher the climate is rather too cold for comfort.

The relative humidity is considerable throughout the year, averaging about 75 per cent. The rainy season is November to April as in the lowlands, but above 3,000 feet no month can be called rainless, and Fort Anderson (Mlanje) has almost 2 inches of rain even in July and August. The rainfall is far heavier than in the valleys; Lauderdale has as much as 108 inches, Zomba has 55 inches, which may be regarded as a typical figure except in the highest and most exposed positions. But Blantyre has only 36 inches, being perhaps sheltered by the mountains on the north. The mountains round the north end of Lake Nyasa are exceedingly rainy, with possibly 100 inches in parts.

By far the largest portion of Northern Rhodesia consists of plateau, varying in altitude from over 6,000 feet in the north and east to about 3,500 in the south; but the valleys of the Zambezi, Kafue, and Luangwa are much lower. The distinction between highland and lowland climate holds here also, but unfortunately even the highlands of Northern Rhodesia, especially south of Lake Tanganyika, are not altogether free from malaria. The capital has now been moved, partly for reasons of health, from Livingstone, an uncomfortably hot even if no longer unhealthy town on the Zambezi, to Lusaka, 300 miles north-east, situated on the open plateau 4,000 feet above the sea.

The rains begin with thunderstorms towards the end of October and set in definitely in November, when the equatorial low-pressure system has swung south to cover South Africa and the winds in Rhodesia are northerly. They continue till March, after which the low-pressure system retreats northward. The mean annual rainfall is about 50 inches in the north and 30 inches in the south in the Zambezi valley.

There are three well-marked seasons in the year. May to September is dry and rainless, cool and comfortable, the mean monthly temperature at the average altitude of the plateau being about 62°. The end of September, October, and early November is a hot season, with a monthly mean of about 77°; the earlier weeks are very dry, but the later part of this season has a good deal of cloud and some thunderstorms in the hot hours of the day. December to March is the rainy season, with heavy rain, much of it in thunderstorms, and damp air, breaks in the rains and fine weather being the exception; the mean monthly temperature is about 70°, the drop from the hot season being due to the screen of dense cloud and the cooling effect of the heavy rain. Except during the rains the climate is very sunny.

CHAPTER XV
PORTUGUESE EAST AFRICA

THERE are two main types of climate, coastal and interior.

The warm Mozambique current, a continuation of the Equatorial current of the Indian Ocean, washes the coast, giving great heat and humidity. The temperature along the whole 1,000 miles is strikingly uniform, the annual mean being 72° at Lourenço Marques, 76° at Beira, and 79° at Mozambique; the latter town is slighter warmer than Mombasa, 800 miles nearer the Equator. The mean annual rainfall on the lowlands is 30–40 inches in the north (Mozambique 33 inches), increases to over 50 inches between Quelimane and Beira (Beira 62 inches), and thence decreases southward to about 30 inches round Lourenço Marques. North of the Zambezi River the rainfall decreases at first from the coast inland, but increases again to over 60 inches in the highlands round the north of Lake Nyasa. Similarly in the south there is a comparatively dry region with about 25 inches between the coast and the edge of the plateau which has about 30 inches. Summer is everywhere the rainy season, especially the period December to May. The humidity of the air is always considerable, and very high during the rains, and in conjunction with the high temperature makes the coast decidedly unhealthy. The sultry nights are enervating as in most tropical lowlands.

The highlands of the interior are, of course, much cooler and are said to be healthy, so that even European colonization may be possible, but few details are available.

CHAPTER XVI
MADAGASCAR

Fig. 21 shows that while central and southern Madagascar may be considered as under the influence of the south-east trades always, the north-west of the island has a marked seasonal change, since the north-east trades of the North Indian Ocean extend thus far in January as north-west winds after crossing the Equator. The belt of lowest pressure in January crosses Madagascar in about 15° S. lat. Summer is

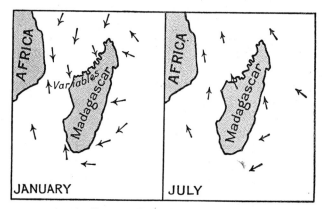

Fig. 21. Prevailing winds.

the rainy season, not because the south-east trades are then strongest, for they blow strongest in winter, but chiefly owing to the influence of the doldrums belt of rising air, into which the winds blow from the east on the east coast, and from the north-west on the north-west coast, their ascent being, of course, hastened by the mountains. The east coast has no dry season, for the ascent of the mountains by the south-east trade wind gives 5 inches of rain even in July. September, October, and November are the driest months, but each has over 3 inches of rain.

The east and north-west of the island, both windward slopes in summer, have abundant rainfall, amounting to more than 100 inches per annum in many parts. The south and south-west, on the other hand, which are very low-lying, and partly in lee of the eastern block of high land, are decidedly dry, almost arid, with as little as 16 inches a year in places. In consequence of its clearer skies this region has higher temperatures in summer than the rest of the island, despite its higher latitude.

Much of the interior is over 5,000 feet above the sea, and hence the control of temperature by altitude is important.

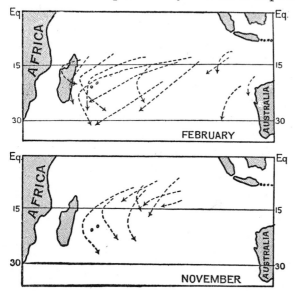

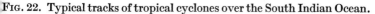

FIG. 22. Typical tracks of tropical cyclones over the South Indian Ocean.

Tropical cyclones are frequent in Madagascar, Mozambique, and the off-lying islands, the Comoro group, Réunion, and Mauritius. They are to be expected chiefly in January, February, March, and April; out of 328 storms recorded in Mauritius, 241 occurred in these months, none in August and September.

NUMBER OF CYCLONES RECORDED IN MAURITIUS IN 35 YEARS

Jan..	. 71	Apr. .	. 50	July .	. 2	Oct.	. 5
Feb..	. 61	May .	. 19	Aug..	. 0	Nov.	. 25
Mar..	. 59	June .	. 3	Sept..	. 0	Dec.	. 33

Total . . . 328

The cyclones originate over the warm ocean, latitude 5° to 15° S., longitude 60° to 90° E. (the Seychelles are very rarely within their range) and travel first in a south-westerly direction towards Madagascar (Fig. 22). They often follow a parabolic course, and the summit of the parabola shows a tendency to swing north and south with the sun, the cyclones commonly recurving about 22° S. lat. in January and February, and sometimes as far north as 14° S. lat. in May; as a general rule they recurve between 18° and 22° S. lat. Their track often forms almost a semi-circle round the islands of Réunion and Mauritius, which are then the scene of widespread devastation. After recurving the cyclones move away towards the south-east.

CHAPTER XVII

BRITISH SOUTH AFRICA
(SOUTH OF THE RIVER ZAMBEZI)

ALTHOUGH this area extends through almost 19° of latitude it has so many features of topography and climate in common that it may well be treated as a whole.

During the summer of the southern hemisphere atmospheric pressure is relatively low, the low pressures having migrated south with the sun from the Equator. There is a fairly steep gradient from the subtropical anticyclones of the South Atlantic and South Indian Oceans, and the wind blows in to the continent, from the north-east, east, south-east, and (probably owing to topographical influences) south-west in Natal, from south and south-east in the east of the Cape Province, bringing rain and cloud over the whole country except the neighbourhood of Cape Town.

In winter anticyclonic conditions establish themselves over the land. The wind tends to be light, the weather fine and rainless, and the sky clear. On the east coast, however, easterly winds continue in winter also, east being the general wind direction on the coast as far north as Mozambique throughout the year. Southern Rhodesia has light easterly winds all the year, north-easterly in summer, south-easterly in winter. Hence South Africa has, speaking generally, rainy summers and rainless winters. But an important exception is the south-west and west coastal district of the Cape Province, which has its rains in winter and a rainless summer, in other words a 'Mediterranean' climate.

MEAN WIND DIRECTION (per cent.)

	Cape Town.		Durban.		Johannesburg.	
	Jan.	July.	Jan.	July.	Jan.	July.
N. . . .	3	28	1	3	38	28
NE. . . .	1	1	25	23	12	7
E. . . .	1	1	18	12	11	8
SE. . . .	2	2	5	4	11	7
S. . . .	72	39	3	4	7	16
SW. . . .	3	7	29	20	5	12
W. . . .	4	3	16	27	3	6
NW. . . .	13	18	1	3	11	16
Calm . . .	1	1	2	4	2	1

In summer the subtropical high pressures lie a little south of the continent, and partly cover the coastal belt just mentioned, so that the weather is fine and dry. In winter they move north, and Cape Town and its neighbourhood are left on their poleward side, and so are open to the depressions of the stormy westerlies. The rainiest district is the extreme south of the province, which lies nearest to the disturbances. It is of interest to note that although winter is the season of storms and rain, yet the mean atmospheric pressure is higher then than in summer, being 30·16 inches in July, 29·90 in January, at Cape Town—a good example of the fact that not absolute pressure, but the nature of the pressure distribution in the district, determines the weather conditions.

Altitude has a most important influence on the climate of South Africa, most of which is plateau of considerable height. The altitude zones usually distinguished are (i) the coastal plain from sea-level to about 1,000 feet, (ii) the Little Karroo, about 1,500 feet, (iii) the Great Karroo, 2,000 to 3,000 feet, (iv) the High Veld, about 4,000 to 6,000 feet. This last is the plateau of which so much of South Africa consists, the other three belts being steps or terraces between it and the sea.

The plateau is lowest in the west, along the line joining the Victoria Falls on the Zambezi to the confluence of the Molopo and Orange Rivers. Much of its eastern edge is tilted steeply upwards, to form the Drakensberg Mountains, over 10,000 feet high. The low-lying valleys of the Zambezi and Limpopo carry the coastal climate far inland.

Temperature. The temperature of British South Africa is remarkably uniform, owing to the fact that the highest plateau is in the north, and the general level tends to sink towards the south, so that increase in latitude is counteracted by decrease in elevation. Another factor is that the amount of rain and cloud decreases southward, and hence there is an increase in the duration of sunshine to balance the diminution in the angle of incidence of the sun's rays. This uniformity is illustrated by the figures shown in the table on p. 83.

These plateau stations are typical of most of the area. They are much cooler than stations in similar latitudes in the northern hemisphere. This is not entirely due to their altitude, as is seen on comparing Beira, on the coast of Portuguese

East Africa, lat. 20° S., where the mean annual temperature is 75·7°, with Bombay, lat. 19° N., where it is 79·3°. One explanation is the small area of the land mass of South

	Latitude.	Altitude. Feet.	MEAN TEMPERATURE			
			Jan.	July.	Year.	Range.
Salisbury . .	17° 48′	4,800	69	56	65	15
Bulawayo . .	20° 10′	4,470	71	57	66	15
Pretoria . .	25° 47′	4,392	72	52	63	20
Bloemfontein .	29° 8′	4,568	72	48	61	24
Graaf Reinet .	32° 15′	2,460	72	51	63	21
Cape Town . .	33° 56′	115	70	55	62	16

Africa, and the vastness of the surrounding seas as compared with those in the same latitudes of the northern hemisphere.

The lowlands are hotter than the plateau, especially in winter and on the east coast, which is washed by the warm Mozambique current; the mean temperatures at Mopeia (Portuguese East Africa) and Salisbury, Komati Poort and Pretoria illustrate this.

The effect of the cool Benguela current on the west coast, and the warm Mozambique on the east, is evident from the following temperatures in almost the same latitude:

MEAN TEMPERATURE °F.			
	Feb.	July.	Annual.
Port Nolloth . .	60	55	58
Durban . . .	76	64	70

The low temperature at Cape Town (annual mean 62°) is due to the cool Benguela current. The temperature of the sea surface close to the shore is almost the same for more than 700 miles north of Cape Town, the coldest water being off the south of South-west Africa. This shows that the cool water is due rather to upwelling along the coast from the deeper strata of the ocean, owing to the pull of the south-east trades which blow over the surface, than to the northward flow of cold water from the Antarctic, though this latter influence cannot be ignored; but if it were the main cause the water would become warmer, however slowly, as it flowed on to warmer latitudes. Warmer water is found not towards the north, but away from the coast, and this corroborates the view that the coldest water reaches the surface along the coast itself from the depths.

Round the coast from the Cape of Good Hope towards the east and north the warm Mozambique current becomes increasingly evident. Thus Port Elizabeth has a mean annual temperature of 64°, East London 65°, and Durban 71°. North of this, however, the change towards lower latitudes is smaller; Lourenço Marques has 72°, Beira 76°.

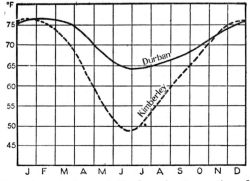

Fig. 23. Mean temperature at Durban (east coast) and Kimberley (interior plateau, altitude 4,042 feet).

In summer (Fig. 31), owing to the clear skies, the plateau enjoys remarkably high temperatures by day, and even the mean monthly temperature is almost as high at Kimberley, 4,042 feet above the sea, as at Durban on the coast, where there is much cloud and humidity (Fig. 23). But in winter the plateau is far cooler, Kimberley having a mean July temperature of 51°, while Durban has 64°; this is the result of the rapid loss of heat by radiation through the clear plateau air. Spring is decidedly warmer than autumn on the plateau, but near the coast autumn is much warmer than spring, an ordinary marine characteristic. The mean temperature at Kimberley in April is 64°, in October 67°; thus the temperature curve lags behind the sun less than usually occurs, a result partly of the clear skies and dry air of the plateau, which enable the ground to heat and cool rapidly, and partly of the fact that the summer rains continue into autumn but have not started in spring, so that April is a cloudier month than October. In Rhodesia the warmest month is November, before the clouds and rain reach their height and lower the temperature, especially the daily maxima. Elsewhere January or February is the warmest month and July the coolest.

The range of temperature is far greater inland than on the coast (see table on p. 83). But in Rhodesia, even so far from the sea as at Salisbury and Bulawayo, the mean annual range

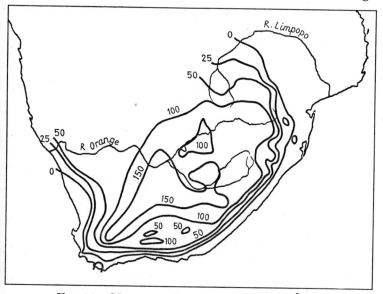

Fig. 24.   Mean annual number of days with frost.

is small, owing to the low latitude; it is much greater in the south, reaching its maximum in the Great Karroo and the south of the Orange Free State Province. The daily temperature range also is greatest on the high plateaux, the land heating rapidly under the unclouded sun, and losing its heat equally rapidly through the clear air at night. The mean daily range is generally about 27° on the high Veld. At Pretoria it is 29° (23° in February, 34° in August), at Bulawayo 24° (19° in February, 28° in September). The range is greatest during the dry months when the sky is clearest, in July and August over most of the region, but in January and February in the south-west of Cape Province. Very high temperatures are sometimes recorded in the interior, up to, but rarely exceeding

100° in Rhodesia, and, what is more important for the farmer, also very low ones. The thermometer may fall considerably below freezing-point at night in any month of the year on the southern part of the plateau, and in winter 'severe frosts, capable of freezing standing water, are practically unknown along the coast but are of fairly frequent occurrence in the interior. As a matter of fact frost is liable to occur at inland stations during any month of the year, but more particularly from May till mid-September, although killing frosts are apt to occur as early as March and as late as October' (Fig. 24). In some cases the cooling is a local radiation effect on calm clear nights, in others strong south winds in rear of a low-pressure system import abnormally cold air which sweeps over large areas. Even the Rhodesian plateau is not immune from ground frosts in winter, but the air temperature is rarely below 32°, and snow is hardly known except on the mountains. The lowest temperature on record is 6°, at Palmietfontein in the north-east of the Cape Province, 4,500 feet above the sea.

Föhn winds, known as Berg winds, descending from the plateau to the coast, are noteworthy, especially on the cool west coast (mean annual frequency about 50 days). They blow from the east at Port Nolloth, from the north on the south coast of Cape Province, from the north-west in Natal. They are most frequent in the winter half-year, and cause the highest temperatures recorded, up to 105° at Port Nolloth. They may continue for as long as two or three days and be very oppressive, and the hot drying wind sometimes does much damage to crops.

Rainfall. The main features of the rainfall distribution are easily understood. The rainfall of the whole region, except the south-west of the Cape Province, probably originates in the evaporation from the South Indian Ocean and is carried into the continent by the SE., E., and NE. winds. Most rain falls during the summer months, when the monsoonal effect is strongest, and the heat of the land causes instability. The tropical cyclones of the South Indian Ocean sometimes extend their influence over Rhodesia and add to its late summer rain. After crossing the narrow coastal plain the east winds rise to the plateau, and all the eastern belt receives a fair rainfall, amounting to over 45 inches a year in the highest

parts of the Drakensberg, and over 40 inches along the
coastal strip, some 40 miles wide, south-west from Durban,
where the sea winds are first compelled to give up moisture.
The interior of Natal between these two areas of greatest
rainfall has about 30 inches of rain a year.

Beyond the crest of the Drakensberg the land slopes down
steadily to the west and the rainfall becomes less, as is shown
by the following records from stations lying on or near the
29th parallel:

MEAN ANNUAL RAINFALL

	Altitude. Feet.	Inches.
Durban . . .	260	43
Pietermaritzburg . .	2,218	36
Drakensberg . . .	10,000	45 (approx.)
Bloemfontein . . .	4,568	22
Kimberley . . .	4,012	16
Upington . . .	2,800	11
Pella	1,800	3
Port Nolloth . . .	40	2

Any latitude south of the Zambezi, except in the extreme
south of the Cape Province, would give a similar series of
records.

The 20-inch annual isohyet follows closely the western
boundary of Southern Rhodesia, the Transvaal, and Orange
Free State Province, all the country east of the line having over
20 inches of rain. Bechuanaland has between 10 and 20 inches,
except the south-west district which, with the north-west and
centre of the Cape Province, has less than 10 inches.

Not only is the rainfall heavier on the east coast, but it
begins earlier in the season and goes on later than in the
interior. Durban has rain in every month of the year, the
real rainy season lasting nine months, from August to April
(Fig. 25). In most of that part of the interior where the
annual rainfall exceeds 25 inches the rains begin in October
and last till March, a period of six months; April is a transition
month, and the dry season definitely starts in May. But in the
drier region with 20 inches or less a year the rains are delayed,
and start only in November, and in many parts in December, a delay which is a great disadvantage for agriculture.

The difference in the total yearly rainfall of two stations, one
west of the other, is largely accounted for by the poor spring
rains at the drier western station. This may be illustrated
from Johannesburg and Vryburg:

MEAN SEASONAL RAINFALL (Inches)

	Winter.	Spring.	Summer.	Autumn.	
	June–Aug.	Sept.–Nov.	Dec.–Feb.	Mar.–May.	Year.
Johannesburg .	0·9	8·6	16·8	6·9	33·2
Vryburg . .	0·8	2·1	13·1	6·4	22.4

The eastern half of Bechuanaland has an annual mean of
about 15 inches, but the rains are so short and unreliable
that even native cattle-rearing is precarious.

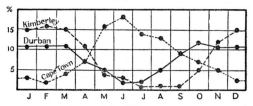

FIG. 25. Mean monthly rainfall (percentage of annual total).

However in Southern Rhodesia the spring rain is much the
same everywhere (except that the elevated eastern escarp-
ments receive more than the rest of the country), and the
difference in the mean annual totals is due chiefly to the
better rains received in late summer and autumn in the east:

	Winter.	Spring.	Summer.	Autumn.	
	June–Aug.	Sept.–Nov.	Dec.–Feb.	Mar.–May.	Year.
Salisbury . .	0·2	5·1	20·7	6·0	31.9
Bulawayo . .	0·0	4·3	15·1	4·1	23.6

The spring rains fall almost entirely in local thunderstorms of
convectional origin, which are equally frequent both in the
east and in the west, and therefore the total spring rainfall is
fairly uniform in amount. But the summer rainfall is brought
by the general monsoonal inflow from the Indian Ocean,
which sets in about December, and the amount is naturally
greater on the east side of the continent. Much of the autumn

rain is associated with the tropical cyclones of the South
Indian Ocean, and their influence also is, of course, strongest
in the east. They are probably not felt far inland.

At many stations in Southern Rhodesia there is a slight
break in the rains in the middle of December. This is not
noticeable in the monthly totals, but appears clearly in the
means for 10-day periods (Fig. 26). It coincides with the
retreat of the sun to the tropic of Capricorn, the rainiest
periods being about the time when the sun is overhead, just
as in the southern Sudan the rainfall diminishes when the
sun is over the tropic of
Cancer. The rain-bearing
winds in Rhodesia are
shown in Fig. 27.

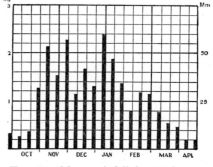

FIG. 26. Mean rainfall for 10-day
periods at Bulawayo.[1]

Southern Rhodesia re-
ceives 95 per cent. of its
annual rainfall during the
summer half-year, Pre-
toria 87 per cent., Durban
70 per cent. The line
separating the summer-
from the winter-rain
region runs west from
the coast between East
London and Port Elizabeth, through the Little Karroo and
thence NNW. to the coast of South-west Africa between
Angra Pequena and Walvis Bay (Fig. 28). Cape Town receives
77 per cent. of its mean annual rainfall in the winter half-year
(Fig. 25). Port Elizabeth is typical of the transition region
in having both winter and summer rain, 55 per cent. in winter,
45 per cent. in summer (Fig. 29). The winter rain of this
south-west coastal belt is brought largely by north-west
winds, blowing into the passing depressions of the 'Roaring
Forties'.

The thunderstorms of South Africa are very violent and
destructive. Groups of cattle are sometimes killed by a single
flash of lightning, and patches of grass fired. Hailstones of
great size often fall at such times, and do much damage to

[1] Goetz, 'The Rainfall of Rhodesia', *Proc. Rhodesia Sci. Assoc.*
1909.

fruit. A large part of the rain falls during thunderstorms, and much of it is lost to agriculture owing to the rapid run-off.

Another most serious disadvantage to the agriculturist is the uncertainty which unfortunately characterizes the rainfall of the whole plateau. Bloemfontein has had as little as 15 inches and as much as 34·5 inches in a year, the annual mean being 25·6 inches. In November 1891, 7·5 inches fell, and in November 1877 none at all.

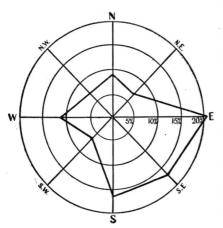

FIG. 27. Rain wind-rose for Bulawayo, showing the percentage of the total rainfall associated with each wind direction. (Goetz.)

In winter the air is very dry and clear, and the sky almost cloudless. At Johannesburg, in the months June to September, the mean cloud covering is less than two-tenths of the sky; even in February, the cloudiest month, the mean is only five-tenths. The Union of South Africa is justly famous for its sunny skies. This is perhaps the most striking feature of the climate to a visitor from North-west Europe. The mean daily sunshine (in hours) is

	J.	F.	M.	A.	M.	J.	J.	A.	S.	O.	N.	D.	Year.	Per cent. of possible.
Cape Town	9·7	9·8	8·4	6·5	6·1	4·8	4·9	5·9	6·8	7·9	9·2	10·2	7·5	66
Johannes-burg	7·8	7·5	7·2	8·7	8·8	9·0	9·2	9·9	9·3	9·0	8·9	8·6	8·7	73

In Rhodesia, however, some winter days are unpleasant with drab cloud and strong east winds, though a whole day with a completely overcast sky is very rare; the mean sunshine is 9 hours a day in winter, 6 hours a day in summer. An important result of the absence of cloud is the large range of temperature on the plateau. Owing to the scanty rainfall and dry atmosphere the wind often raises clouds of dust, and this is considered to be the greatest disadvantage in the plateau climate from the physiological point of view, especially for persons suffering from lung troubles, who find the dry climate very suitable in other respects. Except for this, it is decidedly

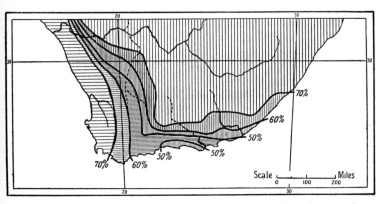

FIG. 28. Proportions of rainfall in summer (vertical lines) and winter (horizontal lines).

healthy. In Rhodesia spring is very dry, and the air is not only dusty but also smoky from bush fires, so that the sky is grey and the visibility poor. The only malarial districts are the coastal plain and the hot low river valleys of the Zambezi and the Limpopo, which carry the unhealthy conditions far inland. The coast of Natal is healthier than the coast farther north.

Main Climatic Divisions of the Cape Province. The Cape

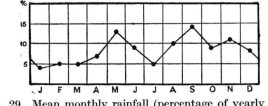

FIG. 29. Mean monthly rainfall (percentage of yearly total) at Port Elizabeth.

Province is the least uniform province of the Union in respect of climate, and may be divided into the following nine main regions (Fig. 30). The mean temperature and rainfall at typical stations may be found on pp. 98 and 102.

Divisions 1 to 4 are coastal.

1. (Typical station, Port Nolloth.) The north-west coast is desert, a continuation of the desert coastal strip of South-west

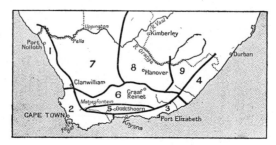

Fig. 30. The major climatic regions of the Cape Province.

Africa. Its main feature is the very low rainfall, almost everywhere less than 5 inches, and only 2·3 inches at Port Nolloth. Almost all the rain falls in winter. The temperature is remarkably low owing to the cool current which washes the coast, and the relative humidity is high, and fogs frequent. Away from the coast conditions improve; the air is drier

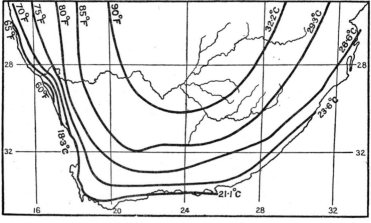

Fig. 31. Mean temperature in January.

and the sky clearer; the rain is somewhat less scanty and the temperature is higher. The mean temperature for February is 75° at Clanwilliam, some distance inland, and only 60° at Port Nolloth (Fig. 31). Berg winds are prominent.

2 (Cape Town) is at once marked off from 1 by its heavier rainfall, and the 10-inch isohyet may be taken as the boundary between them. We have left the desert and reached a fairly well-watered land. Cape Town receives 25 inches annually, but the rainfall in this neighbourhood is very variable according to locality, even exceeding 200 inches in small elevated areas near the town. Table Mountain is often capped with dense clouds, especially at the beginning of stormy weather, the phenomenon being known as the Tablecloth. About 70 per cent. of the rain falls in winter. Summer is dry and warm. The climate is of a 'Mediterranean' type, and consequently wheat is successfully grown, and vines flourish owing to the warm autumn. But the temperature, especially in summer, is far lower than at places in the same latitude on the Mediterranean Sea. The mean at Tangier for the warmest month of the year is 76°, at Beirut 83°, but at Cape Town only 70°, since Table Bay contains the cool water of the Benguela current. False Bay, however, only fifteen miles away across the Cape Flats, is often filled by the warm Agulhas current, and is then strikingly warmer than Table Bay. The sea temperature has been observed to be 67° in False Bay while it was only 51° in Table Bay.

The next division along the south coast, 3 (Port Elizabeth), is chiefly distinguished by having rain both in summer and winter (Fig. 29), the annual total being from 20 to 30 inches. The air is damp throughout the year. Temperature is somewhat higher than in 2, especially in the east, and the range is smaller.

Division 4 (Durban) is a region of well-marked summer rainfall, about 70 per cent. of the annual total being received in the summer half year. The mean temperature at sea-level ranges from about 65° in winter to 77° in summer. The rainfall is about 30 inches.

The remaining divisions are inland.

The Southern Karroo, 5 (Oudtshoorn), is the first of the terraces rising from the south coast. The average altitude is about 1,500 feet. It is a transition region to the higher plateau.

The Great Karroo, 6 (Graaf Reinet), is the next terrace, 2,500 feet above the sea. The mean temperature in July is about 51°, in January 72°. The mean daily range at Graaf Reinet is 25° in June and 34° in January, the latter figure especially being notably high. In summer a reading of 108° has been recorded; on winter nights frost is usual. The rainfall is very scanty, under 10 inches in the west and centre, in The Ghoup as low as 5 inches. There is no rain except in summer, most of it falling in heavy showers in January, February, and March. The rest of the year is a long dry season when practically desert conditions prevail, and vegetation is burnt up, brown and dusty. The effect of the first rain showers of summer in rousing the plants to life, and carpeting the Karroo with bright flowers, has often been described. The remarkable xerophytic adaptations of the plants bear witness to the scant and uncertain rainfall; sometimes a year may pass without a shower. In the east, however, the Great Karroo has a better rainfall, the annual mean rising to 20 inches.

The rest of the Province consists of the High Veld, with an average altitude of about 4,000 feet, but much higher in the east in the Drakensberg. It may be divided into an arid western part, 7, with under 10 inches of rain annually and far less in the north-west where there is under 5 inches, a central tract, 8 (Hanover), with a rainfall from 10 to 25 inches, and the more elevated eastern part, 9, with over 40 inches in the highest mountains, and everywhere more than 25 inches. The mean temperature at Hanover, a central town, 4,500 feet above the sea, is 69° in January and February, and 43° in June and July, the mean annual being 57°, 6° less than at Graaf Reinet, 5° less than at Cape Town, the lower latitude being more than counteracted by the greater altitude. However it is chiefly in winter that the plateau temperatures fall below those of the coast, and in summer they are remarkably high (see p. 84). The mean daily range at Hanover is 31°, and varies little with the season. The whole of 8 and 9 gets its rain almost entirely in summer; in the north 80 per cent. falls in the summer half-year, and July, August, and September are practically rainless.

MEAN TEMPERATURE (°F.)

MEDITERRANEAN AFRICA

Station.	Alt. Feet.	Jan.	Feb.	Mar.	Apr.	May.	June.	July.	Aug.	Sept.	Oct.	Nov.	Dec.	Year.	Range.
Mogador	33	57.0	58.8	60.3	63.1	64.8	67.5	68.2	68.2	68.5	66.7	62.6	58.8	63.7	11.5
Marrakech	1,542	51.6	54.7	59.2	66.7	69.4	77.2	82.0	85.3	75.9	69.8	62.4	54.1	67.3	33.7
Algiers	72	49.3	50.4	52.5	55.8	61.0	67.8	73.4	74.7	70.3	63.7	56.8	51.8	60.6	25.4
Constantine	2,165	43.1	45.7	50.4	53.8	62.6	70.9	79.3	78.3	72.3	61.2	51.6	44.4	59.5	36.2
Géryville	4,280	38.8	42.4	46.2	52.3	60.3	70.2	78.4	77.2	68.0	55.9	46.4	40.1	56.3	39.6
Biskra	410	52.7	56.5	60.8	68.2	76.6	85.3	92.3	90.7	84.4	72.5	61.2	53.2	71.2	39.6
Tunis	141	48.4	51.3	54.3	58.3	64.4	72.0	77.7	78.6	74.5	66.7	58.8	52.3	63.1	30.2
Tripoli	56	54.0	56.1	59.9	64.8	68.5	74.3	78.8	80.2	78.3	74.1	65.3	57.7	66.2	26.2
Las Palmas (Grand Canary)	30	62.8	62.8	63.7	64.9	67.3	70.5	72.1	73.8	72.7	71.4	67.5	64.2	67.8	11.0
Funchal (Madeira)	82	59.4	59.2	59.7	61.2	63.5	67.1	70.2	72.1	71.4	68.4	64.4	61.2	64.8	12.9

THE SAHARA

Station.	Alt. Feet.	Jan.	Feb.	Mar.	Apr.	May.	June.	July.	Aug.	Sept.	Oct.	Nov.	Dec.	Year.	Range.
El Golea	1,257	49.1	53.6	61.5	70.5	77.0	87.6	93.4	91.4	84.6	72.1	58.6	49.8	70.7	44.3
In-Salah	919	54.7	59.4	67.8	76.1	85.6	94.3	99.3	97.0	91.6	80.1	68.2	57.7	77.7	44.6

THE SUDAN WEST OF LAKE CHAD, NIGERIA

COAST

Station.	Alt. Feet.	Jan.	Feb.	Mar.	Apr.	May.	June.	July.	Aug.	Sept.	Oct.	Nov.	Dec.	Year.	Range.
Gorée	20	68.5	66.2	68.2	68.9	71.6	78.3	81.1	81.5	82.4	82.0	78.3	72.0	74.8	16.2
Freetown	223	81.3	82.3	82.4	82.4	81.5	80.3	78.6	77.9	79.1	80.1	81.2	81.4	80.7	4.5
Accra	60	79.7	80.3	81.3	81.1	80.0	77.5	75.7	74.7	76.2	78.3	79.8	80.1	78.7	6.6
Lagos	25	80.9	82.2	83.3	82.5	81.8	79.3	78.0	77.7	78.4	79.5	81.4	81.5	80.5	5.6
Akassa	20	78.3	79.2	79.5	79.9	78.8	77.4	76.1	75.9	76.1	77.2	78.4	78.8	77.9	4.0

INTERIOR

Station.	Alt. Feet.	Jan.	Feb.	Mar.	Apr.	May.	June.	July.	Aug.	Sept.	Oct.	Nov.	Dec.	Year.	Range.
Bismarckburg	2,329	77.4	79.3	78.4	76.5	75.2	72.5	70.2	70.2	71.4	73.4	76.5	76.6	74.8	9.1
Misahöhe	1,542	76.3	77.9	77.7	76.8	76.5	73.9	71.4	71.1	72.1	73.9	76.1	76.5	75.0	6.8
Wagaduga	2,493	74.7	75.6	85.3	88.5	86.7	81.1	78.6	77.7	79.3	81.1	80.6	75.9	80.4	13.8
Kayes	197	77.2	80.8	88.7	94.1	96.4	90.5	83.7	81.7	82.2	84.5	83.1	77.2	84.9	19.2
Timbuktu	820	71.1	73.6	83.1	91.6	94.5	93.7	89.2	86.5	89.2	88.9	80.8	71.1	84.4	23.4
Kuka	869	70.7	74.8	88.9	92.3	91.0	89.6	82.9	79.2	83.5	85.1	79.5	72.7	82.6	21.6

MEAN TEMPERATURE (°F.), *continued*

THE SUDAN EAST OF LAKE CHAD, EGYPT, ABYSSINIA, RED SEA, SOMALILAND

Station.	Alt. Feet.	Jan.	Feb.	Mar.	Apr.	May.	June.	July.	Aug.	Sept.	Oct.	Nov.	Dec.	Year.	Range.
Port Said	11	56.1	57.2	60.4	65.1	70.3	75.4	78.4	79.5	77.5	73.9	67.5	59.4	68.4	23.4
Alexandria	105	56.1	57.2	60.1	63.7	68.5	73.4	77.0	78.1	76.3	73.0	66.4	59.4	67.5	22.0
Cairo (Abbasiya)	98	52.7	55.4	60.8	67.6	74.1	79.0	81.0	80.6	76.1	71.8	64.0	55.9	68.2	28.3
Asyut	182	52.9	55.9	63.0	71.8	78.8	83.8	84.9	84.4	79.3	74.3	64.8	56.3	70.9	32.0
Wadi Halfa	421	57.9	61.0	68.5	78.1	84.6	88.2	88.5	87.4	84.6	79.5	70.0	60.1	75.7	30.6
Atbara	1,163	68.7	70.9	77.5	84.4	90.9	92.8	90.7	89.6	90.3	86.9	79.3	71.7	82.8	24.1
Khartoum	1,280	70.3	73.4	79.2	86.0	90.7	91.4	88.5	86.5	88.2	87.4	80.2	72.1	82.8	21.1
Hillet Doleib	1,283	80.8	82.9	87.1	88.3	85.1	81.3	79.9	79.5	81.3	82.0	81.7	79.2	82.4	9.1
Mongalla	1,440	80.4	81.7	82.6	81.0	79.0	77.4	75.9	75.7	77.2	78.1	79.0	79.2	79.0	6.9
El Obeid	1,866	67.3	70.5	75.9	83.1	85.8	84.7	80.8	79.0	80.1	81.3	76.1	68.7	77.7	18.5
Kassala	1,666	74.3	76.8	81.7	87.3	90.3	87.8	82.8	81.3	83.3	85.8	83.3	76.3	82.6	16.0
Addis Ababa	8,005	60.1	62.4	64.8	64.4	65.7	63.5	61.7	61.0	61.3	61.7	59.2	58.6	62.1	7.1
Harar	6,089	65.8	67.5	68.9	69.4	69.4	68.4	66.0	65.3	67.1	68.0	67.1	67.1	67.5	4.1
Port Sudan	18	73.2	73.0	74.7	79.2	84.0	88.3	92.1	92.3	88.3	83.7	80.4	75.9	82.0	19.3
Berbera	31	76.1	76.1	78.1	81.7	87.3	95.7	97.4	96.6	91.2	83.3	79.1	77.1	85.0	21.3

KAMERUN

Station.	Alt. Feet.	Jan.	Feb.	Mar.	Apr.	May.	June.	July.	Aug.	Sept.	Oct.	Nov.	Dec.	Year.	Range.
Duala	39	79.3	79.9	79.2	78.8	78.3	76.8	74.7	74.5	75.6	75.9	77.9	78.6	77.4	5.4
Yaundé	2,461	73.6	73.9	73.6	72.3	72.1	70.9	70.2	70.7	71.1	70.7	72.3	73.0	72.0	3.7

THE CONGO BASIN

Station.	Alt. Feet.	Jan.	Feb.	Mar.	Apr.	May.	June.	July.	Aug.	Sept.	Oct.	Nov.	Dec.	Year.	Range.
Banana	7	80.4	80.8	81.5	80.4	78.6	74.7	72.5	72.5	75.9	78.6	79.9	79.9	77.9	9.0
Bolobo	1,083	78.1	78.6	79.0	78.4	78.1	77.9	77.4	78.1	78.1	77.0	76.8	77.0	77.9	2.2
New Antwerp	1,230	79.2	80.1	79.2	78.1	79.2	78.4	76.5	76.3	77.0	77.4	77.9	78.1	78.1	3.8
Luluaburg	2,034	76.1	75.7	76.3	77.0	76.6	76.3	76.5	76.3	75.9	76.3	74.0	77.2	76.5	1.5
Elizabethville	4,500	72.1	71.8	70.7	70.6	66.0	60.6	60.3	64.2	70.9	74.8	74.0	71.4	68.9	14.5

KENYA COLONY (BRITISH EAST AFRICA) AND UGANDA

Station.	Alt.Ft.	Jan.	Feb.	Mar.	Apr.	May.	June	July.	Aug.	Sept.	Oct.	Nov.	Dec.	Year.	Range.
Mombasa	50	79·9	80·3	81·8	80·6	78·4	76·5	75·3	75·7	77·0	78·4	79·4	79·9	78·5	6·5
Machakos	5,650	64·4	66·4	66·2	65·3	63·6	59·9	61·0	59·0	62·4	64·9	63·3	62·8	63·2	7·9
Fort Hall	4,500	64·7	64·8	67·4	65·3	62·9	61·4	61·0	60·2	64·8	67·3	64·3	65·0	65·4	7·2
Nairobi	5,450	63·8	64·7	65·2	63·9	63·4	61·6	58·5	59·3	61·6	64·8	64·0	62·3	63·2	6·7
Kabete	6,004	63·7	64·8	64·6	63·5	61·3	59·2	58·5	58·8	59·2	62·8	61·9	61·5	61·7	6·3
Eldama Ravine	7,240	62·0	61·3	63·1	62·9	62·4	61·2	59·5	58·5	58·8	58·6	58·9	60·9	60·9	4·6
Kisumu	3,800	76·9	76·1	75·4	73·3	73·4	72·5	71·8	71·7	73·3	75·4	74·8	76·2	73·9	5·2
Entebbe	3,863	71·1	76·1	71·3	73·3	69·8	69·4	68·6	68·6	69·4	70·1	70·1	70·2	70·0	2·7
Kampala	4,298	72·0	72·3	70·5	70·2	69·3	68·9	67·7	68·1	68·7	69·3	70·0	70·0	69·7	4·6
Wadelai	1,900	80·5	82·2	79·3	78·7	77·4	76·5	76·5	76·0	77·0	77·7	78·7	79·7	78·2	6·2
Gondokoro	1,500	82·5	84·5	86·0	84·0	81·3	79·2	77·8	77·3	77·5	78·0	79·0	80·7	80·7	8·7

TANGANYIKA TERRITORY

Station.	Alt.Ft.	Jan.	Feb.	Mar.	Apr.	May.	June	July.	Aug.	Sept.	Oct.	Nov.	Dec.	Year.	Range.
Dar-es-Salaam	43	81·5	81·3	80·4	77·9	76·3	74·3	73·4	73·6	74·5	76·6	79·2	80·8	77·5	8·1
Tabora	3,983	71·2	72·0	70·5	71·5	70·9	70·7	71·3	72·9	76·3	77·7	75·9	70·7	72·6	7·2
Muanza	3,937	72·1	71·4	72·1	71·8	72·1	68·4	71·8	71·2	72·5	70·3	70·9	70·5	71·0	4·1

SOUTH-WEST AFRICA

Station.	Alt.Ft.	Jan.	Feb.	Mar.	Apr.	May.	June	July.	Aug.	Sept.	Oct.	Nov.	Dec.	Year.	Range.
Swakopmund	20	62·6	63·1	63·3	59·9	60·6	58·5	56·5	54·9	56·1	58·1	58·6	61·5	59·4	8·4
Windhoek	5,456	74·3	71·8	69·8	66·2	60·4	55·8	55·6	58·8	65·8	70·3	72·2	74·1	66·2	18·7

NYASALAND AND NORTHERN RHODESIA

Station.	Alt.Ft.	Jan.	Feb.	Mar.	Apr.	May.	June	July.	Aug.	Sept.	Oct.	Nov.	Dec.	Year.	Range.
Zomba	3,130	72·9	72·0	71·2	69·3	65·7	63·0	62·1	64·9	69·4	74·1	75·6	73·0	69·4	13·5
Lauderdale	2,539	72·8	73·6	72·1	70·2	65·8	62·1	62·4	64·9	70·5	74·5	75·6	73·2	69·8	13·5
Fort Johnston	1,558	78·6	77·4	77·9	76·8	73·2	68·9	68·0	70·9	74·8	80·4	82·0	79·2	75·7	14·0
Nkata Bay	1,400	77·2	75·6	76·6	75·0	72·0	67·7	66·9	68·6	73·6	77·1	78·0	78·0	74·0	13·1
Abercorn	5,100	68·2	65·8	67·2	67·1	65·9	64·4	63·5	67·0	69·8	71·6	69·7	67·8	67·3	8·1
Broken Hill	3,920	69·8	69·5	69·0	67·4	64·0	61·5	61·3	64·8	71·2	76·4	73·9	69·4	68·2	15·1
Livingstone	3,000	75·7	74·5	75·5	72·8	67·7	63·9	64·6	67·9	77·2	80·8	79·0	77·1	73·1	16·9

H

MEAN TEMPERATURE (°F.), *continued*

PORTUGUESE EAST AFRICA

Station.	Alt. Feet.	Jan.	Feb.	Mar.	Apr.	May.	June.	July.	Aug.	Sept.	Oct.	Nov.	Dec.	Year.	Range.
Mozambique	13	81·9	81·5	82·8	81·0	77·7	73·9	73·8	74·5	77·2	80·1	82·8	83·3	79·2	9·5
Mopeia	82	82·9	82·2	81·3	77·9	73·2	70·0	70·0	71·8	76·6	81·7	84·2	82·9	77·9	14·2

MADAGASCAR

Station.	Alt. Feet.	Jan.	Feb.	Mar.	Apr.	May.	June.	July.	Aug.	Sept.	Oct.	Nov.	Dec.	Year.	Range.
Tamatave	16	79·3	80·6	78·3	76·5	72·5	69·3	68·4	69·3	71·2	73·8	76·5	78·6	74·5	12·2
Antananarivo	4,593	70·2	69·8	69·4	67·1	63·3	59·2	57·9	59·4	63·5	68·0	70·2	70·0	65·7	12·3

BRITISH SOUTH AFRICA

Station.	Alt. Feet.	Jan.	Feb.	Mar.	Apr.	May.	June.	July.	Aug.	Sept.	Oct.	Nov.	Dec.	Year.	Range.
Port Nolloth	16	59·5	59·9	59·3	57·7	56·8	55·4	55·2	53·8	55·0	58·1	59·0	60·3	57·6	6·5
Cape Town	40	69·9	70·3	68·1	63·2	58·9	55·7	54·7	55·6	57·9	61·2	64·4	67·9	62·3	15·6
Port Elizabeth	181	69·4	69·7	68·0	65·1	61·6	59·3	57·9	58·4	59·8	61·8	64·5	67·6	63·6	11·8
Port St. John's	22	72·4	72·3	70·2	69·2	65·0	61·8	61·1	61·3	63·7	65·1	67·7	71·1	66·8	11·3
Durban	260	76·3	76·8	74·9	71·8	67·8	64·8	64·3	65·8	67·6	69·5	72·0	74·6	70·5	12·5
Pietermaritzburg	2,225	73·3	73·4	71·4	67·8	61·9	57·6	58·6	62·4	65·2	67·4	69·1	71·8	66·6	15·8
Graaf Reinet	2,500	71·8	72·3	68·2	61·8	56·5	53·0	51·0	53·8	59·0	63·8	68·5	71·5	62·7	21·3
Hanover	4,500	69·4	69·4	64·0	57·3	50·0	42·9	42·9	47·7	52·4	58·1	63·3	69·2	57·2	26·5
Kimberley	4,042	76·2	74·8	70·8	63·8	55·9	50·3	50·7	55·3	61·8	67·4	71·0	75·1	64·4	25·9
Pretoria	4,471	71·7	70·6	67·8	62·9	56·7	52·6	51·7	56·7	63·4	67·6	69·2	71·1	63·5	20·0
Komati Poort	1,000	80·5	79·4	77·0	73·0	68·1	63·1	62·9	67·4	72·7	76·0	76·9	80·6	73·1	17·7
Bulawayo	4,470	71·5	70·2	68·9	66·0	61·2	57·4	57·2	61·2	67·6	72·4	72·5	71·8	66·5	15·3
Salisbury	4,880	69·7	68·8	68·2	65·7	60·6	56·9	56·1	60·2	66·4	70·7	70·7	69·6	65·3	14·6

MEAN RAINFALL (inches)

MEDITERRANEAN AFRICA

Station.	Alt. Feet.	Jan.	Feb.	Mar.	Apr.	May.	June.	July.	Aug.	Sept.	Oct.	Nov.	Dec.	Year.
Mogador	33	2·2	1·5	2·2	0·7	0·6	0·1	0	0	0·2	1·3	2·4	2·0	13·2
Marrakech	1,542	0·8	0·9	1·7	1·3	0·4	0·4	0	0·2	0·4	0·9	1·5	0·7	9·3
Algiers	72	4·0	2·6	3·3	2·0	1·7	0·7	0·1	0·1	1·2	3·4	4·1	4·0	27·4
Constantine	2,165	2·5	2·3	2·7	2·6	1·5	1·2	0·3	0·5	1·0	2·2	2·0	3·4	22·2
Géryville	4,280	0·9	1·2	2·4	1·7	2·2	0·7	0·2	0·5	1·2	1·5	1·3	1·5	15·3
Biskra	410	0·5	0·7	0·8	1·2	0·6	0·4	0·2	0·1	0·6	0·8	0·4	0·6	6·9
Ouargla	505	0·5	0·3	0·3	0·1	0	0·1	0	0·2	0·2	0·5	0·2	0·3	2·6
Tunis	141	2·1	2·0	1·9	1·5	0·9	0·5	0·1	0·2	1·0	1·9	2·1	2·4	16·5
Tripoli	56	3·3	1·8	0·9	0·5	0·3	0·1	0	0	0·5	1·8	2·4	4·7	16·3
Las Palmas (Grand Canary)	30	1·4	0·9	1·0	0·7	0·3	0	0	0·1	0·2	1·1	2·8	2·6	11·1
Funchal (Madeira)	82	3·4	3·6	3·4	1·9	1·1	0·4	0·1	0·1	1·2	4·0	4·7	3·2	27·2

THE SUDAN WEST OF LAKE CHAD, NIGERIA

COAST

Station.	Alt. Feet.	Jan.	Feb.	Mar.	Apr.	May.	June.	July.	Aug.	Sept.	Oct.	Nov.	Dec.	Year.
Gorée	20	0	0	0	0	0	0·9	3·6	9·9	5·2	0·7	0·1	0	20·5
Freetown	223	0·4	0·3	1·2	4·1	11·5	20·0	35·6	36·6	28·5	12·6	5·1	1·4	157·2
Accra	60	0·6	1·0	1·8	3·7	5·7	7·0	1·7	0·6	1·0	1·9	1·5	0·7	27·2
Lagos	25	1·1	2·1	3·7	5·7	10·5	18·7	10·7	2·8	5·3	7·8	2·6	0·8	71·6
Akassa	20	2·6	6·5	10·0	8·6	17·0	18·6	10·1	9·3	19·3	24·7	10·6	6·5	143·8

INTERIOR

Station.	Alt. Feet.	Jan.	Feb.	Mar.	Apr.	May.	June.	July.	Aug.	Sept.	Oct.	Nov.	Dec.	Year.
Misahöhe	1,542	0·6	1·7	3·9	5·4	6·7	10·5	7·9	5·4	8·9	6·2	2·7	1·8	61·7
Bismarckburg	2,329	1·4	1·9	3·3	5·4	6·7	7·0	6·1	4·4	10·7	5·7	0·8	1·2	54·6
Wagaduga	2,493	0	0	0·1	1·8	2·5	4·5	6·2	10·6	5·0	1·3	0	0	32·0
Kayes	197	0	0	0	0	0·6	3·9	8·3	8·3	5·6	1·9	0·3	0·2	29·1
Timbuktu	820	0	0	0·1	0	0·3	0·9	3·5	2·8	1·1	0·4	0	0	9·0
Lokoja	230	0·6	0·5	1·5	4·9	6·0	5·5	7·5	6·9	10·2	4·3	0·4	0·3	48·6
Bauchi	2,200	0	0	0·1	1·3	4·1	5·7	10·4	11·6	6·3	1·5	0	0	41·0
Kano	1,570	0	0	0·1	0·5	3·2	4·8	6·9	11·3	5·0	0·4	0	0	32·2
Zinder	1,460	0	0	0	0·1	0·6	1·9	6·3	9·6	2·9	0·4	0	0	21·7

MEAN RAINFALL (inches), *continued*

THE SUDAN EAST OF LAKE CHAD, EGYPT, ABYSSINIA, SOMALILAND

Station.	Alt. Feet.	Jan.	Feb.	Mar.	Apr.	May.	June.	July.	Aug.	Sept.	Oct.	Nov.	Dec.	Year.
Port Said	11	0.9	0.4	0.4	0.2	0.1	0	0	0	0	0.1	0.5	0.7	3.3
Alexandria	105	2.1	0.9	0.5	0.2	0	0	0	0	0	0.3	1.3	2.6	8.0
Cairo (Abbasiya)	98	0.4	0.2	0.2	0.1	0	0	0	0	0	0.1	0.1	0.2	1.3
Khartoum	1,280	0	0	0	0	0.1	0.3	1.6	2.2	0.7	0.2	0	0	5.1
Hillet Doleib	1,283	0	0.2	0.2	1.1	3.1	5.4	5.9	7.1	4.3	2.8	0.6	0	30.6
Mongalla	1,440	0.1	0.7	1.5	4.2	5.4	4.6	5.2	5.8	4.9	4.3	1.8	0.3	38.9
El Obeid	1,866	0	0	0.1	0	0.4	1.2	3.6	4.5	3.4	0.7	0	0	14.0
Kassala	1,666	0	0	0	0.7	0.5	1.3	4.0	4.4	2.4	0.5	0	0	13.0
Roseires	1,532	0	0	0.1	0.7	2.2	4.3	7.3	7.8	5.6	1.3	0.3	0	29.6
Gambela	1,345	0.3	0.4	1.4	3.1	6.0	7.1	8.2	9.3	7.4	3.4	1.6	0.5	48.8
Addis Ababa	8,005	0.6	1.9	2.8	3.4	3.0	5.7	11.0	12.1	7.6	0.8	0.6	0.2	49.6
Harar	6,089	0.4	1.3	3.0	4.7	5.0	3.5	5.1	6.3	3.7	1.4	0.6	0.4	35.3
Port Sudan	18	0.4	0.2	0.1	0	0	0.4	0.4	0	0	0.3	1.7	0.7	3.9
Massaua	coast	1.6	0.7	0.6	0.5	0.4	0.1	0.1	0.2	0.2	0.3	0.9	1.9	7.4
Berbera	31	0.1	0.3	0.7	0.5	0.4	0	0.1	0.1	0	0.1	0	0.1	2.4
KAMERUN														
Yaundé	2,461	1.6	2.7	5.9	9.1	8.1	4.5	2.6	3.3	7.6	8.9	5.9	2.0	62.2
Debundja	16	8.0	10.9	17.1	17.3	24.8	59.7	64.4	57.7	65.2	45.2	26.6	15.1	412.2
Libreville	66	10.4	9.3	13.7	13.4	9.3	0.5	0.1	0.7	4.1	13.4	13.9	9.3	98.2
CONGO BASIN														
Banana	7	3.5	3.6	4.0	8.4	2.2	0	0	0.2	0.2	1.9	8.3	4.6	36.9
Bolobo	1,083	5.0	7.0	4.6	7.2	5.6	0.4	0	2.7	3.8	6.5	9.6	10.2	62.6
New Antwerp	1,230	4.1	3.5	4.1	5.6	6.2	6.1	6.3	6.3	6.3	6.6	2.6	9.3	66.9
Luluaburg	2,034	7.2	5.4	7.9	6.1	3.1	0.2	0.1	2.5	6.5	6.6	9.1	6.6	60.8
Mobaye	1,312	0.5	1.5	4.6	6.4	15.2	7.3	4.4	6.6	7.2	8.8	5.4	1.1	68.6
Djole	394	5.8	6.6	10.5	10.1	6.7	0.8	0	0	0.9	9.1	10.9	6.5	67.9
Elizabethville	4,500	9.3	10.3	9.5	1.3	0.5	0	0	0	0.3	0.5	4.0	11.4	47.1

KENYA COLONY (BRITISH EAST AFRICA) AND UGANDA

Station.	Alt. Feet.	Jan.	Feb.	Mar.	Apr.	May.	June.	July.	Aug.	Sept.	Oct.	Nov.	Dec.	Year.
Mombasa	50	0·8	0·7	2·5	8·0	12·6	4·0	3·5	2·3	2·0	3·3	4·2	2·0	46·0
Kismayu	66	0	0	0·2	1·6	5·0	3·3	2·0	0·9	0·6	0·2	0·5	0·2	14·5
Makindu	3,280	2·0	1·1	3·8	4·9	0·9	0·1	0	0	0	0·6	5·5	4·7	23·7
Nairobi	5,450	1·9	3·6	4·2	8·9	5·6	2·2	1·1	1·1	1·2	2·3	5·3	2·8	39·9
Fort Hall	4,500	1·5	2·2	4·9	12·8	6·3	1·7	0·9	0·8	1·0	4·8	7·8	2·9	47·7
Naivasha	6,290	1·1	1·6	3·0	5·8	3·0	3·3	2·0	2·4	1·8	2·1	2·7	1·7	30·4
Eldama Ravine	7,240	1·1	2·4	3·7	6·4	5·7	4·7	4·3	5·1	2·8	2·1	2·9	1·6	42·8
Entebbe	3,863	2·6	3·6	5·8	9·7	5·7	5·1	2·9	3·1	3·1	3·5	5·0	5·1	58·0
Kisumu	3,800	2·4	4·0	5·2	7·0	5·1	3·7	2·0	2·9	2·4	2·6	3·9	4·6	45·8
Butiaba	2,025	0·4	1·3	2·6	4·5	5·2	2·6	2·0	3·5	3·6	3·5	3·1	1·0	33·2
Gondokoro	1,500	0·1	0·8	2·0	3·5	6·5	3·9	5·0	4·9	4·4	4·7	1·9	0·4	38·1
Wadelai	1,900	1·1	0·7	4·4	3·8	4·9	3·4	3·9	4·6	4·0	6·6	4·5	0·9	42·8
TANGANYIKA TERRITORY														
Dar-es-Salaam	43	3·3	2·1	4·8	11·9	7·4	1·1	1·7	1·1	1·1	1·2	2·9	2·7	42·3
Tabora	3,983	5·7	5·2	6·7	5·2	0·8	0·2	0	0	0·3	0·5	3·2	5·7	33·5
Muanza	3,723	2·5	3·2	6·5	8·7	3·3	1·9	0·1	1·5	1·8	3·1	5·1	4·9	42·6
Ujiji	2,790	4·6	4·9	5·3	5·2	2·5	0·4	0	0	0·5	0·6	4·1	4·4	32·5
SOUTH-WEST AFRICA														
Swakopmund	20	0	0·1	0·2	0	0	0	0	0	0	0·1	0	0·2	0·7
Windhoek	5,456	3·9	2·7	3·0	1·7	0·2	0	0·1	0·1	0	0·4	0·8	1·8	14·8
Grootfontein	5,020	6·6	5·0	3·7	1·9	0·2	0·2	0	0	0·1	0·6	1·6	4·2	23·9
NYASALAND AND NORTHERN RHODESIA														
Zomba	2,948	11·1	10·7	8·5	4·0	1·0	0·6	0·3	0·4	0·4	1·5	5·7	11·1	55·3
Lauderdale	2,540	18·3	19·6	14·0	12·7	5·5	3·8	2·9	2·0	3·3	4·0	7·2	15·2	108·5
Fort Johnston	1,590	8·5	7·0	4·0	2·9	0·3	0·1	0	0·1	0·2	2·1	1·9	6·4	33·5
Nkata Bay	1,400	8·1	12·4	13·2	11·6	3·3	2·4	2·2	1·1	0·3	0·4	0·9	10·2	66·1
Kalomo	4,090	7·6	7·1	2·2	0·5	0	0	0·3	0	1·1	0·4	3·6	7·2	30·1
Leaui	3,300	7·6	8·2	4·6	0·9	0·2	0	0	0	0·1	0·9	2·8	6·6	32·7

MEAN RAINFALL (inches), *continued*

PORTUGUESE EAST AFRICA

Station.	Alt. Feet.	Jan.	Feb.	Mar.	Apr.	May.	June.	July.	Aug.	Sept.	Oct.	Nov.	Dec.	Year.
Mozambique	13	7·9	8·7	7·4	4·4	2·3	1·0	0·5	1·3	0·5	0·1	0·3	4·9	39·3
Mopeia	82	7·4	7·9	4·9	3·3	0·9	1·0	0·8	0·8	0·2	1·1	3·0	10·8	42·1

MADAGASCAR

Station.	Alt. Feet.	Jan.	Feb.	Mar.	Apr.	May.	June.	July.	Aug.	Sept.	Oct.	Nov.	Dec.	Year.
Tamatave	16	15·0	14·3	17·8	12·0	9·8	14·4	13·2	8·5	7·1	5·3	3·9	9·6	130·9
Antananarivo	4,593	12·0	11·5	7·4	2·0	0·6	0·3	0·2	0·3	0·6	2·5	5·1	11·3	53·7

BRITISH SOUTH AFRICA

Station.	Alt. Feet.	Jan.	Feb.	Mar.	Apr.	May.	June.	July.	Aug.	Sept.	Oct.	Nov.	Dec.	Year.
Port Nolloth	40	0	0·1	0·2	0·2	0·4	0·3	0·2	0·4	0·2	0	0·2	0·1	2·3
Cape Town	40	0·7	0·6	0·9	1·9	3·8	4·5	3·7	3·4	2·3	1·6	1·1	0·8	25·3
Knysna	950	2·0	1·8	2·0	1·8	2·1	2·7	1·9	2·4	2·9	2·6	3·4	2·5	28·1
Port Elizabeth	180	1·2	1·3	1·8	2·0	2·4	1·7	1·9	2·1	2·2	2·1	2·1	1·7	22·5
Durban	260	4·6	4·9	5·4	3·4	1·9	1·2	1·2	1·7	3·2	5·1	5·0	5·1	42·7
Pietermaritzburg	2,225	5·1	6·2	5·1	2·6	1·1	0·3	0·1	0·8	1·8	2·5	5·3	5·0	35·9
Oudtshoorn	1,085	0·5	0·8	0·8	0·6	1·1	0·7	0·3	0·6	1·0	0·9	1·5	0·3	8·6
Matjesfontein	2,593	0·3	0·7	0·4	0·6	1·1	0·5	0·6	0·5	0·4	0·6	0·6	0·2	6·5
Graaf Reinet	2,500	1·7	1·4	2·7	0·9	1·2	0·4	0·2	0·7	1·3	0·9	2·5	1·4	15·3
Kimberley	4,042	2·5	2·8	2·9	1·4	0·8	0·2	0·3	0·2	0·6	1·0	1·5	1·9	16·2
Pretoria	4,471	5·5	3·9	3·5	1·1	0·6	0·1	0·2	0·2	1·1	1·8	3·7	4·2	25·9
Bulawayo	4,470	5·9	4·0	3·1	0·7	0·3	0	0	0	0·1	0·9	3·3	5·2	23·6
Salisbury	4,880	7·5	7·4	4·5	1·0	0·5	0·1	0	0·1	0·3	1·1	3·7	5·8	31·9
Helvetia (Melsetter)	5,000	8·1	20·8	6·8	5·4	1·5	0·8	0·9	1·1	0·8	2·7	4·3	7·1	60·3
Victoria Falls	2,924	5·3	6·5	2·6	0·4	0	0	0	0	0·3	1·2	1·6	4·3	22·2

PART III
ASIA (WITH EUROPEAN RUSSIA, FINLAND, BALTIC STATES)

CHAPTER XVIII
GENERAL FEATURES

ASIA, the largest continent, has an area of seventeen and a quarter million square miles, and from a meteorological point of view the land mass is considerably larger, since Europe and North Africa must be included. It belongs essentially to temperate latitudes; only the southern peninsulas project south of the tropic, and no part reaches the Equator, though Singapore is almost on the line.

The core of the continent consists of vast plateaux, buttressed by great ranges of mountains. Turan and Siberia are low plains, lying north of the central mountains and plateaux, and are thus cut off to a large extent from warm southern influences, since the barrier is high enough to form a more or less impassable wall in the lower strata of the atmosphere. For this reason the winters are exceedingly cold in the northern parts of these plains, the 'cold pole' of the earth being situated in the north-east of Siberia on the Arctic Circle. This region is colder in winter than the corresponding part of North America, where the absence of a transverse mountain barrier permits mild winds from the south to moderate the winter cold.

The winter cold of Asia intensifies the subtropical high pressures so that they extend far north over the continent, and form a great cushion of heavy air, centred over the Gobi desert (Fig. 34, January). The main current of the westerlies is deflected round the north of the high-pressure system, the centre of which is a region of comparatively light winds.

In summer the land heats rapidly and not only is the large high-pressure system of winter dissipated, but the normal subtropical high pressures are changed to low pressures (Fig. 34, July). The centre of lowest pressure is over Baluchistan and Sind, and a vast 'secondary' extends north-

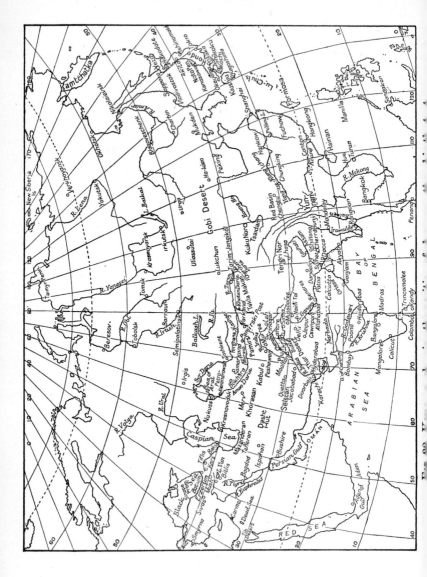

Fig. 88. H...... ....l ... .l ....

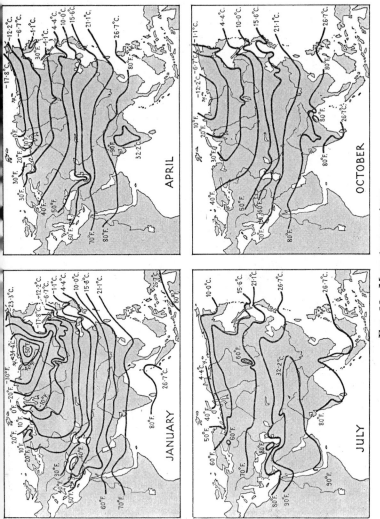

FIG. 33. Mean temperature.

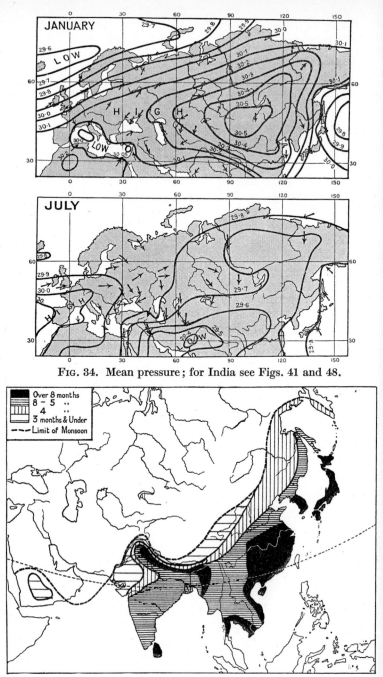

FIG. 34. Mean pressure; for India see Figs. 41 and 48.

FIG. 35. The duration of the monsoon rains.

eastward and covers the whole interior of the continent. The pressure change from winter to summer is the largest found on the globe, and the resulting seasonal change of wind is remarkably complete. The climate of southern and eastern Asia is often taken as typical of a monsoonal régime, but

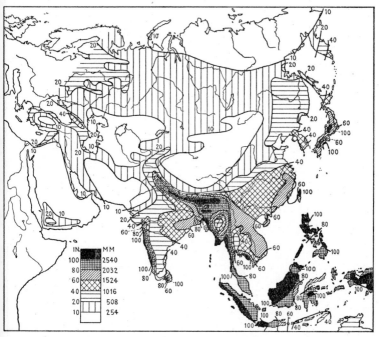

Fig. 36. Mean annual rainfall.

this is somewhat misleading, since the conditions here are really unique. North America is the only comparable continent, and there the monsoonal reversal of pressure, wind and weather is much less complete, owing, for the most part, to the nature of the relief, and partly to the smaller area of America.

Climatically, perhaps the most striking phenomenon in Asia is the rainy summer monsoon. Fig. 35 shows the limits of the monsoon rains, and their duration. In general, summer is the rainy season, and winter is almost or quite rainless (see rainfall maps, Figs. 37 to 40). It will be the aim of the chapters

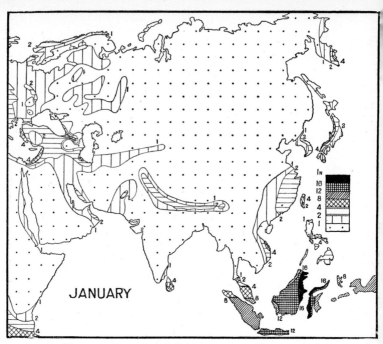

FIG. 37. Mean rainfall in January. (Herbertson.)

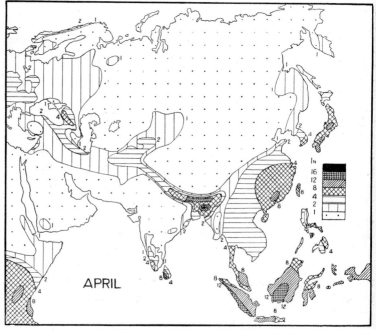

FIG. 38. Mean rainfall in April. (Herbertson.)

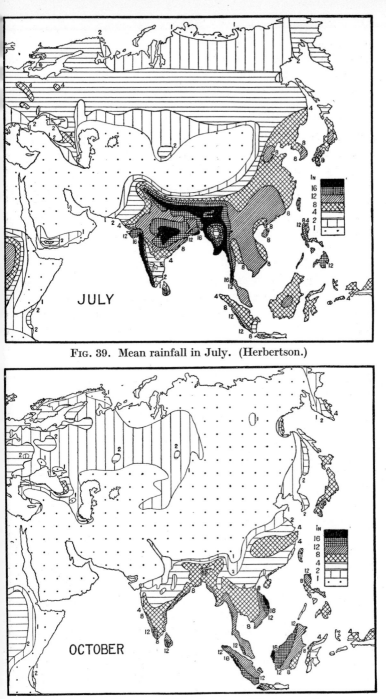

Fig. 39. Mean rainfall in July. (Herbertson.)

Fig. 40. Mean rainfall in October. (Herbertson.)

which follow to point out the main differences in the meteorology and climate of the monsoon countries, to indicate the
contrasts between the tropical and the extra-tropical monsoons, and show that while the winter monsoon is the dry
season in most parts, yet it brings much rain to certain
regions, the west coast of Japan, part of China, the coast of
Annam, the Malay Peninsula, and the east of Ceylon. While
in India as a whole the distinction between the rainy summer
and dry winter monsoon holds good, yet in every month of
the year some part of that country is receiving rain which is
important economically.

Oceanic conditions. Some features of the Indian Ocean are
described on pages 13–15. The east coast of Asia receives
the waters of the north Equatorial current of the Pacific. In
summer this current is deflected north past the Philippines,
and off Formosa joins the current which has flowed north-east
from the Java Sea and up the China Sea under the influence
of the summer monsoon. The combined waters form the Kuro
Shio which flows north-east on both sides of Japan, and then
strikes east across the North Pacific towards North America.
The water is very warm, the surface temperature being about
82° from Singapore to the south of Japan. But along the
Japanese coast the temperature falls rapidly to 70° off
Hakodate, and 60° off the south of Sakhalin; in the Sea of
Okhotsk it is about 50° and on the shores of Bering Strait
only 40°.

In winter the North Equatorial current strikes the Philippines and is deflected northward as in summer towards Japan.
The surface temperature round the Philippines is about 79°,
off the south of Japan about 60°. But an inshore current of
cold to cool water sets southward along China and Annam,
driven by the strong winds of the north-east monsoon, and
consequently there is a very marked drop in the surface
temperature as the mainland is approached. In February
the sea temperature on the east side of Formosa is about
70°, on the Chinese coast in the same latitude only 60°. In
the Yellow Sea it is below 50°, and it falls to 32° in the Gulf
of Pechili. In the Sea of Japan it ranges from about 50° in
the south to under 32° in the north off Vladivostok. The Sea
of Okhotsk and the Bering Sea have surface temperatures

well below 32°, and are largely ice-covered; the cold water flows south past the Kurile Islands along the east side of Yezo and to about lat. 39° N. on the east of Hondo; the west side of Hondo has somewhat warmer water derived from the small branch of the Kuro Shio which finds its way through the Korea Strait.

CHAPTER XIX

INDIA, CEYLON, AND BURMA

(THIS chapter is largely based on the *Climatological Atlas of India*, published by the Government of India, which should be consulted by the reader.)

A country so vast in size and diverse in surface as India must needs have great variety of climate. But a certain unity results from the monsoonal changes which are common to the whole, and description can best be based on the seasonal rhythm, and follow out the main features of the climates of India month by month.

The year is popularly divided into three seasons, the cold season lasting from October to March, the hot season from March to June, and the rains from June to October, but a more convenient division for the present purpose is that adopted by the Government Meteorological Department of India, viz.

(*a*) the season of the north-east monsoon.
    (i) January and February, cold weather season.
    (ii) March to mid-June, hot weather season.
(*b*) the season of the south-west monsoon.
    (i) Mid-June to mid-September, season of general rains.
    (ii) Mid-September to December, season of retreating monsoon.

Cold Weather Season. January is the typical cold weather month. Central Asia is the seat of very high atmospheric pressure, and over India there is a slight but continuous southward gradient, giving north-west, north, and north-east winds (Fig. 41). It would seem at first sight that the pressure distribution and winds are a direct continuation of those of Central Asia, but this is an erroneous view. The isobars shown on our maps are 'reduced to sea-level'. In reality between India and Central Asia the lofty ranges of the Himalayas and the wide plateau of Tibet project high above the lower atmosphere. There are practically no regular observations of pressure from Tibet, but on theoretical grounds it is probable that the pressure at that altitude is very different, not only in intensity, which is obvious, but also in distribution, from that at sea-level. The gradient in the middle and higher atmosphere to which Tibet belongs is directed

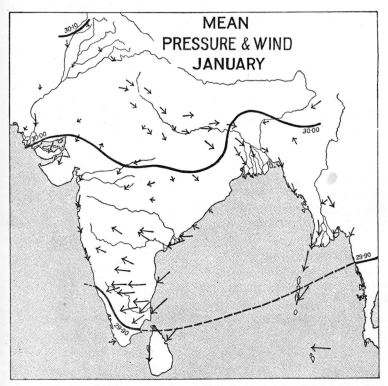

FIG. 41. The constancy of the winds is indicated by the length of the arrows. (*Climatological Atlas of India*.)

towards Central Asia. The winds trend inwards towards the heart of the continent and owing to rotational deflection appear as westerlies, which are known by observation to prevail in Tibet in winter. They must be part of the upper circulation, which maintains the high pressures over Central Asia, and these in turn cause outblowing winds in the lower atmosphere, which are the chief feature of the meteorology of East Asia. But India is quite cut off by the mountain barrier from these outblowing winds. The north-west winds

of the plains of north India must be regarded as local in
origin, that is to say, the downward settling of the air which
feeds them must be going on over the north of India itself,
and not over the interior of Asia. On reaching the lower
layers of the atmosphere the currents become horizontal, with
a general movement towards the south. In north India the
winds are north-west and west, guided apparently by the
open Ganges plain. In the gorges of the Himalayas through
which the rivers reach the plains the wind blows downstream
to the plains of India often with considerable force by night,
but the night winds are balanced by the valley breezes which
blow up the valleys during the day, so that these currents
are only of local significance. Occasionally, it is true, wind
currents have been traced which have crossed the ranges into
India from Afghanistan, and indeed from Russia. But even
in the extreme north-west of India we do not find such cold
waves as in China and Mesopotamia, which could hardly fail
to appear if the Himalayas did not shut off India more or
less completely from the cold interior of Asia.

The winds in north India are very light, averaging only
two or three miles an hour; this, as has been pointed out,
would seem to explain the fact that windmills are not used
by the natives. In Burma the winds are north and in peninsular India and in Ceylon generally east and north-east, but
northerly on the west coasts. The air movement is rather
more rapid in the south than in the plains of north India,
but the wind cannot be described as strong.

The goal of the north-east winds of the winter monsoon is
the equatorial trough of low pressure, situated somewhat
south of the Equator over the Indian Ocean. Still farther
south over the south Indian Ocean lies the subtropical high-
pressure system of the south hemisphere, and the south-
east trades blow from it to the doldrums, where they meet
the air currents of the north-east monsoon, and rise with
them into the higher regions of the atmosphere.

January is a beautifully fine month in most of India. The
offshore winds give little or no rain. The sky is remarkably
cloudless; hardly anywhere does the cloud covering exceed
two-tenths and in the west of the Deccan and in Burma it
is less than one-tenth. Thus during the cold season India

enjoys a climate almost as sunny as is known anywhere on the Earth. The cloudiest parts are the north-west and the extreme south, but even there the sky is far clearer than in

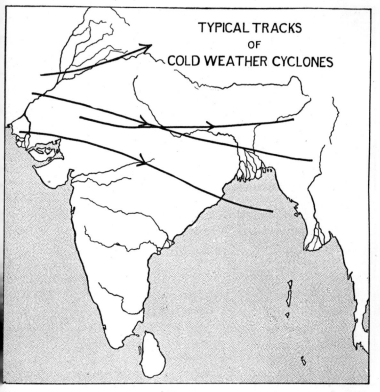

TYPICAL TRACKS
OF
COLD WEATHER CYCLONES

FIG. 42.

England, and the visibility is extremely good except during the rainy spells now to be described.

The clouds of the north-west of India are due to the cold-weather storms which are an important exception to the generally fine conditions. At intervals from the second half of October till June depressions advance from the west, coming over Persia and Afghanistan into north-west India (Fig. 42). Some of them have crossed from the Mediterranean Sea, others are probably secondaries associated with Mediterranean depressions, and bring the same type of weather. In the early and late months their tracks lie over the north of Afghanistan and the western Himalayas and Karakoram, but from December to April they come farther south and

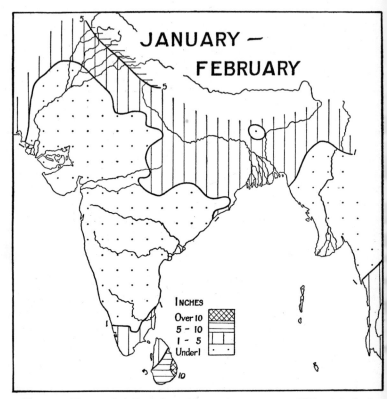

Fig. 43. Mean rainfall of the cold-weather seasons. (*Climatological Atlas of India.*)

influence the weather of the Punjab, Rajputana, Sind, and less prominently the Ganges plain as far as Patna. In the Peshawar Vale there is considerable rain in January, February, March, and April, most in March. In the Vale of Kashmir the maximum is in April, but March has almost as much. In November and December these disturbances may give cloud without much rain. In March and April with the increasing heat of the sun a local convection effect is added, and thunderstorms, hailstorms—the hailstones being sometimes very large—and occasionally tornadoes may mark their passage. They are very important in that they provide an appreciable rainfall (from ·5 to 2 inches in January, i.e. nearly as much as that of an English January), on which the winter crops of wheat and barley in the north of India depend (Fig. 43). The rain is heaviest on the north-west frontier, and in the Punjab; the Ganges plain benefits occasionally, but

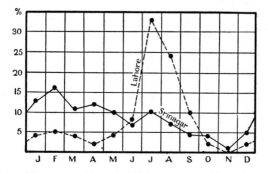

FIG. 44. Mean monthly rainfall (percentage of yearly total).

the storms usually die out before they can reach Bengal. The inner ranges of the Himalayas (Srinagar, Fig. 44) and probably all the highest parts of the chain derive the greatest part of their annual snowfall from them. In the Vale as well as on the mountains of Kashmir most of the winter precipitation is snow, and in north-west India there is occasionally snow as low as 1,000 feet. At Peshawar (Fig. 57) and in Afghanistan also the winter precipitation exceeds the summer; even the arid Khyber Pass has 12 days with precipitation in March and in April. But in the Punjab and farther east the effect on the annual rainfall curve is merely a secondary maximum in the early months of the year, which is far surpassed by the summer maximum (Lahore, Fig. 44). A failure in the winter rains causes considerable distress among the agricultural population all over north-west India.

Ceylon and the extreme south of India provide another exception to the fine dry weather of most of India, since they are situated less than 10° from the Equator and are therefore liable to be influenced by temporary northward migrations of the equatorial low pressures. The east and south of Ceylon

have heavy rains, brought by the north-east monsoon, which
has crossed the warm waters of the south of the Bay of
Bengal, and is forced to rise over the central mountains of

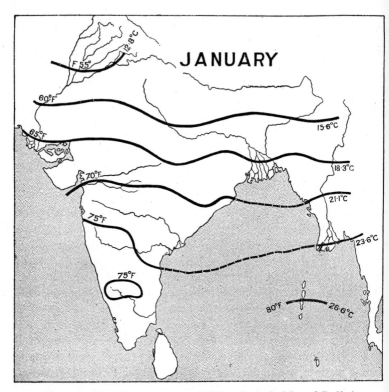

Fig. 45. Mean temperature. (*Climatological Atlas of India.*)

the island. On the east coast there is a rainfall of over
5 inches in January.

The temperature in India in January (Fig. 45) is comparable
with that in Europe in July. On the north-west frontier the
mean is below 55°, at Peshawar 50°; in the Indo-Gangetic
plains, north and central Burma, and the north of the Deccan
from 55° to 70°, as in North and Central Europe; and in the
centre and south of the peninsula, Ceylon, and south Burma,
from 70° to 80° as in Spain, Italy, and Greece. In north India
Europeans find the conditions very pleasant.

'In his consciousness of awakened energy the expatriated Europe-an feels that it also is the cold season, refreshing and invigorating, and affording a climate than which Italy itself can offer nothing more delightful. The thinly-clad native, inured to heat, and living in a draughty hut, with perhaps a single meal a day of not very stimulating food, is less enraptured with the delights of the cold weather. In the early morning his limbs are benumbed and his faculties torpid, and he swathes his head and mouth in a fold of his body cloth, and cowers over the embers of his little fire, till the warmth of the ascending sun restores him for some hours to his state of normal activity' (BLANFORD).

The daily range of temperature is far larger than in Europe. The heat of the day in north-west India is not much greater than in England in July, but the nights are considerably colder, and frost is frequent; Peshawar has recorded tem-peratures below 25° and enjoys dry and bracing weather. In Rajputana frost is rare, in Bengal and Assam unknown, and the air is much less bracing owing to the abundant moisture; at night fog often lies thick on the low plains. On the coasts of the peninsula and Ceylon the temperature is much more uniform as well as higher than in the north-west. In Ceylon, which is the hottest part at this season, the ther-mometer rarely falls below 70° or rises above 85°, and, com-pared with that of the north of India, the air is damp, having a mean relative humidity of 70 per cent. But in the west of the island it is much drier in January than during the rest of the year, and the dryness is considered the disagreeable feature of the January weather.

In February there is but little change. Pressure and winds remain much the same, except on the west coast of the penin-sula where the winds are now westerly and north-westerly. Depressions continue to appear in the north-west, and in some districts give more rain than in January.

Hot-weather Season. In March the hot-weather season begins. With the northward movement of the sun tempera-ture rises rapidly, especially in the interior of the Deccan, and the atmospheric pressure diminishes, becoming somewhat lower over the heated land than over the sea; the Bay of Bengal is covered by a slightly marked anticyclone. The wind is still north-west over the plains, but on the coasts the sea breezes become stronger, blowing from the west on the west coast of the peninsula and from the south on the east coast and in Bengal. These sea breezes bring moist air,

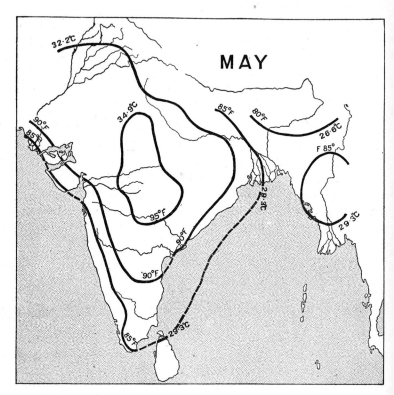

FIG. 46. Mean temperature. (*Climatological Atlas of India.*)

and a little rain to the south of India and Ceylon, and to Bengal and Assam, but the rest of India is unaffected by them, and the relative humidity of the air is becoming less with the rising temperature.

In April and May the sun is far in the northern hemisphere, and the heat becomes greater and greater (Fig. 46). The north of India is hottest owing to the dry air and cloudless skies. In the plains the mean temperature is above 85° in April and above 95° in May. On an average day in May the thermometer will exceed 105° in the United Provinces, and occasional readings up to 120° must be expected. In Sind the heat is still greater, and Jacobabad, situated near the Thar desert, is one of the hottest stations in India. It is true that the diurnal temperature range is great, over 25°, but even a drop of 30° from such furnace heat at midday leaves the night temperature 75° to 80°, high for a July midday in England. Few parts of the world are hotter. Work must be suspended during the hottest hours, and any activity out of doors is impossible as long as the sun is above the horizon. It is inadvisable to venture into the open without taking careful precautions against the sun, for the heat and the glare, both direct and reflected, are intense. A good description of the weather at this time by a resident is given later (p. 145). The air is very dry indeed, humidities as low as 1 per cent. being sometimes recorded; all vegetation is burnt up, not a green thing is to be seen. The sky is almost cloudless, but it cannot be described as clear or blue, since there is a constant dust-haze, a grey pall, through which the sun shines as a pale disk. There is no rain at all.

In the south of India the heat is far less. In Ceylon and on the west coast of the peninsula the mean temperature in April and May is between 82° and 85°, and at midday 100° is not likely to be exceeded. But though the days are cooler, the nights are warmer than in the north, the diurnal range of temperature being considerably less. Moreover, the air is moist and there is considerable rainfall especially in western Ceylon. The south of India and Ceylon have a much warmer climate in the cold season than the plains of north India, but a considerably cooler one in the hot season. Both the annual and the diurnal range of temperature are much less in the south (Fig. 47).

While the temperature rises the pressure over India is becoming less and less. By April (Fig. 48) a definite low-pressure system has formed over the land, surrounded by feeble gradients, which become considerably steepened in May; indeed in May the gradient is almost as steep as when the south-west monsoon is at its height. A similar system, possibly deeper, and developed earlier, but instrumental observations to establish this are lacking, forms over the south of Arabia. The wind is onshore round the coasts of India, bringing considerable humidity. In the south-west of the peninsula and in the centre and west of Ceylon there is a mean rainfall (Fig. 49) of over 5 inches in April, and over 10 inches in May, the 'mango-showers' of south India. Assam and Burma also have considerable rainfall and damp air, sultry hot and unpleasant, but with these exceptions the hot

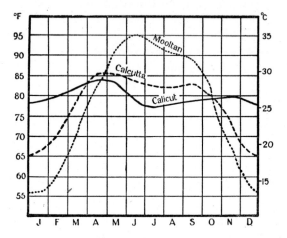

FIG. 47. Mean temperatures. The fall in temperature with the setting-in of the south-west monsoon is clearly marked.

season is one of intense heat and fine, dry, almost rainless weather. The heat, it is true, has already caused a definite low-pressure system to develop, and there are onshore winds on the coasts. But the summer monsoon has not yet started, and the season may be regarded as one of preparation for its arrival.

The hot season is not free from disturbances, which are probably the last feeble manifestations of the winter depressions. In the dry north-west they may take the form of violent squalls of wind of short duration, accompanied by very thick dust-clouds, so thick that it is sometimes dark at midday. The visibility is usually poor in this season, and of course especially so at these times. The squalls occur during the heat of the day, and cause a very welcome cooling of the air, though no rain reaches the ground; they are most frequent in May and June, the average being one a week.

Similar squalls are known throughout the Plains, but nearer the sea the air contains much moisture, owing to the prevailing onshore winds, and the squalls, known here as 'nor'-westers',

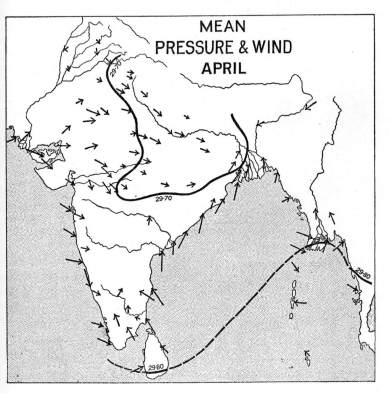

FIG. 48. The constancy of the winds is indicated by the length of the arrows. (*Climatological Atlas of India.*)

generally take the form of violent thunderstorms with sharp showers of rain and large hailstones. The April and May rainfall of Bengal, Assam, and Burma is largely of this kind. In Assam the rain is of great importance for the tea crop. The immediate cause of the squalls is doubtless the existence of a dry, cool, north-westerly wind at some little height above the surface of the earth, blowing over the hot and moist winds from the sea, so that convectional overturning with much precipitation naturally results. The same regions are visited occasionally by tornadoes, or whirlwinds of small diameter, usually some few hundred yards, and trees and buildings may suffer serious damage, and even heavy objects may be carried considerable distances.

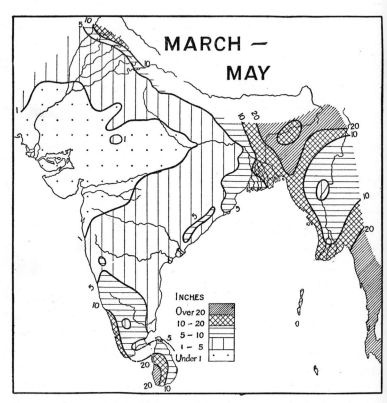

FIG. 49. Mean rainfall of the hot-weather season. (*Climatological Atlas of India.*)

Over the seas round India the mean pressure gradient is slight, and the air currents are weak and variable. These conditions are favourable to the development of tropical cyclones, especially in the south of the Bay of Bengal (see p. 139).

Season of General Rains. In the beginning of June the features of the hot season just described are still more intensified, and the heat and drought become unbearable in the

Plains. But about the middle of the month, quite suddenly, there is a great change. The south-west monsoon sets in, or, to use the ordinary word which well expresses the phenomenon, the monsoon 'bursts'. It is a change not so much in the direction of the wind, as in its force and in the whole face of the weather. The wind blows strongly from the south-west, very strongly over the sea; thick masses of cloud cover the sky and the air is saturated with vapour. A downpour of rain, with violent thunder and lightning, initiates the rainy and moist conditions that will prevail for the next three months. The clouds shelter the earth from the sun and the streaming rain helps to cool the air; over most of India the temperature falls sharply (Figs. 47, 55). Living things feel a sense of relief, and the parched land drinks and becomes luxuriantly green again.

During the hot season pressure diminishes over north India. As early as the end of May there is a definite centre of low pressure over Sind and Baluchistan, in precisely the same place as at the height of the monsoon. Stress must be laid at this point on the exact position of this goal of the in-blowing winds of India; the south-west monsoon is making for north-west India, not for Central Asia. Round the coasts there are fairly constant sea breezes during the hot season. The south-west monsoon is not merely an intensification of these sea breezes, but over most of India a complete and catastrophic change. The south-east trades of the south Indian Ocean cross the Equator, become south-west winds north of the line, when they come under the influence of the right-handed rotational deflection of the northern hemisphere, and surge on over India. Thus the south-west winds of the monsoon are very different from the comparatively gentle west and south-west winds that blow on the west coast of the peninsula in the previous months. It cannot have taken the south-east trade several months to travel from the Equator to India if the way was clear. Certainly the low pressures over India seem to have invited its approach long before it arrives. Possibly the facts may be satisfactorily explained as follows. The normal trough of low pressure which is the goal of the south-east trade, and which lies somewhat south of the line in January, still remains in an attenuated form near the Equator during the hot season of India, and here the south-east trade ends. North of it there is a belt of slightly higher pressure, separating it from the low-pressure system which is being developed over India by the heat. The north-west winds that blow on to the west coast of the peninsula are derived from the north side of these higher pressures (Fig. 50,

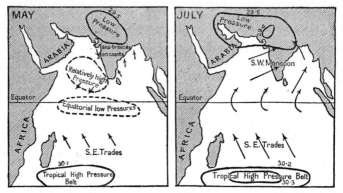

FIG. 50. Diagrammatic sketch of the conditions before (left-hand diagram) and after (right-hand diagram) the setting-in of the south-west monsoon.

left-hand diagram). As the hot season wears on pressure continues to fall over south Asia, and much of the air which has expanded and risen makes its way in the higher atmosphere into the equatorial low pressures, which become filled up in June. There is then a continuous and fairly uniform gradient from the tropical high-pressure belt of the south Indian Ocean, right across the Equator, into the low pressures of north India (Fig. 50, right-hand diagram). The south-east trades find no obstacle to stop them at the Equator, and sweep on over India as the south-west monsoon. The gradient is steeper than in May, since pressure has been increasing in the anticyclone over the south Indian Ocean while decreasing over south Asia, and the wind is very much stronger. The latest isobars for the Indian Ocean (*Meteorological Atlas of the Indian Seas*, and the last issues of the *Monthly Meteorological Charts of the East Indian Seas*) show a well-marked high-pressure system in the neighbourhood of the Equator, with light and variable winds in April; in May there is a uniform gradient over the south Indian Ocean, but a wide area of little or no gradient between lat. 10° S. and the low-pressure system over India.

The summer monsoon blows over India as a fairly steady wind more than twice as strong as the north-east monsoon, and saturated with vapour from its long passage over the tropical ocean. At Bombay its average speed is about 14 miles per hour, but this is more than in most of India. It is still stronger over the sea, especially the Arabian Sea, owing probably to the influence of the low-pressure system of south Arabia. It reaches the west coast of the peninsula first, surges on towards the east and north, and arrives with remarkable punctuality in most years, at the following dates:

Mean date of:	*commencement.*	*ending.*
Bombay . .	June 5	Oct. 15
Bengal . . .	June 15	Oct. 15–30
N.W. Province .	June 25	Sept. 30
Punjab . .	July 1	Sept. 14–21

By July all India is under its influence. The front of the monsoon generally develops into a tropical cyclone in the Bay of Bengal, and often in the Arabian Sea, but once the south-west current has set in the steady movement of air precludes such storms, which are almost unknown till October, when the weak and variable winds of the retreating monsoon again offer favourable conditions.

The main wind direction round India is shown in Fig. 51. There are two well-marked air currents, one meeting the Western Ghats at right angles but not extending far north of the Gulf of Cambay, the other advancing over the Bay of Bengal, and then turning towards the north-west up the Ganges plain. The currents meet and give heavy rainfall over Central India, where there is a long trough of low pressure extending south-east from the low-pressure centre over Sind. No doubt the great wall of the Himalayas plays an important part in directing the south-east winds of the plains, and through them controls the northward limit, and the force, of the Arabian Sea branch of the monsoon. It may be noted also that the mountain barrier, by preventing the inflow of winds from the dry interior of Asia, causes that from the

Indian Ocean to be especially strong. Throughout south and east Asia the winds of the summer monsoon arrive charged with vapour from the warm seas over which they come China like India has heavy summer rains. But the rain is especially heavy over India owing to the favourable arrange ment of the mountain ranges which bound the country Sir G. C. Simpson (*Q. J. R. Met. Soc.*, 1921) lays great stress on this feature. The region may be regarded as a compart ment, with mountain sides at least 6,000 feet high on the

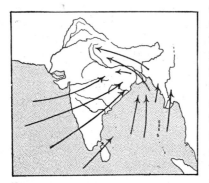

east, north, and west, but open on the south to receive the powerful inrush of the moist ocean winds. The air that enters must rise at least 6,000 feet, most of it higher over India, and the cooling that results from this ascent seems to be the main general cause of the heavy rainfall the local distribution being determined by the position of the ranges in relation to the wind directions.

FIG. 51. The main currents of the south-west monsoon.

The south-west monsoon is essentially the rain-giver of India, and the source of livelihood to its millions of inhabi tants. It is estimated that 85 per cent. of the total rainfall is derived from it. But it must not be thought that it rains continuously. There are breaks, which are sometimes pro longed, and the total rainfall of the season may be reduced to such an extent that the crops fail and famine follows. The rain is associated with the passage of depressions, comparable with those of the westerlies, or with those of the cold season in the north of India, but they move in the opposite direction to the latter. They usually form over the head of the Bay of Bengal (Fig. 59) and move along the trough of low pressure up the Plains, maintaining their cyclonic characteristics clearly marked as far as Rajputana and occasionally into Baluchistan. The rain falls in copious tropical downpours but it is noteworthy that in Bengal and Assam violent thun derstorms are rare during the south-west monsoon, this being a striking contrast to the conditions of the previous three months when nor'-westers with much thunder and lightning were frequent. In the north-west, including the Peshawar Vale, the monsoon rain is comparatively light, but sometimes

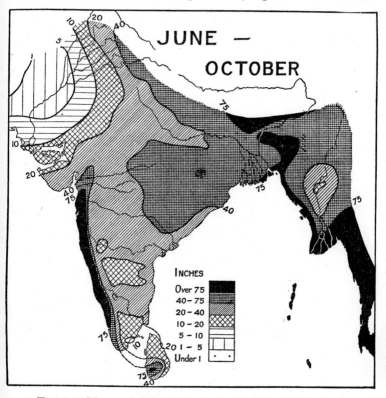

FIG. 52. Mean rainfall during the season of general rains.
(*Climatological Atlas of India.*)

depressions give two or three days of heavy rain, and there are many thunderstorms.

The map of mean rainfall during this season (Fig. 52) shows very clearly the great influence of the relief of the land. The rainfall figures mentioned in the following paragraphs which deal with the monsoon are, except where otherwise stated, the mean totals for the months June, July, August, and September, and thus represent the monsoonal rains. The west coast of the peninsula and Ceylon, and still more the

Western Ghats and the hilly interior of Ceylon, have enormous totals, 50 to 100 inches on the coast, far more on the windward slopes of the hills, but this wet strip does not extend far north of Bombay; the Indus delta is arid, and Karachi has only 6 inches while Bombay has 76 inches. East of the Ghats there is an extraordinarily rapid decrease; less than 100 miles from the coast the rainfall has diminished from over 100 inches to under 20 inches. The following table illustrates more accurately this striking rain-shadow:

Station.	Position.	Mean Rainfall in inches. June–Sept.
Mangalore . .	West coast of peninsula	110
Bangalore . .	Interior ,,	20
Madras .	East coast ,,	15
Colombo . .	West coast of Ceylon	22
Kandy . .	Central Highlands ,,	28
Trincomalee .	East coast ,,	12

Most of the centre and east of the Deccan has between 15 and 30 inches.

Similarly on the east of the Bay of Bengal there is a remarkably rapid transition from the rainy coast and windward slopes of the highlands of Tennasserim and Arakan with their excessively heavy fall, to the comparatively dry interior of Burma with less than 30 inches; here the rainiest months are May and September separated by a pronounced minimum in July. In the north the Arakan Ranges join the Khasi Hills, and here there is the heaviest rainfall, not only of India, but of the whole world. The configuration of the district, therefore, merits study. The Khasi Hills are an east–west range, 150 miles long, with an altitude of about 5,000 feet. In the east they meet the northward continuation of the Arakan Ranges, trending towards the north-east, with a similar altitude. Hence there is a wide depression, opening to the south-west, between the two mountain systems. A large part of the Bay of Bengal branch of the monsoon enters the funnel-shaped depression which lies widely open to it, and the air is forced to rise rapidly as the passage narrows. The result is the phenomenal rainfall, which reaches its maximum, so far as records exist, at Cherrapunji. This station is about 200 miles from the Bay of Bengal, but it must be remembered that the intervening tract consists of low-lying land, which is practically a vast lake at this time owing to the rivers having overflowed their banks. The flood water is warmer than the sea, and the air currents which have blown over it before they reach Cherrapunji contain enormous stores of moisture. Dacca, just outside the mouth of the 'funnel', has a mean rainfall for the monsoon months of 49 inches; Sylhet, in the narrower part of the funnel, but still on low ground, has 106 inches, Cherrapunji at an altitude of 4,455 feet, on the south side of the Khasi Hills above Sylhet, 318 inches. Beyond the ridge the rainfall decreases rapidly; Shillong, only some 25 miles from Cherrapunji, and at a greater altitude, but situated on the northern leeward slope, has only 55 inches, that is to say less than one-sixth as much as Cherrapunji, and at Gauhati, still farther north, in the bottom of the Brahmaputra valley, the rainfall is only 43 inches. At Cherrapunji as much as 905 inches once fell in a year (annual mean 428 inches), and 41 inches, twice as much as the mean rainfall for the whole year in the east of England, has fallen in a single day.

Bengal and Assam have a heavier rainfall than the rest of India with the exception of the west coasts. The amount is greater in the east than in the west, in the south than in the north. Owing to the moist air and frequent thunderstorms of the hot season that precedes it, the 'burst' of the monsoon is not nearly so clearly marked as on the west coast.

The Plains derive their rainfall chiefly from the Bengal branch of the monsoon, and the amount therefore becomes less with increasing distance from the Bay. The following series gives an instructive view of the diminution from Bengal to Sind:

MEAN RAINFALL

Station.	June–Sept.
Calcutta	46 inches
Patna	41 ,,
Allahabad	33 ,,
Agra	22 ,,
Delhi	22 ,,
Mooltan	5 ,,
Jacobabad	3 ,,

The decrease becomes especially rapid beyond the Ganges–
Indus divide west of Delhi towards the Punjab, and the
deserts of Sind are the most arid region in India. It is a
striking fact that the Thar desert lies almost exactly in the
centre of lowest pressures, and the scantiness of its rainfall is

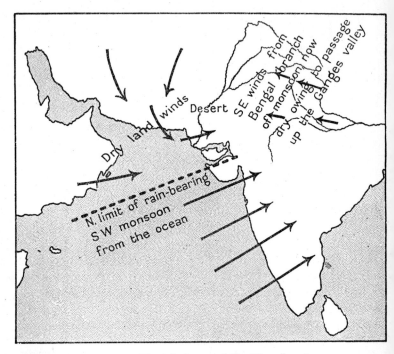

Fig. 53. The winds round the Thar desert.

at first sight surprising. It is the result of the previous history
of the winds that enter it (Fig. 53). On the west the air
currents come from the north-west, across the arid plateau
of Afghanistan and Baluchistan, and they become even drier
in descending to the plains of Sind, and can yield no rain.
The inflow on the east, north, and north-east consists of air
which has lost its moisture during its passage up the Ganges
plains, and when the air descends into the Punjab it is dried
still more by its descent, so that the Thar desert receives no
rain from this quarter. There remains the south coast of
Sind. At Karachi the prevailing winds are west and south-west

and they are especially strong during the afternoon. Here, then, would seem to be a source of rainfall. But these on-shore winds are drawn in from the immediate offing, where the air is by no means saturated with moisture, since it is derived from the north-west current just mentioned as blowing over the plateau of Baluchistan. The wind can pick up but a small amount of vapour during its short passage over the sea, and this is rendered the less effective, so far as rainfall is concerned, owing to the intense heating over the desert sands, itself a result of the cloudless skies. Owing to the heat the air rises and cools, and if the ascent continued high enough dew-point would be reached, clouds formed, and rain pre-cipitated, but before this can happen the rising air is caught up by the very dry upper current from the west which is known to exist here, and carried away. The south-west mon-soon of the Arabian Sea, which gives such heavy rain to the Western Ghats, does not reach the deserts of Sind; its north-ward boundary is the Gulf of Cambay. If it extended to the mouth of the Indus so that a true monsoon current from the ocean swept up the Indus valley, there is no reason why the rainfall there should not rival that of the equally flat and low-lying Ganges delta. The contrast between the fer-tility of the Ganges and the aridity of the Indus basin cannot be explained by the difference in the configuration of the valleys.

The arid west, with a mean annual rainfall of less than 10 inches, includes almost all Sind, the west of Rajputana, the south-west of the Punjab, and much of Baluchistan; the summer rain is in part general though light rain associated with rare depressions from the Plains, in part occasional local heavy thunderstorm rain in the hot hours. Jacobabad, on the Quetta railway west of the Indus, has the lowest recorded rainfall, 3 inches during the monsoon, 4 inches during the whole year. Sometimes there is no rain for a year, at other times far more than the mean annual amount may fall in a few hours in a sudden downpour. The mean annual rainfall at Hyderabad, Sind, is 7 inches, but 13 inches fell in the course of three consecutive days in August 1865, 10 inches on one of them. Doorbaji, Sind, had 34 inches on one occasion within two days, the annual mean being about 5 inches.

These sudden floods are hardly less fatal to plant life than the drought that usually prevails, for they wash away the surface soil here, and cover it up there with sand, and they also do great damage to property. Most of the rainfall which goes to make up the mean annual total is of this spasmodic type. The air in the desert is very much drier than in most of India, but the coast has a fairly high humidity owing to the sea breezes. The sky is cloudless, and the heat extreme (absolute maximum at Jacobabad 126°).

The outer ranges of the Himalayas have exceedingly moist air and very heavy rain during the monsoon, which decreases in general from east to west, as on the Plains:

MEAN RAINFALL

Station.					June–Sept.
Darjeeling .	.	.	.	.	102 inches
Naini Tal .	.	.	.	.	81 ,,
Mussooree .	.	.	.	.	81 ,,
Simla	.	.	.	.	48 ,,
Murree	.	.	.	.	35 ,,

The clouds hang low, and these hill stations are often enveloped for days and even weeks at a time. They offer no refuge from the ubiquitous rain and moisture of the Plains during the monsoon. The monsoon does not cross the main ranges of the Himalayas. The farther one penetrates beyond the outer ranges towards the interior, the less is the rainfall. The elevated valleys in the heart of the ranges, such as that of the Indus round Leh, have a remarkably low rainfall. Leh itself has only 1 inch during the months June to September.

'In July and August the weather occasionally becomes disturbed owing to the extension of the monsoon current into north-west India, which causes low cloud and locally heavy rains over the mountains along the Indus valley. Actually there is very little precipitation at Gilgit or Drosh during the monsoon season' (VERYARD and ROY).

The rivers roll along in high flood and inundate their low flood plains for thousands of miles. The floods in the Punjab are especially destructive. 'About July and August comes the rush of life-giving water to the steaming plains; then is the anxious time for the engineer and bridge-maker; then the swelling brown torrent spreads across miles of river-bed,

curling and eddying with resistless sweep against piers and
abutments, licking the necks of the bridge supports, and
bringing down heavy batteries of floating timber and uprooted trees.' But 'in the early dry months of summer these
channels are frequently nothing but wide white spaces of
glittering sand, with here and there a narrow ribbon of
gleaming water permeating the width of river-bed and offer-
ing no difficulty to the passer-by, except where the main
channel, narrowed to the dimension of a rivulet, may per-
chance present an unfordable obstacle'.

In most of India the air is much cooler during the monsoon, but the range of temperature from day to night is less
than during the hot season. The relief from the heat is welcome, but the continued moisture soon enervates the European. Early in June the highest temperatures were to be
found over Central India, where, as in most of India, the
clouds and rain of the monsoon cool the air considerably.
In arid Sind, however, where there is but little cloud and
hardly any rain, the temperature in July (Fig. 54) is about
the same as in June, and is by far the highest in all India.
The west coasts of the peninsula and Ceylon are now the
coolest regions, since the sea influence is strong, and cloud
and rain are very heavy. In Bengal and Assam the arrival of
the monsoon has not so much effect on the temperature, since
the previous months are not rainless.

In a normal year the south-west monsoon continues till the
middle of September over the whole of India. About that
time the falling temperature causes the atmospheric pressure
to increase in the north of India, and the monsoon currents
begin to lose their strength, and are no longer able to reach
the north-west frontier. The weakening is a gradual process,
in contrast to the suddenness with which the monsoon started.
By the middle of September the monsoon is over in the
Punjab, and by the end of the month it fails to reach the
United Provinces. North-west winds take its place and in
the beginning of October they extend over Bengal. Bombay
is among the last places to lose the monsoon, in mid-October,
as it was one of the first to receive it.

The distribution of pressure over India remains much the
same in July and August as in June. In September the

low-pressure system begins to fill up, and in the beginning of October the pressure is very uniform. The isobars for that month show a tendency to high pressure in north India, and relatively low pressures over the Bay, but the gradient is very feeble.

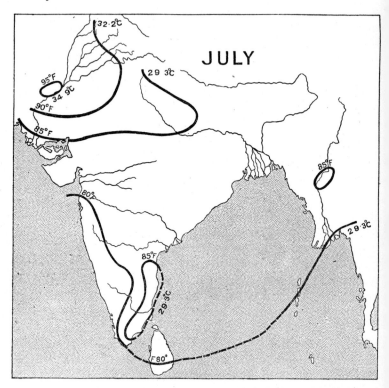

FIG. 54. Mean temperature. (*Climatological Atlas of India.*)

Season of retreating monsoon. As the south-west monsoon withdraws, the sky clears, the sun shines again and, in spite of the lateness of the season, temperature rises for a few weeks, to fall again afterwards to the winter minimum (Figs. 55 and 47). The land is still water-logged with the rains when the heat increases, and consequently this is an unhealthy period in some districts. But especially in the north-west October and November have the best weather of the year, with bright blue skies, clear air, and pleasant temperature.

During November and December the prevailing winds on the east coast of the peninsula south of Orissa blow from the south-east, but they really belong to the retreating south-west monsoon.

'The [south-west monsoon] current then recurves over the centre of the Bay, in the same manner as during the monsoon proper over the north of the Bay and Bengal, and is directed or determined to the west or Madras coast of the Bay, which hence receives frequent

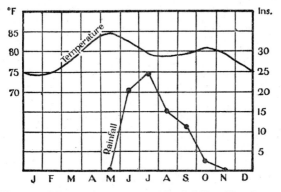

FIG. 55. Mean temperature and rainfall at Bombay.

rain during a short period of two months—the rainy season of the eastern and southern parts of the peninsula south of Orissa and Ganjam. These rains were formerly described as accompanying the setting in of the north-east monsoon on the Madras coast. That, however, is a misnomer, as the true north-east monsoon winds are dry land winds, and the rain-giving winds of this period in Madras are those of the south-west monsoon in its retreat or contraction down the Bay. The period during which this rainfall occurs is hence now usually termed the retreating south-west monsoon' (ELIOT).

These months are the rainiest of the year in the Madras Presidency (Fig. 56). At Madras itself the rainfall is 15 inches for the four months June to September, but 18 inches for the two months November and December. All the east and south-east of the peninsula south of the Godavari delta has heavy rain in November and December, and also the east of Ceylon, where there is a considerable rainfall in January also; but in Madras the rains cease by the end of the year. A considerable portion of the rain of November and December is brought by the cyclones that develop over the Bay during these months.

It is interesting to note that in every month of the year there is a considerable rainfall in some part of India. In

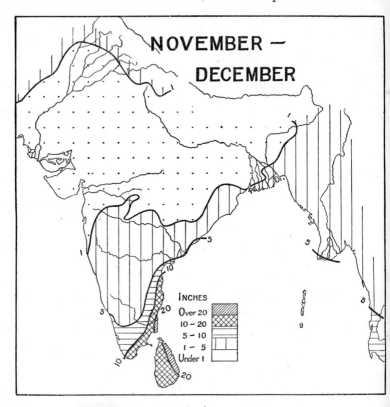

FIG. 56. Mean rainfall during the season of the retreating monsoon.
(Climatological Atlas of India.)

January and February north India gets rain from the winter depressions (Peshawar, Fig. 57). In March thunderstorms begin to be frequent in Bengal and Assam, and continue to give heavy rain till the monsoon starts in June (Goalpara, Fig. 57). The general monsoonal rains continue till October, and then during the retreat of the monsoon in November and December there is heavy rain in Madras (Madras, Fig. 57).

The temperature over the whole country is remarkably

uniform in October (Fig. 58), the mean being about 80° every-where at sea-level. In November it is becoming cooler in the north, and the nights in the far north-west are chilly; in December the cold-weather season starts.

When the monsoon is at its height only comparatively shallow depressions occur, forming at the head of the Bay and travelling inland. True tropical cyclones are rare until

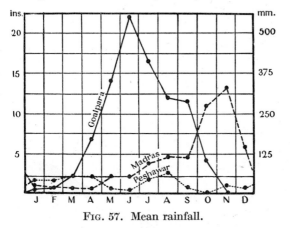

FIG. 57. Mean rainfall.

the monsoon dies away. At this period the barometric gra-dient over the Bay is slight, and the winds are weak and variable, conditions favourable for the local development of excessive heat and moisture in the stagnant air; pressure falls, and in a day or two a tropical cyclone may form, to move slowly forward on its destructive path. The total number of tropical cyclones recorded is:

	Jan.	Feb.	Mar.	Apr.	May.	June.
Bay of Bengal, 1877–1903 .	0	0	0	1	8	4
Arabian Sea, 1877–1903 .	0	0	0	1	5	6

	July.	Aug.	Sept.	Oct.	Nov.	Dec.	Total.
Bay of Bengal, 1877–1903 .	4	2	6	8	17	6	56
Arabian Sea, 1877–1903 .	0	0	0	2	7	0	21

A few of the usual tracks followed by the storms are shown in Fig. 59. The early storms of the year develop in the extreme south of the Indian seas, about 10° N. lat. The place of origin moves northward with the sun, till in July, as

we have seen, it is in the head of the Bay of Bengal, but the
storms that originate there are usually not of tropical violence.
As the sun returns southward, the place of origin of the
cyclones follows it, and in November most of them develop
south of 12° N. lat. They usually die out, or at any rate

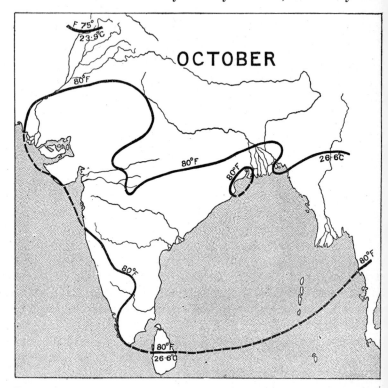

Fig. 58. Mean temperature in October. (*Climatological Atlas of India.*)

decrease very much in intensity, if they cross any large land
area. But while their centre still lies over the sea, they can
work fearful devastation on the coasts, and Madras, Bengal,
and Burma especially have suffered enormous material damage
and thousands of lives have been lost. Cyclones have been
known to cross the peninsula from the Bay of Bengal to the
Arabian Sea, degenerating into feeble storms accompanied by
rain during their passage over the land, and developing again
into hurricanes on reaching the Arabian Sea.

Droughts. The actual rainfall in any year may be either above or below, often very considerably above or below, the mean. Deficiencies are of most practical importance in India. They may occur either during the cold season, if the winter

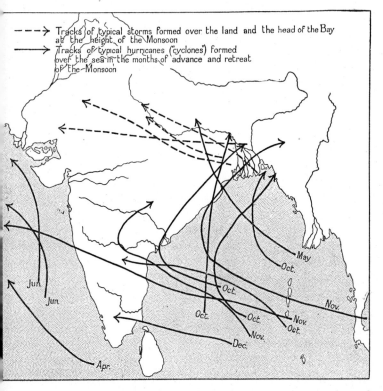

Fig. 59. The broken arrows show the tracks of typical storms formed over the land at the head of the Bay at the height of the monsoon, the full arrows the tracks of typical hurricanes formed over the sea in the months of advance and retreat of the monsoon.

depressions of north India are few or feeble, or during the south-west monsoon, which may be late in appearing, early in ending, or which may give but poor rains owing to frequent and long spells of clear dry weather. The rainfall is most variable in the arid west, in and around the deserts of Sind, but here deficiencies are not of much importance since there are few crops which depend on the rainfall. It is least variable in the districts of heaviest mean rainfall, and here again even the greatest deficiencies matter little, since the mean rainfall is far more than sufficient for agricultural requirements. They are most serious in the intermediate districts with a mean rainfall between 15 and 45 inches and a very dense population. The normal rainfall just about suffices for the crops, and any great deficit causes failure and consequent famine.

'The effect on crop-production is greatest and most disastrous in the following areas: (1) Central Burma; (2) The Deccan, including the Bombay and Madras Deccan districts, and Hyderabad; (3) North-Western and Central India, more especially the South Punjab, East Rajputana, and the United Provinces' (ELIOT).

When a failure in the winter rains is followed by a poor monsoon in north India, or when, as often happens, the summer monsoon is poor two years running, the consequences to the natives are, of course, intensified.

'A sudden cessation of the rains of 1896 resulted in famine over an area of about 307,000 square miles, with a population of nearly 70,000,000; on the average 2,000,000 persons were relieved daily during the twelve months from October 1896 to September 1897, and the number rose to more than 4,000,000 at the time of greatest distress. . . . In the height of the famine there were for weeks together more than 6,000,000 persons in receipt of relief. On a comparison of the Census figures of 1901 with those of 1891 it is estimated that during these two famine periods the death-roll exceeded the normal mortality of non-famine years by about 5,000,000.'

Climatic regions. From the preceding sketch, based on the seasonal changes, it must be obvious how manifold are the climates of India, considered regionally; the north has very different conditions from the south, the coasts from the interior, the west coasts from the east coasts. Altitude introduces further and even greater variations, ranging from the Plains through the hill stations to the everlasting snows of the Himalayas. Fig. 60 shows the major climatic regions; their characteristics have been already indicated, and need not be repeated here. We shall describe as samples only (i) the Carnatic, as representing south-east India and east Ceylon, (ii) Bengal, a moist coastal region, (iii) the Punjab in the semi-arid plains of the northern interior, (iv) Simla, a typical hill station, (v) the Vale of Kashmir, an intermont

basin near the front of the Himalayas, and (vi) Leh, in an
elevated valley in the far interior of the mountains.

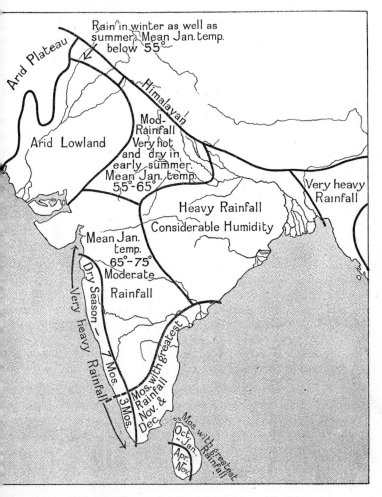

Fig. 60. The major climatic regions of India.

The Carnatic. The climate is distinguished by uniform high
temperatures, and moist air throughout the year, and by the
fact that most of the rain falls in October and November,
during the retreat of the monsoon rather than during the
monsoon proper. The term 'cold season' is a misnomer here

for the early months of the year, since the mean temperature of even the coolest month, January, is 75°; May is the warmest month with a mean temperature of nearly 90°, and June is almost as warm. The annual temperature range is about 13°. The daily range also is small. In January the thermometer rises in the day to about 85° and does not fall at night much below 70°, so that the nights are very oppressive in Madras as compared with north-west India. In May the average daily maximum temperature is about 100°, and the average minimum about 80°. The lowest temperature ever recorded was 57°, the highest 113°. The uniform high temperatures are the less bearable because of the high humidity of the air, which ranges from 65 to 81 per cent. April especially is very ener- vating owing to the hot moist sea winds from the south.

In April and May there are occasional thunderstorms known as 'mango-showers'. The arrival of the south-west monsoon does not cause any very decided increase in the rainfall, since the winds have lost most of their moisture on the west coast of the peninsula; but the rainfall increases slowly till Sep- tember, which has 5 inches. Then in October it becomes heavier, just at the time when over most of India the rains are stopping and the fine weather of late summer is beginning. The retreating monsoon recurves over the Bay as already described, and gives very heavy rainfall to the Carnatic in October (11 inches) and November (13 inches). December has only 5 inches, and by the end of the year the south-west monsoon has entirely withdrawn, leaving Madras under the influence of the dry land breezes of the north-east monsoon. The rainfall is very slight in January and February, decreasing to a minimum in March. The October, November, and Decem- ber rainfall is collected in large tanks on which the irrigation of the province depends.

Bengal. Here is the transition between the constantly high temperatures and great humidity of the south of the peninsula and the dry bracing air and great range of temperature which characterize the north-west.

Bengal is low-lying, and there is much inland water, rivers and creeks, irrigation canals and ditches, and swamps. Sea breezes begin in February, and the prevailing winds continue from south till October, making the air damp and relaxing.

Moreover, Bengal as a whole is one of the rainiest provinces of India.

'The customary division of the year into three seasons, the cool season, the hot season, and the rains, holds good in Bengal as in the more westerly provinces, but the first is shorter and less bracing, and the heat of the second, if less intense owing to the greater dampness of the air, is on this account, perhaps, more trying to the European constitution. The rains are also longer and more copious' (BLANFORD).

In March and April nor'-westers, accompanied by dust- and thunderstorms, give heavy rain. During the hot season Calcutta enjoys an advantage in the fresh sea-breeze which lasts through the late afternoon and evening and slightly cools the air.

'At length in the early part of June, the clouds gather more thickly, while the barometer falls to a lower point than it has reached since the beginning of the year; and in the first or second week, heavy and continuous rain ushers in the monsoon. This first burst of the rains usually accompanies a cyclonic storm, formed either at the head of the Bay or over the delta itself. . . . Its immediate effect is a great fall of the day temperature; and the comparative coolness, supervening on many weeks of close oppressive weather, brings a sense of relief. . . . When, however, in September the rainless intervals become longer, and the day temperature begins to rise, while the air, still highly charged with moisture, is almost motionless, the relaxed energy of the human system fairly rebels against this further trial of its endurance, and all who are not compelled by their vocations to remain at their post hasten to escape to the temporary refuge of a hill station. September and October are thus the most trying and unhealthy season of the year' (BLANFORD).

Punjab. The following account is given by the Rev. J. M. Merk, a resident in the province:

'Like the rest of India, the Punjab has really but three seasons: the summer or hot season, the rains, and the winter, which, in India, we speak of simply as the cold season. The hot season begins in April, but in March it is already so warm that barley and wheat ripen and are harvested. From April to June, as a rule, there is no rain. The west wind holds sway, and blowing from the sandy wastes of the Indus region, is a veritable hot wind. A denizen of the temperate zone can hardly realize the

L

desiccating, truly scorching heat of the wind. When exposed to
it, one may imagine he is facing an open furnace. The thermometer rises in the shade to over 120°. In order to enjoy fresh air
at this season one must take exercise in the early dawn, between
4 and 5 in the morning; for no sooner has the sun risen than the
heat sets in again. After 7 a.m., save of necessity, no European
leaves his house, and should business oblige him to do so, he must
protect himself from the sun with a sunshade and a thick head-
covering. . . . At sunrise, or soon after 5 a.m., houses must be
closed, only a small door being left open for communication with
the outside world. Thus the house of a European is more like
a gloomy prison than an ordinary dwelling-house. So long as
the hot winds blow strongly and steadily, rooms may still be
kept in some measure cool by means of "tatties" or grass screens
set up in front of the doorway, and continually sprinkled with
water, or by the fan vanes of the so-called "thermantidote",
which a servant keeps revolving and sprinkles with water; and
at night the punkah is worked. Whoever cannot provide himself
with these artificial cooling appliances must suffer the daily
torment of insupportable and exhausting heat. Man and beast
languish and gasp for air, while even in the house the thermometer
stands day and night between 95° and 115°. Little by little the
European loses appetite and sleep; all power and energy forsake
him. Vegetation suffers equally; almost all green things wither;
the grass seems burnt up to the roots; bushes and trees seem
moribund; the earth is as hard as a paved highway; the ground
is seamed with cracks; and the whole landscape wears an aspect
of barrenness and sadness. At length, in June, the hot winds
cease to blow, and are followed by a calm; and now indeed the
heat is truly fearful; grass screens and thermantidotes avail
naught; all things pine for the rains; but no rain, not even a
shower, can one hope for, till the south and east winds shall have
set in. And even then, the rains do not extend to the whole of
the Punjab; Lahore has but little rain, Mooltan scarcely any
and the peasant of the Western Punjab is dependent entirely on
artificial irrigation for the watering of his crops.

The southerly and easterly winds bring first clouds and violent
storms with heavy rain showers, which are repeated daily, or, at
all events, every 2 or 3 days, and, finally, the rains, which, in
the Himalayas, set in at the beginning of July and cease at the
end of August or in the middle of September. In July the tree
begin a second time to burst into leaf; grass springs up once
more, and soon a vegetation is developed that, fostered by warmth
and moisture, is scarce to be kept within bounds. The peasan

now works hard at ploughing, sowing, and weeding his fields. Rice is sown in June, during the great heat; in September it is reaped, and within two months maize is sown and harvested. . . .

After from 4 to 6 weeks of heavy rain, often falling uninterruptedly for 2 or 3 days in succession, it clears up, and sometimes some weeks pass without further rain; after which a week or two more of rainy weather brings the season to a close. Grateful as is the coolness brought by these showers, the more oppressively hot and sultry it is when the rain ceases and holds off, if only for half a day. The atmosphere weighs on one like a heavy coverlet; and then comes the daily and nightly plague of mosquitoes. Insect and reptilian life is now active; of evenings it hums and buzzes and croaks all around, frogs make their way into the house, and with them more serious and unwelcome visitors, scorpions, and snakes, for which reason it is unwise, at this time of year, to go about in the dark.

One can hardly picture to oneself in our European climate how serious and disagreeable are the effects of excessive moisture, as experienced towards the end of the rains. Woodwork swells, and doors and windows can be fastened only with much difficulty. Shoes and all articles of leather become thickly coated with fungus, books become mouldy and worm-eaten, paper perishes, linen becomes damp in the presses, and despite the oppressive heat one must often light a fire on the hearth, only to neutralize in some degree the influence of the damp.

The period which immediately follows the rains up to October is the most unhealthy season in the year. Decaying vegetation under an ardent sun generates miasma, the consequences being fever, dysentery, and not infrequently cholera. Towards the end of the rains, one rejoices indeed to see the heavy dark clouds disappear, but the heat soon becomes once more so great that one longs for the cold season, and more than ever turns an anxious eye to the wind vane, watching for some sign of the cool westerly and northerly winds. With the beginning of October these winds set in steadily, clearing the skies, and now the blue firmament appears in all its splendour, so glorious in the torrid zone. . . . From October to Christmas, as a rule, the weather is clear and fine, the air is pure and most delicious, and one can hardly imagine a more charming climate; but it must never be forgotten that an Indian sun shines overhead, and that even in the cold season one must never expose the unprotected head to its rays. The European now once more breathes freely, and it is a delight with the head well covered to move about in the open air. For 5 or 6 weeks white men can work vigorously and with pleasure.

In December and January the fire burns all day long on the hearth, and in the morning and evening is especially grateful. The nights are positively cold; even on the plains, ice and hoar frost form, and near the ground the thermometer sometimes sinks to 23°. During the second half of the cold season we have in the Punjab a good deal of rain, without which indeed the barley and wheat harvest is poor; the pulses also require the winter rains. In February we have a short spring; many trees unfold their leaves, and every bush furnishes its quota of flowery adornment. But this spring is of short duration, and in March it is already warm on the plains and the hot summer is at hand; an occasional dust-storm, however, for a while keeps off the summer heat. A dust-storm is indeed in itself unpleasant, the air being so charged with dust as to bring an Egyptian darkness, no matter what may be the hour of the day.'

Simla on a ridge in the front ranges of the Himalayas has the same seasonal changes as the Punjab, which Simla overlooks, but the altitude being about 7,000 feet the temperature is much lower at all times; even the hot season at Simla is pleasant for Europeans, who find it a haven of comfort after the furnace heat of the Plains. The hottest month is June, when the mean temperature is 67°, about the same as in Central Europe in that month; the mean daily maximum temperature is 74°, the mean daily minimum 61°. January is the coldest month, with a mean temperature of 39°, the same as in England. Frost is frequent at night in winter, the lowest temperature on record being 19°. There are sometimes heavy falls of snow, and occasionally the snow-covering is several feet deep after a bad storm. The air is bracing and, except during the south-west monsoon, dry.

In January, February, and March, the depressions of north India cause heavy falls of rain and snow, the total precipitation amounting to about 3 inches in each month, twice as much as in the plains of the Punjab. In April, May, and the first half of June there are often thunderstorms with heavy showers of rain. These are the representatives of the dust-storms of the Plains, and indeed they sometimes bring clouds of dust even as far as the hills. They nearly always occur in the afternoons. The air is remarkably dry in April and May, the mean relative humidity being only 45 per cent. The end of June brings the monsoon with the sudden and complete change of weather already described for India as a whole. The rain pours down during July and August, and the crisp dry air of April and May is replaced by the monsoon currents which are always damp and often saturated. The clouds hang low on the front ridges of the Himalayas, much lower in summer than in winter. Simla is often enveloped in cloud for days, even weeks, at a time during the monsoon, and the hill-stations farther east are still worse off in this respect, the mean rainfall being 50 inches. In the middle of September the rains cease; and the weather is then beautifully clear, mild, and settled till the end of the year, and the sky is cloudless. This is the most charming season of the year at Simla, and all Europeans who can do so make for it or some other hill-station. It is a favoured resort during the hot season also, but during the rains the ubiquitous damp and heavy rain make it undesirable. In the cold season it has some visitors, but many Europeans find it too cold.

Vale of Kashmir. The vale is a flat-bottomed depression, about a hundred miles long and fifty wide, through which the river Jhelum flows. It is behind the front ranges of the Himalayas, and its climate differs materially from that of the Plains; it resembles rather that of Central Europe. At Srinagar in the centre of the vale, 5,250 feet above the sea, the mean January temperature is 31°, about the same as at Berlin, and considerably less than in England, or at the most frequented hill-stations in the Himalayas, which are some thousands of feet higher. The warmest month is July, not June as in most of north India, with the high mean temperature of 73°. Thus the range of temperature is very large, a common feature in such enclosed basins. The air is always damp, the mean monthly relative humidity ranging from 71 to 82 per cent.; it is highest in the cold months. But the annual rainfall is comparatively small, only 27 inches. The driest months are October, November, and December, each of which has less than 2 inches; the other months have about 3 inches each. The heaviest precipitation is in the early months of the year, and is derived from the winter depressions. The four months January to April have 14 inches, the four months of the summer monsoon only 8 inches. The summer monsoon does not give much rainfall beyond the outer ranges of the Himalayas. Most of the winter precipitation in the vale of Kashmir is in the form of snow.

'We are apt to think of Kashmir as part of India, and therefore as necessarily warm. As a matter of fact it lies 34 degrees north of the Equator, in the same latitude as the northern part of South Carolina. In altitude it stands over 5,000 feet above the sea. Consequently the climate is comparatively cool. From November to March it is so cold as to be not only bracing but even rigorous. The spring and fall are mild and delightful, and the summer is warm. The great amount of water spread over the plain for irrigation, and the summer storms on the mountains make that season damp though but little rain falls on the plain. . . . The temperate climate of the region, combined with the beautiful scenery, makes Kashmir a most attractive summer resort for the people of India, especially the English' (ELLSWORTH HUNTINGTON).

Kashmir seems to be suitable as not merely a summer resort but also a permanent colony for British settlers.

At *Leh* in Ladakh conditions are much less hospitable. We are here 11,500 feet above the sea in the Upper Indus valley, which is settled by a scanty population between the altitudes of 9,000 and 12,000 feet; below 9,000 feet there are impassable gorges, above 12,000 feet the climate precludes agriculture. The mean atmospheric pressure at Leh is about 20 inches. The mean temperature for the year is 41°, for January 17°; the four winter months have a mean below 32°. The lowest temperature on record is − 19°, and the mean daily minimum in January is 9°. Temperature rises rapidly as summer comes on; in July the mean is 63°, and the mean daily maximum is 78°. Thus the range of temperature is very large. Water has been made to boil (boiling-point 191°) by simply exposing it to the sun in a small bottle blackened on the outside, and shielded from the air by a larger vessel of transparent glass. The rays of the sun are very powerful, but the shade temperature at the same time may be low. The precipitation is remarkably scanty, the total for the year being only 3 inches, and no month having over half an inch. The maximum is in the summer, July and August having half an inch each; there is a secondary maximum in winter. The mountains round about must have a very much heavier fall, and snow sometimes lies very deep even in the valley in winter. Agriculture depends entirely on irrigation. The mean relative humidity is low, below or only just above 40 per cent., from May to November; in the winter months it rises to 70 per cent. The air is thus usually dry, and always bracing.

CHAPTER XX

CHINA

DETAILED information concerning the climate of the Chinese Empire is meagre; most of the observations have been made on the coast, and the interior is poorly represented. Few travellers have given any but the most general remarks on the climate, and the inconsistencies between some of them show that the statements are based on too brief periods of observation.

In winter atmospheric pressure is very high over Central Asia, and the gradient over China steep (Fig. 34). Strong winds blow out from the deserts of the interior, which are very cold at this season, and descend as a great cataract over the plateau edge, which is here undefended by mountain ramparts, to China. Their descent warms them somewhat, but still they are felt as icy blasts, especially in northern China, and they are so strong that they carry clouds of dust, and on the China Sea navigation is often interrupted by the bad visibility. The mean direction is north-west in north China, north in central China, and north-east in the south. Over the China Sea this monsoon usually commences as a gale which continues for several days.

The winter monsoon is at its strongest in December, January, and February, a season of very cold dry windy weather. In April the high-pressure system over Central Asia is breaking up, and the winds over China are variable, though, in general, still from the north-west in northern China; in southern China the summer monsoon is starting, and the prevailing winds are south-east and east. In May the summer low pressures are already developed over the interior of the continent, and they deepen in June and July. The prevailing winds over all China are south and south-east, warm and rainy. They are not of great force, in general only half as strong as the winter winds, for the barometric gradient is not steep; this is an interesting contrast to the conditions in India, where the summer monsoon winds are more than twice as strong as those of the winter monsoon. The low pressures into which the south-east winds of China blow are a great secondary extension from the centre of lowest pressure in north-west India. The summer monsoon, the season of rain and cloud and damp enervating heat, comes to an end in September. In October the barometric gradient is reversed, and the dry winds from the interior commence.

The wind reversal from winter to summer is striking:

NORTH CHINA. PERCENTAGE WIND FREQUENCY (HANN)

	N.	NE.	E.	SE.	S.	SW.	W.	NW.
Winter . .	17	8	5	6	6	8	18	32
Summer .	10	9	12	26	16	10	7	10

In winter especially the direction is remarkably constant, and hence the mean temperature is very low, since the almost constant west, north-west, and north winds blow from precisely the coldest quarter, viz. north-east Asia. In summer the prevailing winds are from the warmest quarter. On the China Sea the normal monsoon is often interrupted, both in summer and winter, by winds of gale force from other quarters.

China has, in its most marked form, an 'east-coast' climate. The January isotherms (Fig. 33) fall gradually southward in their course from west to east over Eurasia, and attain their most southerly position just before they reach the Chinese coast, indeed, according to some maps, on the coast itself. The 32° isotherm touches its lowest latitude for the whole globe, 35° N., in the east of Eurasia; it runs farthest poleward on the west of the same land mass. All northern China has a mean January temperature below freezing-point, northern Manchukuo below zero. The sea is sometimes frozen in the Gulf of Chihli for many miles from the shore, even 50 miles in severe winters. At Hong Kong, situated just inside the tropic, the mean for the coldest month, February, is only 58°, the lowest mean known near sea-level in the same latitude in the north hemisphere. Frost and snow occur everywhere in China, even at Hong Kong and Canton, where, however, they are very rare. Shanghai has recorded 10°. The low winter temperatures are the result of the lack of a good mountain barrier against the north-west winds, China presenting in this respect a great contrast to India which is sheltered by the Himalayas. The coasts of China are more exposed than the interior where there are mountain ranges running from west to east as wind-breaks. The valleys between the ranges are sheltered and hence are not so cold as the coasts. Thus in the Yangtse valley, at Shanghai on the coast the mean January temperature is 38°, at Hankow, about 500 miles up the river, 40°, and at Cheng-tu, in the Red Basin of Szechwan, 44°; Cheng-tu is 1,500 feet above the sea, but it is well sheltered by the mountain ranges which buttress Tibet on the east. The whole of the Red Basin enjoys comparatively mild winters, and snow and frost are almost unknown, but nearer the sea the Po-Jang Lake in Kiangsi often has a thick sheet of ice in winter. In the north of China even rapid rivers, such as the Hoang-ho in Kansu, are usually frozen in winter.

There is a great difference in temperature in winter between the north and south of China, Hong Kong being 36° warmer than Peking in January. The difference between the temperatures of Fort William and Lisbon, almost the same latitudinal distance apart on the west coast of Eurasia, is only 10°.

The north-west winds descending from the deserts of the interior are naturally very dry. The mean relative humidity at Peking in winter is 58 per cent. The sky is almost cloudless, and there is no rain. When the icy wind blows strong it carries clouds of dust, which are a noted scourge of Peking, and are often met with hundreds of miles out to sea. A milder form of the same visitation is the almost constant dust haze. The dust on settling forms the characteristic loess of the north of China. As a rule these dusty storms are confined to the winter months, but

'steady westerly gales often prevail day and night, with but a day or two's interruption at intervals, throughout the months of March, April, May, and on into June. The result of these long-persistent, hot, dry land-winds is not only to render Peking almost uninhabitable at that season with any comfort, but so to parch up the country that a view across the western hills over brown burnt-up grass and the dry parched plain is one of mid-winter, and, but for the heat, it is hard to realize that the month is June. On such occasions it is pitiful to see the winter wheat only sprouting above the ground to wither and die, and the country people walking round their fields with bunches of the parched stalks held in their hands above their heads for Heaven to witness and relent' (LITTLE).

In central and south China droughts are almost unknown.

In summer the temperature is remarkably uniform; the July mean is 78° at Peking, 80° at Shanghai, 82° at Hong Kong. The range from winter to summer is large, 54° at Peking, 43° at Shanghai, 24° at Hong Kong.

Manchukuo, the Great Plain of China, the Si-kiang Valley, and Szechwan illustrate the main varieties of Chinese climates. Manchukuo has very long cold winters, for the land is snow-covered and the rivers frozen for five months in the south, six months in the north, where the Amur is closed by ice from October till May. The strong dry dusty north-west wind makes the cold the more penetrating despite the usually bright sky. Except in the south temperatures down to − 25° are frequent, and furs and wadded cotton garments are necessary. The change from winter to summer is rapid, and four months, June to September, have mean temperatures above 60°, and two months above 70°. The summers are long, and warm enough, except in the north, for two crops of cereals.

The Great Plain of China has about three months with means below 32°, but none below 20°, so that the winters are much less severe than in Manchukuo. The summers are much warmer, with four months above 70°, and July is almost as warm as in the Si-kiang Valley. The hot humid summers are perhaps more enervating here than in the south of China where the winter is much warmer and therefore the seasonal contrast less pronounced, or in Manchukuo where the winters are very cold but the summers less hot than in the Great Plain. In most parts two crops can be raised, one being a winter cereal, and in favoured districts three crops a year.

In the Si-kiang Valley frost is practically unknown near the sea, and snow only falls occasionally on the hills. The coldest month is almost as warm as July in England. There are seven months with mean temperature above 70°, four of them above 80°. Thus there is practically no winter.

Szechwan is far inland, and most of it is over 2,000 feet above the sea, but it is specially favoured in winter, by comparison with most of China, in having lofty mountain walls to shelter it from the cold winds. The mean temperature in January is far above freezing-point, being 49° at Chungking, altitude 750 feet. Summer is long and hot, having five months with mean temperature above 70° (August 85°).

Summer is the rainy season. The winds of the south-east monsoon have travelled far over the warm ocean, and are saturated with moisture. The rainfall is heaviest in the south and east, and diminishes towards the north and the interior. The coast south of the mouth of the Si-kiang receives over 80 inches per annum. The 40-inch isohyet runs along the north of the Yangtse basin. The north of China, including Peking, has about 25 inches, and Manchukuo 20 to 40 inches. The rains swell the rivers and cause heavy floods. The Yangtse rises as much as 70 feet in August at Chungking. The average rise at Hankow is about 40 feet. Most of the rain falls within four months, so that the monthly totals are large; exceptionally heavy downpours may wash away the soil from the treeless hills, flood the plains, and bury and ruin the fertile cultivated surface. The loss of life and the damage to land and property are as serious as in the not infrequent droughts.

Over all China most of the rain is brought by the summer monsoon, but there are three rainfall régimes, those of north, central, and south China; north China includes all China proper north of the Yangtse basin, central China is the Yangtse basin, and south China all the country south of the Yangtse basin (see rainfall curves for Peking, Shanghai, and Hong Kong, Fig. 61). The conditions are simplest in north China. Peking has 23 inches, 91 per cent. of the annual total, in the months May to September. The other seven months of the year have each less than 1 inch of rain. The rainfall increases from the setting in of the summer monsoon till July and August, and then decreases again as the monsoon weakens —a typical monsoonal régime.

In south China the régime is somewhat similar, but the rainfall is far heavier than in the north. At Hong Kong the mean annual rainfall is 84 inches, and no month has less than 1 inch. Heavy rain begins at the end of March, and increases to an early summer maximum in June. Each month during the summer monsoon has more than 3 inches of rain, and each of the five months May to September has 10 inches or more. Thus the main features of the rainfall régime in south China are the heavy summer rains, the early summer maximum, and the fact that some rain falls in the winter months though the amount is insignificant by comparison with the large annual total.

In the third régime, that of central China, most of the rain is derived from the summer monsoon, but the periodicity is not nearly so strongly marked as in north China. At Shanghai only 60 per cent. of the total falls in the five months May to September, and no month of the year has less than 1 inch. The rainiest months are June and July, and there is considerable precipitation even in winter. The typical monsoonal régime is much modified. In the interior, e.g. Ichang, there is less rain in winter, about the same amount in summer, 78 per cent. of the total falling in the months May to September.

The following table shows more clearly the contrast in the winter conditions at Shanghai and Peking—

	SHANGHAI. *Rainfall.*		PEKING. *Rainfall.*	
	Total Amount.	*No. of Days.*	*Total Amount.*	*No. of Days.*
	Inches.		Inches.	
January . . .	2	12	0	2
February. . .	2	9	0	3
March . . .	3	13	0	4
April . . .	4	15	1	4
May . . .	4	11	1	7
June . . .	7	14	3	11
July . . .	6	13	9	14
August . . .	6	11	6	11
September . .	4	11	3	8
October . . .	3	11	1	3
November . .	2	7	0	3
December . .	1	6	0	2
Year . . .	45	133	25	72

At Shanghai the mean relative humidity exceeds 75 per cent. in every month. The summer months have the highest mean, 84 per cent., but January and February have 79 per cent. At Peking, the relative humidity in winter is only 58 per cent. (49 per cent. in April), in summer it is 71 per cent. The amount of cloud at Shanghai is greatest in June, 7·4 (expressed in tenths of the sky covered), but it is 6·3 in January and 6·8 in February. At Peking it is only 2·1 in winter, 4·9 in summer.

It is not possible to give a complete or satisfactory explanation of the peculiarities of the rainfall of central China from

the data available. Its early summer maximum is common
to Japan and most of the other islands off the coast of China.
In Japan these early rains are known as 'Plum rains' (p. 163).
It seems clear that in the early summer shallow depressions
form in the middle of the Yangtse basin, move slowly seaward
down the valley, and then travel to the north-east over
Japan. Their exact origin cannot be said to be understood.

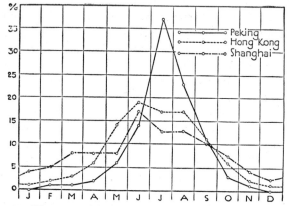

FIG. 61. Mean monthly rainfall (percentage of the yearly total).

The rapid but unequal heating of the wide plains of Szechwan,
which slope south and are, therefore, well exposed to the
sun's heat, is perhaps the most probable of the causes that
have been suggested. The secondary maximum of rainfall in
August is due to the typhoons, which are most numerous off
the coast of central China in that month. Usually they recurve towards the north-east before they reach land, but
sometimes they pass right over the coast, which suffers fearful
havoc from their fury (p. 169). They are always accompanied
by heavy rain even at a considerable distance from the centre.

The winter rain of central China is associated with shallow
depressions which appear in the interior of the country, and
move seaward, frequently down the Yangtse valley, as in
summer. The winds on their east sides are east and south-
east, and blowing from the sea they are rainy and comparatively warm; in the rear there are strong north winds, an
intensification of the usual north-west monsoon. The eastern
half of Korea has a few inches of rain in winter owing to its

acing the north winds of the winter monsoon, but the heaviest
ains fall in summer.

In conclusion we sum up the main features of the three
major climate regions of China. The first region, China north
of the Yangtse basin, is very cold in winter when strong dry
north-west winds from the interior of Asia blow almost continuously. The wind often rises to gale force, with clouds of
dust. The range of temperature is large, for the summer
months are almost as warm as in south China. The monsoonal change of wind and weather is complete. Winter is
almost rainless except near the sea where wild snow-storms
occur. The south-east winds of summer bring the rain, most of
it in late summer, but the total is less than in the rest of China.

Central China also has cold winters for the latitude, but not
so cold as north China; the mean sea-level temperature is
above 32°. The seasonal change is not so sharply marked as
in north China, for the winter months are damp, and have
some rain, though not so much as falls during the summer
monsoon. The fertile Red Basin of Szechwan is warmer in
winter than the coast, which is more exposed to the north
winds; frost and snow are rare. The Yangtse valley itself is
damp and cloudy, especially in winter; at Chungking, the
sun is often not seen for weeks together. But the rest of the
province, lying well above the river-level, enjoys clear skies
and very fine weather. The climate of Cheng-tu is described
as delightfully bright and dry in winter. The name of the
province Yunnan denotes 'south of the clouds', with reference
to the cloudy valley of the Yangtse. Yunnan is said to be
very sunny during most of the year. The summer rains last
from the beginning of May till the end of September. Most
of the province is more than 6,000 feet above the sea, and
is therefore healthy for Europeans. But the deep valleys in
the west are extremely malarious and are avoided as far as
possible even by the natives.

The third region, including all China south of the Yangtse
basin, is subtropical in character, but has remarkably cool
winters for the latitude, though frost and snow are very rare
near sea-level. The rainfall is very heavy, and by far the
greater part is derived from the summer monsoon; winter,
however, is not quite rainless. The rainiest month is June.

CHAPTER XXI

JAPAN

JAPAN shares in the monsoons of eastern Asia and resembles China in the main features of its climate, most of the rain falling in summer and the range of temperature being considerable. The prevailing winds are north-west in winter, south-east in summer. But modifications are caused by the insularity of Japan. The winters are milder than on the mainland, the 32° isotherm for January being 250 miles farther north; the mean temperature in January at Vladivostok is 7°, at Sapporo, in the same latitude beyond the Japan Sea, 20°; at Shanghai 38°, at Kagoshima 45°. The warm Kuro Shio influences Japan, but it does not raise the winter temperature very much since the main current flows on the east of the islands which is in lee of the prevailing winds in winter, the season when a warm current is most effective in warming the winds that blow over it, and only a small stream penetrates into the Sea of Japan; the British Isles are much more favourably situated in relation to the North Atlantic drift over which the winds blow for two or three thousand miles before reaching Europe at a temperature abnormally high for the latitude. In the case of the Kuro Shio the main influence is indirect. In winter as well as in summer the warm water is the path of depressions, which give unsettled weather with some southerly winds and a certain amount of rain even in winter, so that no part of Japan can be said to have a pronounced dry season or even a dry month.

The north of Japan is washed by the cold Okhotsk current, one branch of which makes its way south as far as lat. 39° N. in winter on the east coast.

The warmest month is August, an insular characteristic. The summers are almost as warm as in the same latitudes in China.

The Japanese archipelago is of great extent from north to south; Sakhalin lies off east Siberia in lat. 50° N., while the tropic of Cancer passes through Formosa. Very great diversities are due also to differences of altitude, for Japan is essentially a land of mountains.

There are four main climatic regions, Yezo, Hondo, Kiushiu and Shikoku, and Formosa. They differ chiefly in the intensity and duration of the winters (SANDERS).

Yezo has the coldest winters, for there are not less than three months with a mean temperature below 32°, when the land, especially in the north and east of the island, is snow-covered even near sea-level. The cold is not of the dry crisp type experienced in Siberia, for owing to the proximity of the sea the island has damp air and a good deal of snow and rain, the precipitation exceeding 2 inches in every month. After a more or less severe five months' winter, very severe in the mountains, there is a quick transition to summer, and in August the mean temperature is 70° in the south, 65° in the north of Yezo. Summer is the rainy season. The annual rainfall is less than in the rest of Japan, being about 40 inches in most of the island.

In Hondo the winters are much less severe; only in the extreme north and in the mountains is the mean temperature in January as low as 32°, and in the south it is 40°. But readings of 20° occur at Tokio in most winters, and frost may occur even in April. In summer also it is appreciably warmer than in Yezo, the centre and south of Hondo having four months with a mean temperature above 70°. The summer rains are heavy, and fall mostly in early and late summer. It is a season of moist air and much cloud, frequent rain, and enervating weather. Tokio has more than 4 inches of rain each month from March to November inclusive, and the annual total is 60 inches. The winter conditions are different on the east and west sides of the island; the prevailing winds are north-west, dry when they leave the continent, but humid and somewhat warmer after the passage of the Sea of Japan. Meeting the mountainous west of Hondo they rise and give heavy precipitation, rain near sea-level, snow in the interior, and the weather is very unpleasant, cold, damp, cloudy, and foggy. The winter precipitation is much heavier than the summer, for the prevailing south-east winds of summer are offshore (Fig. 62).

'The masses of snow which accumulate in the mountainous region and even on the west coast of Japan are enormous. There are villages which frequently experience a fall of over 20 feet of

snow. I was surprised several times by the first snows when
trying to get across a mountain pass. In such cases retreat was
a necessity. During the winter people in the mountains of course
do very little work. I know a village in the north of the main
island, called Kiriake, where the inhabitants after their breakfast
go to the baths, which are fed by hot springs, and remain in them
for the whole of the day enjoying the heat' (NAUMANN).

The highest summits bear snow most of the year. But after
crossing the mountains the winds descend to the east coast

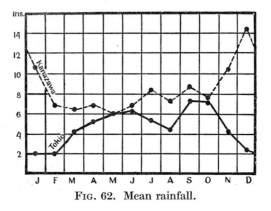

FIG. 62. Mean rainfall.

and give generally clear, sunny, and pleasant weather,
especially on the south-facing slopes. Rain, however, is by
no means rare, for the warm waters off the south-east of
Hondo favour cyclonic activity which gives Tokio more than
2 inches of rain in each of the winter months, but the summer
rains from the monsoon winds are much heavier. The yearly
total in Hondo, Kiushiu and Shikoku exceeds 60 inches except
on the east side of Hondo and round the Inland Sea; considerable areas of the exposed coasts and mountains have
more than 80 inches. Rice is the characteristic crop of
Hondo, and in the south and centre cotton and tea flourish.
Wheat and barley are grown as winter crops harvested in
June.

Kiushiu and Shikoku have a subtropical climate, the mean
temperature of the coldest month being well above 40°, and
nine months have a mean above 50°. The summers are not
much warmer than in Hondo, but the humid air is more
enervating.

'On the ocean side of Southern Japan, the palm tree, the orange tree, and the camphor tree flourish. Some small islands near this coast may be found covered with flowers at the beginning of February, when the lake of Suwa in the interior of the main island is frozen over so firmly that fairs are held upon it.'

Formosa has no cold season; the coolest month has a mean temperature above 60°, and frost and snow are unknown near sea-level owing partly to the low latitude, partly to the winds blowing from the north-east over a warm sea, instead of the north-west as in most of Japan. The summers are rather warmer than farther north, and there are seven months with a mean above 70°. The rainfall is heavy, and there is the usual monsoonal summer maximum, but the winters are by no means dry, having more than 3 inches in each month. The mountains which cover all the interior rise steeply from the sea to over 10,000 feet, and have very heavy rain in winter and summer from the easterly winds, the yearly total exceeding 100 inches.

The summer rain of Japan. The south-east monsoon naturally gives the heaviest rain in the east and south, and the south coasts of Kiushiu and Shikoku have more than 80 inches in the year. But the heaviest rain occurs not when the monsoon is at its height but in June and September. The wettest period is the second half of June and the beginning of July. During these weeks the sky remains wholly overcast, rain falls every day, and the weather is depressing and unpleasant. The air is so moist that walls and pavements become wet, and furniture and clothes mouldy. This rainy spell is called the 'Bai-u', meaning plum-rains, as it comes when the plums are ripening; it is the most critical period for rice cultivation. The summer rise of temperature is considerably checked by the pall of cloud of the Bai-u.

The early summer maximum is found not only in all Japan except Yezo but also at Hong Kong, in central China, the Lu-chu Islands, and Korea, but not in north China and Manchukuo, nor in the Bonin Islands. In Japan the Bai-u rainfall is about the same on the east and west coasts, diminishing towards the north. Okada points out that the monsoon is not at its strongest during the Bai-u, but is weak and often interrupted by calms and light variable winds. He suggests as an explanation of the heavy rain the frequent shallow depressions which originate in South China or in the neighbourhood of Formosa, and travel very slowly through the area. He says 'the cyclones are perturbations of heat origin, and develop as a result of unequal heating of the earth's surface by strong insolation. Most of the Yangtse depressions develop in the province of Szechwan.' The explanation seems hardly adequate.

The second rainfall maximum, in September, is due largely to the typhoons which pass over or near Japan in that month (p. 169). They tend to form east of the Philippines, and to move first to the north-west and then to the north-east, following the warm waters of the Kuro Shio. Indeed the Kuro Shio is a favourite course for depressions all the year, a fact which helps to explain the absence of a dry season in Japan.

The rainfall is heavy over the whole of Japan during the south-east monsoon, heaviest on the south-east and south coasts. Almost everywhere this is the rainiest season of the year, except on the west coast of Hondo. The annual total also is greatest in the south of Japan, that is on the south coasts of Kiushiu, Shikoku and Hondo, where it exceeds 100 inches in places, and on the west coast of Hondo, the central part of which has a similar amount. The rainfall is least in the south of Sakhalin and east of Yezo, where it is less than 30 inches, and around the Inland Sea, where the surrounding hills reduce the total to less than 40 inches.

CHAPTER XXII

SOUTH-EAST ASIA AND THE EAST INDIES

THE warm seas in which the East Indies are set help to intensify the hot and moist equatorial climate, but the whole region enjoys the great advantage for the tropics of having high mountains close at hand with many hill-stations at various altitudes for recreation and recuperation. The mean annual temperature is about 80° on the islands, and the mean annual range is very small, 2° at Batavia, 3° at Singapore; at Batavia the highest recorded reading is 96°, the lowest 65°, and the mean daily minimum temperature in August is 72°. In Siam and especially in Annam the range is much greater owing to the cool winters brought by the north-east monsoon; at Hué the February mean is only 68°, and in Annam the temperature may fall below 50° on winter nights, and a fire is welcome. But the summers are unbearably sultry owing not so much to any very high temperatures as to sticky hot vapour-laden air and the streaming rain of the monsoon. The southernmost islands of the East Indies are too small to have very cool winters, but at Kupang, Timor, the mean temperature is only 77° in July, and the lowest temperature on record is 59°. The seasons, where seasons are of any significance, depend not on temperature but on the amount of rain. The archipelago lies between the great monsoon areas of south-east Asia and north Australia, and the monsoonal air currents which control the climate in those countries blow over them (Fig. 63). These general winds are light and fairly steady, but there are endless local peculiarities, almost every one of the numerous straits and channels being known to mariners for its own squalls or other weather features. Thus the Malacca Straits have 'Sumatras', strong squalls with violent thunder, lightning, and rain, which blow at night during the south-west monsoon; they blow from the south-west and are in origin land winds intensified by strong mountain breezes. The hot seas and the many mountains cause the rainfall to be very heavy, and the region as a whole is one of the rainiest on the earth. The mountains and the west and south coasts of Sumatra and Java have many stations with annual means

of over 250 inches, and even the plains on the east of Sumatra
have more than 80 inches. But the rain falls in very heavy
downpours, and the number of rainy days is not unduly high.
Indeed there is more sunshine, and the skies are much clearer,
than in north-west Europe; Batavia receives its 72 inches of
rain a year in 357 hours and enjoys 2,326 hours of sunshine.
The least rainy islands are those near Australia, Timor and
its neighbours in the east of the Lesser Sunda Group, and

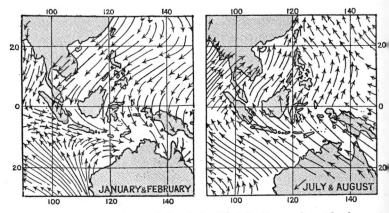

FIG. 63. The prevailing winds of the East Indies region; the longest
arrows denote the most constant winds.

there are also small areas of rain-shadow in the Asiatic part
of the region such as central Siam, and in most of the islands;
Java has a specially complex rainfall map owing to its position
and varied relief; its north coast is in a rain-shadow and has
an annual mean of less than 40 inches. The monthly totals
are in many cases more striking than the annual; Tavoy on
the coast of Tenasserim has 48 inches in July, Baguio in
Luzon, 5,000 feet above the sea, has a mean of 47 inches in
August, and in July 1911 it recorded 133 inches. The East
Indies probably has more thunderstorms than any other part
of the world. Buitenzorg, Java, records 322 days a year with
thunder, but this is a somewhat extreme figure for the region.
    The rainfall seasons are different in different islands and
even on the two sides of the same island or peninsula in some
cases. Latitude accounts for many of the differences, some
of the islands being in the north, some in the south hemi-

sphere. But there are many local differences which are due
to purely local causes, such as the lie of the mountains and
the trend of the coast. The influence of mountain ranges is
important everywhere. Thus Bangkok in Siam has the normal
seasons of India, with rain in the northern summer, but the
coast of Annam, backed by a mountain range at right angles
to the winter monsoon which blows from a warm sea, receives
most of its rain in the winter months with a pronounced
maximum in October and November. The same contrast is
found between the west and east sides of some of the Philippine Islands; Baler on the east coast of Luzon has 9 inches
of rain in January, Manila on the west coast only 1 inch, but
in August Manila has 16 inches, Baler only 6 inches. But,
speaking generally, south-east Asia has its rains, with hot
sultry weather, oppressively damp air and cloudy skies in
the months May to October, a cool dry season with bright
skies and clear and comparatively invigorating air in winter,
especially in December and January, and a hot dry season
in February, March, and April. Penang, on the west
side of the Malay Peninsula, has a similar régime, but
the dry season is less dry, the driest month, February, having
3 inches of rain. Tenasserim, however, being farther from
the Equator, has a dry rainless winter, in strong contrast to its
summer with more than 80 inches of rain in the three months
June, July, and August. At Singapore, only 100 miles
north of the Equator, the dry season may be said to have
disappeared, for there is heavy rain in every month; December
has most, 10 inches, and there is a secondary maximum of
7 inches in April; the driest month, May, has 6 inches;
the mean relative humidity probably exceeds 75 per cent. in
every month; the seasons in the north of Sumatra are similar.
The northern half of Borneo shares this equatorial climate;
at Sandakan in British North Borneo the driest month, April,
has 4 inches of rain, and the rainiest months are November,
December, and January, with 15 inches or more each,
during the north-east monsoon; the mean annual range of
temperature is only 3°. Many-sided Celebes presents too complicated a study in rainfall régimes to be described here.

At Batavia, lat. 6° S., the seasons are those of the south
hemisphere. The rainiest months are October to April, and

July, August, and September are decidedly drier with less than 3 inches each, August the driest month having only 1·7 inches. Some parts of the plains of north-east Java where the annual rainfall is below 40 inches have an almost rainless season in August and September. Towards the east of the Lesser Sunda Islands the north Australian régime becomes more and more prominent, and Timor and its neighbours have a very dry season in the southern winter; Kupang, Timor, gets less than 3 inches in the six months May to October, but the rest of the year has over 54 inches; part of Sumba has less than 32 inches a year. The periodicity appears to be stronger here than anywhere else in the Archipelago; the rain is brought by the west winds; the south-east trades, dry when they leave Australia, have not time to pick up much moisture before they reach the islands.

Van der Stok, director of the Batavia Observatory, divides the East Indies into three main rainfall provinces:

(a) North Sumatra and the northern half of Borneo have most rain in April and November, least in July and February;

(b) in the neighbourhood of the Equator the rain is heavy all the year, and the humidity high;

(c) the south of Borneo, the south of Celebes, Java, and the rest of the Sunda Islands have most rain from November to April, least from May to September when the south-east trades blow. In the eastern islands there is a pronounced dry season.

New Guinea, 1,500 miles long, is large and varied enough to claim a separate description; it has extensive plains almost at sea-level clothed with equatorial forest, and at the other extreme large areas above 3,000 feet in the mountain ranges which fill much of the interior, and snow frequently falls on the mountain tops. The trades blow from south-east and east from May to November, the north-west monsoon from December to March. The western end of the island is almost on the Equator, and has equatorial conditions all the year; around and west of Geelvink Bay the annual rainfall exceeds 100 inches, and even the driest month, October, has more than 4 inches, at many stations more than 8 inches. The mean annual range of temperature is very small, only 1·4 at Manokwari.

The rest of the island lies in a WNW.–ESE. direction, and the driest season is when the easterly trades are blowing parallel with the grain of the land. But even July and August have more than 2 inches each, and in most parts probably more than 4 inches; the yearly totals are very high, more than 100 and up to 200 inches on the coasts and low plains, and over twice as much in the mountains. But there are many local variations in both the amount and the season of rain. In some cases the explanation is the trend of the local mountain ranges, as on the north of Huon Gulf where the rainiest season is the period of the south-east trades which meet the mountains almost at right angles; the rainfall exceeds 250 inches, and means up to 33 inches a month are reported for May, June, and July; January and February are least rainy, with more than 8 inches each.

The shores of the Gulf of Papua, in the British Territory of Papua, have varied conditions. The neighbourhood of Port Moresby is an area of low rainfall with only about 40 inches a year; the season of the trades is dry, June to September having about 1 inch a month, and December to March is a pronounced rainy season. Kikori, however, on the north-east shore of the gulf, has 230 inches a year, most in May to June and September to October; December with 11 inches has least. Daru, on the other hand, 150 miles south of Kikori, near the mouth of the Fly River, with a mean annual total of 91 inches, has most rain in January to May, January being the rainiest month, and least in July to October, a relatively dry season with less than 3 inches a month.

In New Guinea the hot air is heavily charged with vapour and there is dense cloud during much of the day, especially in the mountains. It is hottest in the southern summer with a mean monthly temperature about 82° near sea-level; the coolest winter is found in the British Territory of Papua, where the mean temperature of July and August, the coolest months, is about 78°. In the rest of the island the mean temperature near sea-level is a little above 80° for every month of the year.

Typhoons. Fig. 64 shows the usual place of origin and the courses followed in the different months by these devastating storms. They belong to the class known as hurricanes in the

West Indies region and as cyclones in the Bay of Bengal, and their meteorology and characteristics are almost exactly the same. According to a recent report (1919) of the Weather Bureau of the Philippine Islands typhoons are:

frequent from July to November,
less frequent in May, June, and December,
quite rare in January, March, and April,
almost entirely absent in February.

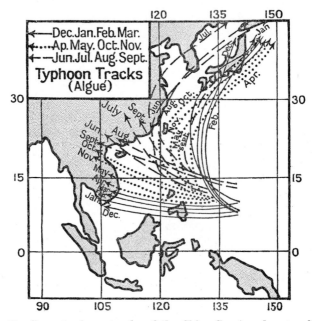

FIG. 64. Some typhoon tracks of the China Sea (much generalized).

It will be seen from Fig. 64 that some typhoons travel almost due west and reach the coasts of Indo-China, and others recurve on a parabolic course, following more or less closely the Kuro Shio; the latter degenerate into the ordinary extra-tropical cyclones of the westerlies before reaching Japan. The Philippine Islands are unfortunate in lying right in the track of a large proportion of the disturbances during their most violent stages. It may be noted from the figure that typhoons have a tendency to originate farther south and to follow a more southerly course when the sun is farthest south.

But it must be remembered that here as in other parts of the globe cyclones are prone to be very erratic both in the speed and the direction of their movement; the tracks shown in Fig. 64 are very much generalized. The following extract from the report of the Weather Bureau of the Philippine Islands on a typhoon in December 1918 illustrates this:

'From the fact that on December 18th to 20th there was a marked increase in the strength of the north-east wind at the Island of Guam (13° N., 144° E.) it is inferred that the typhoon was already developed, though it must have been centred more than 400 miles to the southward. The important indications at Yap (9° N., 138° E.) were the changes in the direction of the wind and the break in the weather. During the 17th to the 19th the wind was north-east, on the 20th it had veered to ENE., then to east in the early hours of the 21st, and after sunrise to south-east. With these wind changes the sky became overcast, with rain squalls, and during the 20th nearly 2 inches of rain fell. . . . By the morning of the 22nd the north-east wind over the Philippine Islands was backing north and north-west, and at 9.30 a.m. a warning was issued "There is a typhoon over the Pacific about half-way between the Western Carolinas and Mindanao, probably moving WbN". . . . The typhoon now became much more pronounced, and successive reports showed that until 6 a.m. on the 24th the core of the system was following a north-westerly course, and having reached 14° N., 128° E., the authorities were convinced that it was curving away to north and north-east, and would soon cease to affect the islands, and before noon on the 24th they did not hesitate to order the typhoon warnings to be lowered. However, suddenly, and without any definite premonitory signs, the north-westward advance was arrested, and the afternoon observations showed that the centre was moving WSW., and to the surprise of the authorities it maintained this unusual course across the middle Philippine Islands and the South China Sea to the neighbourhood of Saigon before the close of the month. The lowest barometer readings were registered at about noon on the 25th, 28·50 inches at Magallanes, 4 miles from the centre, and 28·52 inches at Sorsogon, 3 miles from the centre. On the 22nd the rate of progress of the system was about 11 miles an hour; next day . . . it slowed down to only 3½ to 4 miles. Then after curving to WSW. it advanced at 12 miles until the morning of the 26th when the rate was again reduced to about 9½ miles during the passage across the South China Sea. . . . The area of destruction, while the storm was raging in or near south-eastern Luzon, was about 80 or 100 miles in diameter. . . . The wreck of the steamer *Quantico* took place on the evening of the 25th on the northern coast of Tablas Island; 21 lives were lost. . . . At Romblon, nearly all the houses, even those of strong materials, suffered. . . . Many big trees were uprooted. Light trees like bananas were completely destroyed. The tower of the church was blown down. There was no absolute calm (eye of the storm), but relative calm was observed for about one hour, with light winds, force 1 or 2.'

CHAPTER XXIII

SOUTH-WEST ASIA

(ANATOLIA, SYRIA, PALESTINE, ARABIA, MESOPOTAMIA,
PERSIA, AFGHANISTAN, BALUCHISTAN)

[INFORMATION on the general meteorology of this region will be found in Chapter xxxi.]

In south-west Asia extreme continental conditions approach closely to the shores of the Mediterranean, and the weather is liable to wide and sudden variations according as the dry continent or the warm humid Mediterranean gains the upper hand.

Winter is dominated by the great high-pressure system of Central Asia. Over the Mediterranean there are low pressures (p. 272), but their influence does not extend effectively more than about 20 miles from the coast; thus all the plateau of Anatolia is covered by an extension of the Asiatic anti-cyclone, and another extension covers Arabia. Continental conditions prevail everywhere except on the littoral. The general winds are strong from the north-east, and the weather is cold and dry; but the low pressures over the Cyprus region and the Black Sea impose their own control on the surrounding coasts, giving south winds on the north coast of Anatolia, north on the south coast, south and south-east in Palestine. Usually the Mediterranean depressions do not advance far inland, but sometimes they are very vigorous and travel far to the east, assisted by the Caspian Sea and the Persian Gulf. An important track leads over north Mesopotamia, Persia, and Afghanistan into the plains of India, and the depressions that follow it, all in the winter half-year, give those lands their chief supply of rain, which is nowhere very copious. In Afghanistan there is some, but less, rain in summer also, derived from the Indian monsoon; in north India winter gives only a secondary maximum in the rainfall curve, which is dominated by the summer monsoonal rains. The winter depressions cause unsettled weather, and their approach is indicated by southerly winds.

On the Mediterranean Sea and its coasts these depressions

are the main weather control in winter and give the whole of the rainfall, which is moderate in amount, heavy only on some mountainous coasts, such as the south-east of the Black Sea. The rain is very variable in amount from year to year, and in duration, a very serious consideration in a region which at best is semi-arid, and in which agriculture is almost the only source of livelihood. The first signs of the autumn rains are eagerly watched for; a late beginning of the rains in autumn or an early cessation in spring may be catastrophes. A local effect of importance is the warm indraft in front of depressions, the sirocco of Palestine and Syria, which occurs in all seasons except summer, but is specially important in spring when disturbances are vigorous, and the deserts of Arabia from which the winds are drawn are already hot. The winds that blow in front of the Black Sea depressions descend from the plateau of Anatolia and are appreciably warmed by their descent.

The whole region is liable to be swept by cold waves from the north in rear of deep and extensive depressions. The advance of the wave can often be traced clearly from its origin in Central Europe or Russia to the Black Sea, the Levant and adjoining lands, and far south in Egypt. Such cold waves naturally occur only in the cold months; they are especially severe when abnormally high pressures cover the Balkan Peninsula (WEICKMANN).

Another effect of the depressions that pass eastward in spring along the south coast of Asia Minor into Syria is seen in the frequent thunderstorms of the north of Syria and Mesopotamia where the hot arid steppes meet the mountains on the south-east of Anatolia which still bear their winter snows, so that there are strong temperature contrasts.

In summer the conditions are much simpler and more uniform. The main control is the great low-pressure system of south Asia, into which west and north-west winds blow from the Azores anticyclone. Depressions are very rare, and the weather changes little from day to day. The coasts are cooler than the interior, since they receive prevailing onshore winds, and the cooling influence is increased by the sea breeze which blows from about 8 a.m. till 6 p.m. with almost unbroken regularity.

The sky is almost cloudless, the sunshine intense, and the heat in the steppes and deserts very great, but thanks to the low humidity not in itself unhealthy. The wind blows strong especially by day, and its passage over the parched wastes often raises clouds of dust and sand; dust-storms are not unknown even in winter. The north coast of Asia Minor is peculiar in having east and north-east winds westward of Cape Karembe, blowing through the windy Bosphorus. The south-east coasts of the Black Sea have strong onshore winds, and get heavy rain even in summer, though not so much as in winter.

Hence this region, except the coasts, has but scanty rainfall, in winter owing to the dominance of the continental anti-cyclone, in summer owing to the winds blowing steadily, undisturbed by depressions, from cooler to hotter regions. The winters are cold, the summers very hot with intense sunshine, strong winds, and frequent dust-storms. The land is mostly desert and steppe.

Anatolia. Regions with very diverse climates are included in Asia Minor. The north coast will be described first. It is a well-watered tract, the mountains receiving much rain from the Black Sea depressions in autumn and winter, and a considerable amount from the strong onshore winds in spring and summer. Winter is a season of unsettled weather as on the Mediterranean coasts; the southerly winds in front of depressions are warmed by their descent from the plateau, and the strong northerly winds in rear are often bitterly cold; the mean January temperature at Trebizond is 44° (cf. Marseilles, 43°). In summer north-west winds prevail, constant save for the alternation between the stronger sea breeze by day and the land breeze at night; unlike most of south-west Asia the south-east coasts of the Black Sea have useful rain in the summer owing to the surrounding mountains. The summer temperature (mean for July at Trebizond, 74°) is much like that of the Mediterranean coasts of France and Italy, but the abundant moisture fosters a much more luxuriant vegetation. With the usual Mediterranean figs and olives there are tea gardens and plantations of Turkish tobacco. Partly owing to the shelter of the Caucasus Mountains the coast east of Sinope is more favoured than the

coast between Sinope and the Bosphorus which is more open
to cold north-east winds and does not enjoy such frequent
föhn winds from the plateau; the summers too are dry, the
vegetation has less than the usual Mediterranean luxuriance
and the olive does not flourish.

From the north coast we make our way south through the
forests of the coastal ranges up to the plateau which lies some
3,000–6,000 feet above the sea, enclosed by a mountain rim.
The short journey leads to an entirely different land, with
continental extremes and scanty rainfall. The high pressure
which cover the plateau in winter ward off the genial influence
of the surrounding seas and give cold dry weather. Usually
north-east winds blow strong, dry, and cold from the south
of Russia, but at times a vigorous Black Sea depression
extends over the plateau giving warm south winds till a cold
wave swoops down in its rear as it passes eastward, and bring
bitter weather and deep snow to the bleak open steppes; a
such times thousands of sheep may perish. On the higher
plateau in the east, and in the deep valleys of the headwaters
of the Euphrates, the winters are still more severe, and snow
lies deep. At Sivas (4,400 feet) the mean temperature in
January is 21°, and − 20° has been recorded; the July mean
is 67°; the annual range, 46°, as well as the range from day
to night, is high; the intense cold of winter is followed by
hot summers, during which the aridity is only tempered by
occasional thunderstorms. Spring is the rainiest season, but
late summer is rainless and the great salt lakes bear witness
to the aridity. The mean annual rainfall at Angora is 11
inches, at Sivas 14 inches.

Continuing south across the Taurus, and descending to the
coastal plain of Cilicia, we return to usual Mediterranean
conditions. Owing to the southward exposure and the mountain shelter the climate is very warm. Frost is rare and
never severe, and in summer the maximum temperature may
exceed 110°. But the sea breeze which blows every day with
great regularity especially in summer, setting in about 8 a.m.
prevents excessive heat. The rainfall is about 20 to 25 inches
a year, with a strong maximum in winter and spring. Where
there are good irrigation facilities from the streams, as around
Adalia and Adana, Mediterranean agriculture flourishes luxu-

riantly, and cotton is an important product of the plains south of Adana. The layer of dust inches deep on the ground and the clouds of white dust which whirl through the hot shimmering air behind moving vehicles on a windy day are a reminder of the aridity of the Mediterranean summer. The rich coastal strip is the more impressive by contrast with the arid steppes of the interior, which are only a few miles distant.

The west coast of Anatolia has a similar climate, but the lowlands are wider, and are continued by wide valleys for some distance inland where the plateau itself is considerably lower than in the east. At Smyrna the mean January temperature is 46°, and in most years 6° or 7° of frost is recorded; the mean for July is 81°, and it is rare for the maximum temperature to exceed 100°. The strong Etesian winds and the regular sea breeze during the heat of the day are a boon in moderating the heat on the coast. In the sheltered valleys out of reach of the sea breeze the summer days are extremely hot and enervating.

Mesopotamia. The bold north-west–south-east feature lines exert a strong control on the wind directions. In winter the high pressures on the north give north-west winds, but frequent interruptions are caused by the passage eastward of depressions from the Cyprus region, in front of which the winds are south-east, with cloudy skies, some rain, and temperature much above the normal. The north-west winds in their rear are cold for the latitude and very dry, and they usually give clear bright skies. The mean temperature in January is 40° at Mosul, 49° at Baghdad; 0° has been recorded at Mosul, and once during a spell of nine days the temperature remained continuously below freezing-point, which shows that the winter cold may be severe in the north, at the foot of the snow-covered mountains of Kurdistan; at Baghdad 10° has been registered; snow is not unknown throughout Iraq. The cyclonic winds from the south-east bring all the rain that the land receives, but the total is less than 10 inches, and in lower Mesopotamia less than 5 inches; practically none falls except in winter and spring, June to October being rainless; much of the spring rain falls in thunderstorms. The rainfall is very variable from year to year. Round the Persian

Gulf the south-east winds are called Kaus or Sharki; they are sometimes followed for a few hours by a very strong wind from the south-west, called Suahili, which is dangerous for small craft.

In summer the prevailing winds are still north-west, blowing down the Mesopotamian corridor to the low-pressure system of southern Asia; they are called Shamal. Uninterrupted by cyclones they are remarkably constant, and especially strong during the day when they carry clouds of dust; there is a marked lull at night. The sky is cloudless, the air very dry, the sunshine fierce, and the heat intense. At Baghdad the mean July temperature is 94°, and 123° has been recorded; the maximum exceeds 100° practically every day in July and August, and even Basra near the Gulf has recorded 122°. The heat would be still greater and less bearable but for the strong winds, Mesopotamia being more fortunate in this respect than north-west India, where the heat is more enervating owing to the calmer air, though the temperature is the same (NORMAND). In·Mesopotamia the natives take refuge where possible in underground chambers during the day, and pass the nights on the house-tops in the comparatively cool breeze—but the mean minimum temperature of July nights at Baghdad is 80°. All the scanty steppe vegetation is burnt up, and the plains lie deep in fine dust which is swept up by the wind; the sky though cloudless is white rather than blue owing to this dust and the irregular refraction, and the visibility is often very poor not only over Mesopotamia but far out on the Persian Gulf. Sometimes 'dust devils' grow to great heights, over 5,000 feet having been measured by airmen. The great rivers roll down in heavy flood from their mountain sources in March and April when the snows are melting rapidly and depressions may cause heavy rains; the Tigris has risen 12 feet in a day in its lower course. The very great range of temperature is shown by the fact that the rapid Tigris has been known to freeze in winter at Mosul, where in summer 120° has been registered.

Persia. Mazanderan has a heavy rainfall, especially in winter, owing to the depressions over the Caspian and the influence of the Elburz Mountains, and the luxuriant vegetation includes the orange, date-palm, sugar-cane, and cotton.

The plateau has an even greater temperature range than Anatolia, for in spite of the altitude of 4,000 feet it is but little cooler in summer than Mesopotamia, but the winters are cold, the mean January temperature being only a little above freezing-point; Teheran has recorded 19°. The precipitation is scanty except in the hills, and the land cannot be cultivated unless irrigation is possible. In the rainless summer there is hardly a cloud, and in the middle of the plateau the aridity is extreme, for even in winter there is practically no rain, and in the heat of summer violent winds carry clouds of salt dust over the lifeless desert.

Afghanistan and Baluchistan resemble Persia, but the winters are less cold, the summers less hot, and the rainfall rather heavier; in winter there is heavy snow on the mountains of north Afghanistan. The summer monsoon of India gives a secondary rainfall maximum in July.

Syria and Palestine. The coastal strip has a good Mediterranean climate, notable for its high autumn and winter temperature due to the warmth of the waters of the east Mediterranean; even slight frost is rare. The humidity and rainfall decrease fairly regularly from north to south. From west to east also there is a general decrease, but it is locally interrupted by a large increase on the mountains and on the plateau of Palestine, then a decrease to extreme aridity in the Ghor and to dry though not arid conditions in the Baalbek depression between Lebanon and Anti-Lebanon, and an increase again east of the depression before the final decrease in the deserts of Transjordania and Syria. Except in the most favoured parts irrigation is essential for any serious agriculture, and it is thought that good underground supplies of water are available in most of Palestine. The rainfall exceeds 20 inches except in the south of Palestine; it is over 35 inches at Beirut and about 20 inches at Haifa and Jaffa, and then falls away rapidly towards the south to 12 inches at Gaza and about 3 inches at El Arish. The rains normally begin in October, but are liable to be late; after April little rain falls, and the summers are rainless.

The plateaux of the interior which overlook the coast have a heavier rainfall than the coast itself (Jerusalem 25 inches, Jaffa 20 inches), especially in the Lebanon Mountains.

The Ghor is extremely arid, a rocky desert except in the few irrigated spots; the Dead Sea has about 3 inches, the upper Jordan valley about 10 inches, Tiberias 18 inches. The edge of the escarpment on the east of the Ghor has about 12 inches near the Dead Sea, 25 inches near the Lake of Galilee, but as the plateau descends eastward the rainfall diminishes rapidly to less than 2 inches in the deserts of Syria and Arabia. As soon as the coast is left steppe conditions assert themselves more and more, the winters being cold and dry, frost frequent, and snow no rare visitant; the summers are very hot with frequent dust-storms. The sea breeze sets in regularly every day on the coast. Especially in spring there are sirocco winds which bring dry dusty air and high temperatures from the deserts on the south-east.

Arabia. Most of the peninsula is desert, but the mountains of Yemen get heavy summer rain from the monsoon, and above 5,000 feet it is a rich agricultural region, carefully terraced and irrigated, which produces good cereals, fruits, and especially coffee, in marked contrast to the arid wastes of the coastal strip. Oman, being farther east and north, gets most of its scanty rain in winter. No details are available from the deserts of the interior, but the climate must resemble closely that of the eastern Sahara. The mean temperature in July probably exceeds 95°. A contributing factor in the extreme aridity of the south-east of Arabia is the coolness of the surface water of the Arabian Sea. Aden has only 2 inches of rain (most in spring) and owing to the almost constant wind from the sea the mean temperature in June, the warmest month, is 89°, about 10° less than at Berbera on the opposite shore, and no reading above 102° has been recorded.

CHAPTER XXIV

THE HEART OF ASIA

WITH a width of about 500 miles, narrower or wider as the enclosing mountains approach more or less closely, a vast arid tract extends for some 2,000 miles from the Pamirs, ENE. to the Khingan Mountains. It is really a great basin, or rather a series of basins, since it is enclosed on all sides, especially the west, by much higher ground; but the average elevation above the sea is about 3,000 feet, so that the term plateau is not inapplicable, especially as numerous mountain ranges intersect the region. The tops only of the ranges now project above the deserts of gravel and sand, the products of subaerial denudation which bury the lower parts of the mountains from which they were derived.

Central Asia is often classed as a continuation of the deserts of North Africa and Arabia. It certainly resembles those regions in aridity and in the great summer heat, but by no means in the winter conditions. In winter the heart of Asia is under the influence of the great cushion of dense air that collects over the cold continent, giving the highest atmospheric pressure (reduced to sea-level) on the earth's surface. Calms and gently outflowing winds are the result in the central parts of the high-pressure region, and there can be no, or very little, precipitation. In spring the heated land throws off its burden of air, and the change to the low-pressure conditions of summer is a period of violent winds. In eastern Mongolia the north-west winds descend over China in great storms which carry much dust. In summer the low pressures draw in air from all sides, and under more advantageous conditions of relief a certain amount of rain would probably have been received, despite the fact that the sea is a thousand miles distant. But the deserts are surrounded by mountains; on the south-west of the Takla Makan tower some of the highest ranges on the globe. The Indian monsoon current is for the most part stopped by the wall of the Himalayas, a barrier 5 miles high. In the east a small portion of the monsoon makes its way into Tibet, but it must still cross the 700 miles of plateau, elevated 3 miles above sea-level and ribbed by numerous ranges, before reaching the Takla Makan. Probably it is a safe assertion that none of the monsoon current reaches so far north as to make the descent into this inland basin, and even if it succeeded in doing so it would be so warmed by compression as to be a very dry wind. Similarly on the north and west the mountain barrier, though lower, suffices to ward off the winds from those quarters. Only in the east do moist winds penetrate, and a belt of good steppe land about 70 miles wide borders the south-east of the Gobi. The sea is only 350 miles away, and the south-east monsoon, when it crosses the Khingan, still contains enough moisture to make agriculture possible with the help of irrigation. The northern edge of Mongolia also is by no means desert, the rainfall being sufficient to maintain abundant grass in places, and Urga has 7 inches of rain a year.

A very important factor in the meteorology is the high latitude. Central Asia lies between 37° and 50° N., and therefore there is a great seasonal change in the insolation. The annual range of temperature throughout these deserts is very large indeed.

It is instructive to recall for comparison the conditions of the Sahara. There the desert, far from being confined to the interior of the continent, reaches the sea on the west, north, and east, and mountains are of but minor importance in causing the lack of rain. Owing to the low latitude there is no excessive cold in winter, for even the north of the Sahara has a mean January temperature of 60°. As in almost all deserts the range of temperature is considerable, but not nearly so large as in Central Asia.

The rainfall is probably less than 2 inches a year in the deserts in the heart of Asia; in the east it is somewhat heavier and may amount to almost 10 inches in favoured localities. But even 2 inches must not be expected in the deserts every year, for many years have far less, and the balance is restored by a violent cloudburst at long intervals. Traces of the overwhelming floods that result may be seen in the deep channels, now dry, which the torrents excavated. There are no long series of records, but the available data show that the total precipitation is made up of winter snow as well as summer rain. The mean annual precipitation at Kashgar is 4 inches, of which over two-thirds fall in spring and autumn. At Yarkand half an inch was recorded in the single year a gauge was maintained. A traveller who stayed at Lukchun near Turfan for 10 months reports that it rained 5 or 6 times, and snowed 3 times, the snow disappearing the day after it fell. Urga has an annual mean of 7 inches; July and August are the rainiest months. The number of rainy days has been recorded at Hakiao (lat. 41° N., long. 111° E., in eastern Mongolia) for a few years, and the average found to be 59, 35 being in the summer half-year. This station, lying well to the north and west of the In-Shan and Khingan Mountains, is evidently reached by the south-east monsoon of China. There is a little snow in winter, and occasionally the ground is snow-covered for weeks.

The air is dry. Sven Hedin recorded a mean relative humidity of 28 per cent. in the Takla Makan in May, 69 per cent. in December. The mean summer humidity at Lukchun at 1 p.m. was 20 per cent. The sky seems to be somewhat more cloudy than in the Sahara.

The summers are very hot, with the sun glaring down during the long days through the dry air. Satisfactory records are wanting, but some that are available are given below:

Station.	No. of Years' Record.	Altitude in Feet.	Mean Temp. for July.	Highest Temp. recorded in July.
			°F.	°F.
Kashgar	2	4,255	80	—
Yarkand	1	4,120	82	103
Uliassutai	1½	5,365	65	94
Urga	7	3,445	63	97
Lukchun	2	−100	90	118

Uliassutai and Urga are comparatively cool owing to their higher latitude; the position of Lukchun below sea-level explains its excessive heat. But the Lukchun figures are eclipsed by the reports of Turfan, near which the depression sinks to 300 feet below sea-level. Domestic animals, even camels, cannot live through the summer heat, and have to be driven up the mountains. Ellsworth Huntington tells us that 'according to the Chinese, the summer is so hot that during the day the birds all gather in the shade of the trees beside the rivers. If one of them flies up, he is scorched to a cinder and falls sizzling into the water. Another Chinese yarn affirms that the heat is so great that after blowing on your rice to cool it, you must ply your chopsticks as fast as possible. If you do not, the rice will become hot again and burn you!' During the heat of the day the natives retire to underground chambers. Younghusband, speaking of a journey between the Tian

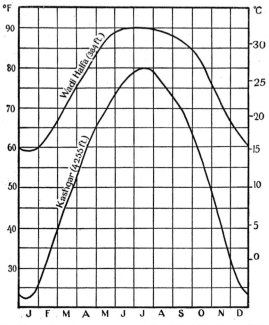

Fig. 65. Mean temperature curves for Wadi Halfa and Kashgar.

Shan and the Altai, says: 'The heat was intense, for the wind blew off the heated gravel as from a furnace, and I used to hold up my hand to protect my face from it in the same way as one would in front of a fire.'

In summer Central Asia resembles the Sahara, but in winter there is a great contrast (Fig. 65). Frost is indeed by no means unknown in the Sahara on winter nights, but the mean January temperature is everywhere above 50°. In the deserts of Central Asia, the mean for the same month is considerably below freezing-point. Standing water and small rivers are frozen right across throughout the winter months and the natives bring home their water-supply in the form of blocks of ice. It is rare for the thermometer to rise above freezing-point even at midday, and at Tarim Jangiköl, 2,890 feet above the sea, Sven Hedin found that the mean daily maximum temperature, during the January he stayed there, was as low as 26°. The mean January temperature was 9°, and the lowest reading he recorded during his winter's stay was —14°. In the middle of the Takla Makan he recorded a minimum of —25° in the beginning of January. On January 2 the maximum temperature was only 8°. Other records are:

Station.	No. of Years' record.	Altitude in Feet.	January. Mean Temp.	Lowest Temp. recorded.
			°F.	°F.
Kashgar	3	4,255	22	—8
Yarkand	1	4,120	21	2
Uliassutai	1½	5,365	—15	—40
Urga	7	3,445	—15	—46
Lukchun	2	—100	13	—5

The dryness and stillness of the air make these low temperatures more endurable than might have been expected. Ellsworth Huntington says he could sleep comfortably under a sheepskin in the open air with a temperature of —6°.

In general, the cold winter lasts from the end of November till the end of March. The west of the Tarim Basin has 3 months, Urga 6 months, with a mean temperature below freezing-point. The transition to summer is accomplished by May, so that spring is a time of extraordinarily rapid increase in temperature. At Tarim Jangiköl the mean temperature when Sven Hedin was there was 17° in February, 40° in March, 55° in April, 69° in May. The difference between February and March was greater than that between January and July in England.

The daily range of temperature is very large throughout the year, about 36° near the Tarim, and 24° at Lukchun in winter, 30° in summer. The annual range reaches remarkable figures, 58° at Kashgar, 77° at Lukchun, 79° at Urga, and 80° at Uliassutai.

Early in spring violent ENE. winds set in, to continue by day till the end of summer. Blowing with gale force they carry with them clouds of dust swept up from the desert, which darken the air and make life miserable. They are known as Karaburan, i.e. 'black storms'. The sand they drive along is one important cause of the rapid changes in the courses of the rivers through the desert.

'The daily winds [in the Gobi] were often extremely disagreeable. It was with the greatest difficulty that we could keep our tents from being blown down, and everything used to become impregnated with the sand, which found its way everywhere, and occasionally we had to give up our march because the camels could not make any head against the violence of the wind' (YOUNG-HUSBAND).

The coarse particles of gritty sand are not carried beyond the limits of the desert, but the lighter particles are blown far outside, and give a characteristic hazy appearance which is very common on summer days. The fine dust gradually sinks to the ground and forms loess. Ellsworth Huntington describes the scenery on the mountain slopes about 14,000 feet above the sea on the south-west of the Tarim basin as follows:

'Instead of the boulders and rough hollows which one usually sees in moraines, these presented surprisingly soft outlines, for they had been deeply buried in loess deposited from the atmosphere. The loess was covered with thick grass, full, as we soon saw, of countless Alpine flowers and dotted with sleek flocks of sheep and herds of cattle. . . . Our gaze went out far beyond [the lower mountains] to where the last low hills gave place to a strange yellow band. It seemed at first to be the sandy desert of the heart of Asia; but during the two hours of our stay on the pass it expanded and rose, and we then knew it for the inevitable dust-haze which shrouds the country more than half the year.'

The dust-storms rage by day only. At night the desert air is usually calm. To quote again from Younghusband's narrative:

'The nights were often extremely beautiful, for the stars shone out with a magnificence I have never seen equalled even in the heights of the Himalayas. Venus was a resplendent object and it guided us over many a mile of that desert. The milky way, too, was so bright that it looked like a bright phosphorescent cloud, or a light cloud with the moon behind it. This clearness of the atmosphere was probably due to its being so remarkably dry. Everything became parched up and so charged with electricity that in opening out a sheepskin coat or a blanket, a loud crack-ing noise would be given out, accompanied by a sheet of fire. The temperature used to vary very considerably. Frosts continued to the end of May, but the days were often very hot, and were frequently hottest at nine or ten in the morning, for later on a strong wind would usually spring up, blowing sometimes with extreme violence till sunset.'

Autumn and winter are free from dust-storms, and the clear, dry, invigorating air and pleasant temperature of the second half of September, October, and the beginning of November are described as forming an ideal climate.

Ellsworth Huntington describes the conditions of agricul-ture in this arid land. The Takla Makan desert is surrounded by a ring of coarse gravel detritus which has been carried down from the mountains by the streams in their rapid course to the depression. The water of the smaller streams disappears rapidly into and percolates through the gravel, and comes to light again at a lower level when it meets with finer deposits of sand and clay, and here there is a fairly continuous zone of moisture and verdure. In the most favoured districts, where the water is abundant enough to fill irrigation channels, there are gardens of unrivalled luxu-riance which produce the most luscious fruits, pears, apricots, grapes, melons. Agriculture depends for its moisture in west Mongolia entirely, and in east Mongolia largely, on the water that seeps through in this way, or on the running streams from the mountains, whose short courses across the desert are made still shorter by the demands of irrigation. Evaporation everywhere greatly exceeds precipitation, and most of the streams, which owed their origin to the rains and melting glaciers of the distant mountains, soon wither away in saline lakes. A belt of trees, reeds, and other undergrowth marks their course. The Tarim, Khotan Daria, and Cherchen Daria alone succeed in extending their ribbon of verdure right across the desert.

The mountains round the Tarim basin have of course more abundant precipitation than the floor of the depression; it is estimated at 25 to 30 inches a year. The higher summits have perpetual snow, and small glaciers. Unfortunately, though there is sufficient moisture the mountain tops are too rugged, and the cold too intense, for even nomads to pasture their herds on them; but the zone between 10,000 and 14,000 feet has excellent pasture which is grazed by the herds of the Kirghiz. Below 10,000 feet scantiness of moisture begins to take effect and at 5,000 feet it is barren desert. According to Sewerzows, the Khirgiz of the Tian Shan pasture their flocks in winter above 10,000 feet in order to keep above the zone of heaviest snowfall, which is also the zone of forest. Above 10,000 feet the snowfall in winter becomes less ('inversion of rainfall'); but it is not so with the summer rainfall, for in summer, owing to the higher temperature, inversion of rainfall begins considerably higher. Hence the zone between 10,000 and 14,000 feet has abundant summer rain and rich pasture, which remains largely free of snow in winter.

From the Pamirs some years' meteorological observations are available, taken at Pamirski Post, a Russian station on the Murghab River, 12,000 feet above the sea. The precipitation is extremely low, only 2 inches a year (Leh in the Indus valley has 3 inches); probably it is a little more at less elevations, for there is much snow in the lower valleys; the mountain ridges get but little snow, and have no glaciers. Pamirski Post has the steppe régime of rainfall, the rainiest season being late spring and early summer. The air is remarkably dry, with a mean relative humidity of 41 per cent. in summer, 59 per cent. in winter, and clear except when hazy with dust. The rays of the sun are very powerful even in winter, when the shade temperature is far below freezing-point. The difference between day and night temperature is very great. The mean temperature in January is 1°, in July 56°; the extreme readings recorded were $-52°$ and 82°. Very strong south-west winds blow up the valleys by day throughout the year.

CHAPTER XXV
TIBET

Not only the climate, but the whole life of Tibet is essentially conditioned by the great elevation. The plateau is an enormous block, elevated more than 12,000 feet above the sea, except in the valley bottoms of the east. Its length is about 1,200 miles, the width 400 miles in the west, and 700 miles in the east. It is walled on the south by the Himalayas, on the north by the Kuen Lun, the Altyn Tagh, and the Nan Shan. On this plateau the atmospheric pressure is only about half, in the highest parts rather less than half, that at sea-level, and visitors suffer greatly from fatigue, shortness of breath, and mountain sickness, as the result of any undue exertion in such rarefied air.

The north-west is known as the Chang (1 in Fig. 66). Here the altitude is greatest, over 15,000 feet everywhere, and on the average 15,000 to 17,000 feet, that is to say considerably greater than that of Mont Blanc. The mean temperature must be about 0° in January, 40° in July. The region consists of a series of wide open flat-bottomed detritus-filled valleys with a general east–west direction, separated by more or less parallel ridges. The climate is very rigorous, and hence the vegetation is scanty. Very much of the surface is bare rock or soil, parts are covered not with vegetation but with salt, which glistens so white in the intense sunshine that the natives who have to cross it wear dark spectacles. But many parts have a fairly good plant covering, consisting chiefly of grasses and other low plants rarely more than 3 inches high, and notable for their great root development, a sign that they find the habitat a very dry one. Wild animals such as antelopes feed on the grass, but even the hardy nomads never take their flocks to these bleak uplands. There are, of course, no trees or shrubs, but it is interesting that flowering shrubs have been found elsewhere in Tibet as high as 19,000 feet, and butterflies as high as 17,600 feet.

South of the Chang is the belt of 'Upland Pastures' (13,000 to 15,000 feet), the summer resort of the Dokpa and their herds (2 in Fig. 66) with abundance of excellent grass.

The great valleys in the south, of the Upper Indus and the Sanpo, and in the south-east, of the Yangtse, Mekong, and Salwen, form the third division, the most important economically (3 in Fig. 66). The south-east of this region is remarkably fertile. Trees flourish up to 13,500 feet above the sea in parts, and travellers have been much impressed by the

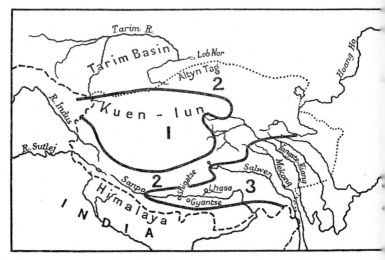

FIG. 66. The main climatic regions of Tibet.

luxuriance of the valley forests of the east of Tibet at altitudes of 12,500 feet. Wheat is grown as high as 12,500 feet, though it cannot be depended on to ripen above 11,500 feet. Millet, maize, and rape are common crops. Some of the alluvial valley-bottoms are very productive, in particular the Lhasa valley has been specially commented upon by the few foreigners who have had the privilege of seeing it. It has the advantage of an extensive system of artificial irrigation.

These general statements on altitude and vegetation probably give the most useful indication possible of the climate in the absence of reliable temperature and rainfall statistics established by long-continued observations. The only readings are those of travellers, taken on their journeys or during a few months' halt. Hence the mean values mentioned in the following paragraphs are not founded on very satisfactory data, and must be taken as merely giving a general idea of the conditions.

The warmest month in the north-west of Tibet is August, but even then frost must be expected every night. The lowest reading recorded in this month is 19°. The air is remarkably clear, containing very few dust or moisture particles, and the barometer stands at about 16 to 17 inches. Consequently insolation is very intense, but the air in the shade is cold; Sven Hedin recorded 147° on a black bulb thermometer (sun temperature) when the ordinary air (shade) temperature was 54° to 61°; the barometer reading was 17·1 inches. There is a large range of temperature between day and night. Winter is exceedingly harsh; Bonvalot traversed the country during the months December to March, and noted a temperature as low as −40° F. on January 6. The lowest reading recorded by Sven Hedin was −40°, at about 35° N. lat., 80° E. long. On the previous day 'the night came down over the enormous snowfields, biting cold. The temperature went down to the freezing-point of mercury (−37°). I had two candles and a nice fire in my tent as it was Christmas Eve. The next morning one pony lay dead and hard on his place among the rest.'

The south-east of Tibet is a less inhospitable land. The mean daily maximum temperature at Lhasa (11,600 feet) is 72° in June, 71° in July, 64° in August. The slight drop in July, and larger drop in August, are presumably due, in part at any rate, to the cloudy skies of the monsoon. The highest maxima in the shade exceed 90°. Probably it never freezes in July and August.

Everywhere in Tibet spring is much delayed since there can be no very great rise in temperature till the snow covering is melted. In the agricultural districts the melting is artificially hastened by scattering stones and earth on the snow to absorb the sun's heat. Seed cannot be sown till April. Autumn is early, and in the central districts all the crops must be gathered by the middle of September, for night frosts then become very severe even as low as 12,000 feet above the sea. In November the smaller lakes freeze over, and Tengri-Nor becomes a sheet of ice early in December. Even geysers are turned into pillars of ice in the depth of winter. The numerous very salt lakes, however, do not freeze. All the rivers are frozen solid except those in the south-east, which are at a less altitude, and have a greater volume. The Lhasa River has only a fringe of thin ice. Kuku Nor, though salt, is often frozen in winter, and devout Buddhists walk over the ice to the holy island of Kiusu. A Russian expedition made meteorological observations for fifteen months in the south-east of the Tsaidam salt steppe region, lat. 36·2° N., long. 97·3° E., at an altitude of 9,380 feet; the mean temperature was 9° in January, 63° in August, and the extremes recorded were −20° and 91°.

With regard to the amount and season of precipitation, the problem arises how far Tibet is influenced by the summer monsoon. The Himalayas undoubtedly form an effective climate barrier. In the west, probably hardly any of the moist monsoon air current is able to cross it, for the mountain wall is very high and continuous, and, moreover, the barometric gradient directs the winds along rather than across the mountains. But in the east the mountains are lower, and the deep and fairly open valleys of the headwaters of the great rivers of Further India and southern China, offer a ready ingress to the moist winds. Hence there is summer rainfall of true monsoonal origin in south-east Tibet, July and August being the rainy months. The mean annual rainfall is estimated at from 10 to 20 inches at Lhasa and Shigatse. In the west most of the precipitation seems to fall in winter, of course in the form of snow, and is doubtless associated with the winter depressions of north-west India and the western Himalayas. Sven Hedin's opinion is that in winter there is more snow in west than in east Tibet, in summer more rain in the east than in the west.

The monsoon currents that succeed in passing the Himalayas find another barrier in the Tangla Mountains, which run from WNW. to ESE. through the centre of Tibet attaining altitudes of over 25,000 feet, where they seem to be finally stopped. North of the Tangla the annual precipitation is probably not over 4 or 5 inches; Leh, the nearest comparable station with good records, has 3 inches. Travellers have suffered severely from lack of fresh water in crossing the stony barren wastes on the north. But as soon as they cross the

Tangla Mountains towards the south they find in summer cloudy skies and only too much rain—monsoonal conditions. Probably the rain is frequent rather than abundant.

Violent and constant winds are often noted in travellers' diaries. They blow especially by day all the year on the higher plateaux, and make the low temperatures harder to bear than the thermometer reading would suggest. They often bring blizzards of snow even in summer-time. They usually blow from the west, except during the monsoon in the south-east. Probably they represent the currents in the higher layers of the atmosphere flowing in towards Central Asia in winter to feed the high-pressure system shown by the sea-level isobars and the outflowing surface winds of the winter monsoon of south-east Asia.

The small precipitation is doubtless the chief reason that the snow-line is so high in Tibet. On the south face of the Himalayas it is as low as 16,000 feet, but in Tibet it is probably 19,000 to 20,000 feet. Other factors combining with the small precipitation are the strong winds, intense sunshine, and rapid evaporation.

CHAPTER XXVI

RUSSIA (IN EUROPE AND ASIA), FINLAND, THE BALTIC STATES

EUROPEAN Russia is included with Asiatic for description in this chapter since the Ural Mountains do not form a real climatic divide. Travelling east through France and Germany from the western seaboard of Europe which is washed by the warm and stormy waters of the North Atlantic, we experience a gradual transition, which, it is true, continues right into the heart of Siberia, but at the Vistula the climate has become definitely continental. That river forms a convenient if arbitrary boundary between the ocean-controlled climates of Western and Central Europe and the essentially continental type to which practically all the Russian territory conforms.

Russia is an enormous unbroken land mass with an area of eight and a half million square miles. Being situated in middle and high latitudes it has a very extreme climate, and eastern Siberia contains the 'cold pole' of the earth, where the winters are the coldest known and the range of temperature is greatest. Canada is the only land which has comparable extremes. In the southern hemisphere the land masses in similar latitudes are attenuated, and consequently the winters are mild.

The region contains vast plains not much above sea-level, and therefore maps of sea-level isotherms give a closer approximation to actual observed temperatures than in the case of many countries where a considerable correction to sea-level has been applied. The highest elevations are the Caucasus and the mountains of Armenia, and the lesser heights of the Urals, the Yaila Mountains, and the mountains of south and east Siberia.

Pressure conditions. In January (Fig. 34), the dry cold of Central Asia so intensifies the subtropical high pressures that the largest high-pressure system known at any season on the earth is formed. Lukchun (57 feet below sea-level), near its centre, has a mean pressure in January of 30·8 inches. The normal high pressures are not only intensified but drawn far north, since the north of the continent is the coldest part, in contrast to the summer conditions when the centre of lowest pressure is in the south. Towards the west there is a well-marked extension of the high pressures along lat. 50° N., across southern Russia and Central Europe to the Atlantic, forming the barometric 'backbone' of Europe, which forms a most important wind-divide. North of it, over all northern and central Russia and Siberia, the prevailing winds are from the south and west; west of the River Obi they belong to the Icelandic low-pressure system of north-west Europe. Variable winds mark the high-pressure axis itself, and south of it the steppes of south Russia and Turan have north, north-east, and east winds, very cold and dry. West and central Siberia has in general southerly winds, exceedingly cold; in the east of Asia the winter monsoon blows from the north-west. In April and October the general pressure distribution and hence the prevailing winds are similar to those of January. The absolute pressure in the centre of the continent is considerably less, and the surrounding gradient is not so steep, but the same high-pressure ridge along 50° N. separates south Russia, with north-east winds, from central and north Russia and Siberia, with south and west winds. Indeed, these features persist from August to April, a period of nine months.

The outstanding feature of the summer conditions (July, Fig. 34), which last for only three months, is the deep trough of low pressure over the south of Asia, with its centre in Afghanistan. A vast extension towards the north-east covers central and north Asia as a shallow depression with gentle gradients; the mean July pressure at Lukchun, 57 feet below sea-level, is 29·6 inches, 1·2 inches less than in January. The North Atlantic anticyclone, now much intensified, projects far over Central Europe, and can perhaps be recognized as far as Lake Baikal in the curve of the 29·7 isobar, so that there is a tongue of high pressure as in winter, but it points now towards the east. North and central Russia has westerly and north-westerly winds, south Russia north-westerly in the west and north and north-easterly in the east, which continue to the Mediterranean. Turan has steady north winds, except Ferghana and other valleys in the mountains, where the wind blows up the valleys, from the west in the case of Ferghana;

the north of Siberia has east winds and in eastern Asia the south-east monsoon is blowing. Round the Caspian Sea there is a seasonal reversal of wind direction, the air flowing in winter from the dry cold land to the relatively warm sea, and in summer out from the relatively cool sea to the hot land (Fig. 67).

Temperature (Fig. 33). In winter the warm Atlantic Drift is a more important source of heat for Russia than direct

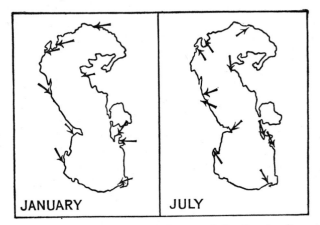

JANUARY   JULY

FIG. 67. The prevailing winds around the Caspian Sea.

insolation. The prevailing westerly winds of the north and centre of the country carry the oceanic influence far inland. In the south, on the other hand, the prevailing north-east winds are cold, since they originate in the heart of the continent. Consequently the isotherms have a general north-west to south-east trend in European Russia and west and central Siberia. Every mile we advance towards the north-east, the colder it becomes, the temperature decreasing with remarkable uniformity into the north-east of Siberia where at Verkhoyansk the winters are among the most extreme known anywhere, as cold as on the Polar icecaps. The heat of the North Atlantic is more than 3,000 miles distant beyond the frozen continent; the Pacific Ocean has not much effect, since the wind blows offshore almost continuously, and, moreover, ranges of hills intervene; the Arctic, being ice-covered, cannot ameliorate the harsh conditions to any great extent. The warm Indian Ocean lies far to the south of the insuperable barrier presented by the lofty mountain ranges and wide deserts of the centre of Asia. Of direct insolation there is none at the winter solstice, for Verkhoyansk is within the Polar Circle. During the long winter nights radiation goes on rapidly from the snow-covered ground through the clear calm dry atmosphere and the cold air stagnates in the valley-bottoms. The mean temperature in January at Verkhoyansk is $-58°$, the mean minimum temperature of the month $-83°$, and $-94°$ was once recorded, this being the lowest reading ever taken on the surface of the earth. The highest temperature ever recorded in January was $-13°$. The winter cold is less intense towards the north. Sagastyr (on the Arctic Ocean, delta of the Lena) is about $25°$ warmer in January. This is due, according to Woeikof, not so much to the influence of the ocean, which is ice-covered for some hundreds of miles from the shore, as to the stronger winds on the flat and treeless tundra and the absence of temperature inversion. The fact that the cold pole is so far east in Siberia is an indication of the relative importance of the Atlantic and Pacific Oceans in determining the winter climate of Eurasia. The prevailing westerly winds, unimpeded by any important mountain barrier, bring heat for hundreds of miles inland from the Atlantic, and the vapour they contain is effective to the same end by checking radiation. The theoretical probability that the low winter readings of eastern Siberia are due to drainage of cold air into the valley-bottoms, in which all the regular meteorological observations are made, and that inversion of temperature is the normal winter condition, is strengthened by the few records available from elevated stations, which are shown to be considerably warmer. The isotherms drawn on our maps represent only the conditions of the valley-bottoms.

Almost the whole of Russia has a mean January temperature below freezing-point. The isotherm of $32°$ F. bisects the Crimea and the Caspian Sea, and follows roughly the line of the Trans-Caspian Railway across Turan, so that only the south of the Crimea, the lower land of Trans-Caucasia, the southern half of the Caspian, and the extreme south of Turan have a mean temperature in January above freezing-point. And even south of the $32°$ isotherm there is a considerable area in and around Armenia which forms an 'island' of cold, with mean January temperature below 32°; thus at Kars, 5,740 feet above the sea, the January mean is 9°. In Trans-Caspia much of the land lying south of the 32° isotherm is mountainous, and hence has actual temperatures much lower than the isotherms show. To appreciate the significance of the January isotherms for the life of the Russians it must be remembered that almost all the vast area to the north and east of the 32° line is snow-covered for some weeks at least every winter, the sledge is the usual conveyance, and the rivers are frozen. The 14° isotherm crosses European Russia obliquely from the north of the Gulf of Bothnia, through Moscow to near Astrakhan. The north-east shores of the Caspian Sea are on the cold side of it, and hence, although the latitude is 47° N., the winters are colder than at Leningrad in lat. 60° N. Almost all Siberia has a January mean below 0° with the exception of the south of the Pacific coastal strip, but even at Vladivostok the mean is only 7°.

The warming influence of seas and lakes on their neighbourhood is clearly marked in winter. Mariehamn, on the Åland Islands in the Baltic, has a mean January temperature of 27°, but at Leningrad, 350 miles east at the head of the Gulf of Finland, which, however, is frozen over, the mean is only 18°. The White Sea and the Peninsula of Kola form another striking example; northward along the meridian of 35° E. the temperature actually rises over the White Sea, to fall over Kola and rise again on the Murman coast. It is worthy of notice that the coldest part of the north-west of Russia is well to the west under the lee of the Scandinavian highlands; this is an exception to the usual increase of temperature in the direction of the ocean, and is a result of the barrier opposed by the highlands to the warm moist winds.

Proximity to the sea and the shelter of the Yaila Mountains combine to give the south of the Crimea, the Russian Riviera, its mild winters. At Yalta the mean January temperature is 39°, and the lowest reading on record 9°; at Ekaterinoslav, 280 miles north, fully exposed to the cold north-east winds that sweep over the steppes, the corresponding figures are 19° and −31°. Even Yalta is considerably colder than the north coasts of the Mediterranean Sea, which, however, are in slightly lower latitudes. The coast of the Black Sea at the foot of the Caucasus is another climatic oasis, thanks to the mountain shelter, a shelter which is perhaps felt even on the south coast of the Black Sea. When, however, a deep depression lies over the east of the sea, the lower western end of the Caucasus is unable to keep back the north-east wind, which sweeps down as the dreaded Bora, an exceedingly strong, cold, dry wind from the steppes, known especially in the neighbourhood of Novorossiisk.

The isotherms curve northward over the south of the Caspian Sea, the northern part of which, however, being frozen, has little or no modifying influence. The Arctic Ocean warms the north of Siberia somewhat, but its frozen surface is not so effective a source of heat as the open Pacific, on the shores of which the isotherms are closely crowded. The most striking effect is shown by Lake Baikal in December (Fig. 68) when the water is freezing but not yet frozen over; there is much fog on the shores of the lake at this time. In the second half of the winter the lake is completely ice-covered and has much less warming influence. The Sea of Aral, being shallow, freezes over rapidly in the beginning of winter, and thenceforward does not appreciably warm its neighbourhood.

To consider next the lowest readings that have been recorded, the warmest part of Russia is the south-west, the coasts of the Black Sea and the southern half of the Caspian, but even here there are few stations where the thermometer has not been known to fall below 18°. The south of Turan has lower records, −15° at Merv, −24° at Nukuss, on the delta of the Amu Daria. The whole of the north-eastern half of European Russia, including the coast of the Arctic Ocean, and all Siberia has experienced temperatures below −40°, all central Siberia below −60°, and Verkhoyansk has recorded −94°.

The Siberian winter is by no means so unpleasant as these low temperatures might suggest. The air in the interior of the continent is bracing and often calm, so that it is possible to protect oneself adequately with furs. Vegetation hibernates, to flourish luxuriantly again in the summer warmth.

'The inhabitants of the south of East Siberia have no cause to envy the winters of Central Europe with their leaden skies, strong damp winds and sudden changes of temperature, which are felt the more because they oscillate about freezing-point. Except on the coasts the sky is beautifully clear, especially between September and April, and of a deep violet-blue which recalls Italy and north India. The air is transparent and calm, and the bright sunshine is so warm that the snow on the roofs melts though the air temperature is below 0°' (WOEIKOF).

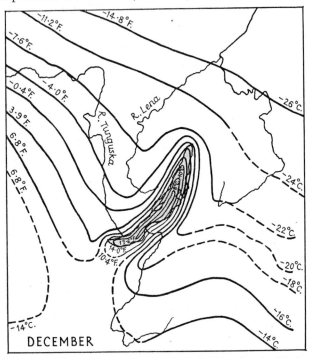

FIG. 68. Mean temperature in the neighbourhood of Lake Baikal in December. Compare Fig. 69.

It is only when the wild Buran blows, the Purga of the tundras, that there is danger to man and beast. During these storms the wind sweeps with extraordinary violence over the open plains. The air is thick with snow, descending from the sky and swept up from the ground, so that it is impossible to see. Though the temperature is not specially low the cold is felt keenly, and any one who is overtaken runs a serious risk of losing his way and being frozen to death. The Buran is known and dreaded in south Russia and throughout Siberia, except in the forests. It often makes it impossible to cross the passes of the Stanovoi Mountains for weeks together in winter.

The air is usually described as being very dry. We may be inclined to challenge this statement on finding that the mean relative humidity in January is over 80 per cent. almost everywhere, and over 85 per cent. in European Russia, figures almost identical with those for England where the air is notably humid. But it must be remembered that in Russia the air is very cold, and, though the relative humidity is high, the absolute humidity is very low. On coming into contact with the human body the air is very much warmed, and becomes much drier than the air in England, raised to the same temperature. Physiologically, therefore, the Siberian winter air is 'dry'. A few figures will make this point clearer. At Oxford, England, the mean relative humidity of the air in January is 87 per cent. and the mean air temperature is 39°; when this air is heated to 60° (a figure chosen as an approximation to the temperature to which air is heated near the body) the relative humidity becomes 42 per cent. At Tobolsk the mean relative humidity in January is the same as at Oxford, 87 per cent., and the mean air temperature is −2°, so that if the air is heated to 60° the relative humidity falls to 8 per cent., about a fifth of the value for Oxford.

In summer the land mass is warmer than the sea. The July isotherms follow the parallels of latitude more closely than those of January, except along the Baltic and Pacific coasts; their general trend is WSW. to ENE. The 50° isotherm, the southern boundary of the tundra, cuts off the northern peninsulas, and the 70° line crosses central Russia and southern Siberia. The highest temperatures occur in the deserts of the south, the south of Turan having a July mean over 86°. The effect of bodies of water is considerable though not nearly so great as in winter. At Mariehamn (Åland Islands) the mean July temperature is 59°, and the absolute maximum 85°, and at Leningrad the corresponding figures are 64° and 97°. Thus the insular station is the cooler in summer as it was the warmer in winter. The interior of the Kola Peninsula is somewhat warmer than the coasts. The isotherms show characteristic southward loops over the Caspian Sea. The Arctic and Pacific coasts are cooler than the interior of Siberia, and indeed the climate of the Pacific coastal strip is described as decidedly unpleasant in summer owing to the chilly damp and foggy south-east winds that almost constantly blow from the sea. Lake Baikal cools its neighbourhood appreciably (Fig. 69).

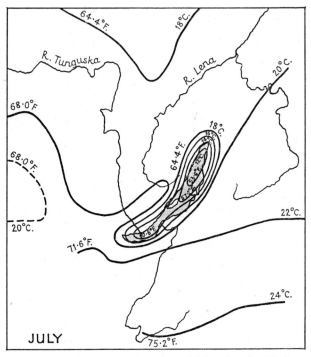

FIG. 69.   Mean temperature in neighbourhood of Lake Baikal in July.

The highest temperatures recorded are about 86° in the tundra in the extreme north of Russia and along the Baltic coast. It is a striking illustration of the regulating effect of bodies of water that no higher maxima occur in lat. 55° on the Baltic than in lat. 71° in the Arctic deltas of north-east Siberia. The summer maxima, like the summer means, are highest in the south of Turan, where they exceed 105°.

The distribution of temperature is far more uniform in July than in January:

				January.		July.	
				Mean Temp.	*Absolute Min.*	*Mean Temp.*	*Absolute Max.*
				°F.	°F.	°F.	°F.
Batum	.	.	.	43	18	77	95
Tashkent	.	.	.	30	—15	80	109
Leningrad	.	.	.	18	—35	64	97
Moscow	.	.	.	14	—44	66	99
Tomsk	.	.	.	—3	—60	64	95
Yakutsk	.	.	.	—46	—84	66	102
Verkhoyansk	.	.	.	—58	—94	59	93
Range between extreme stations	.	.	.	101	108	21	16

A most important factor, especially in continental countries situated in the 'temperate' latitudes, is the range of temperature from summer to winter. In Russia the difference between summer and winter is so great that a statement of the mean annual temperature, which includes such widely different extremes, is without practical significance. The map showing lines of equal range of temperature (Fig. 70) is strongly reminiscent of that of the winter isotherms whose influence evidently outweighs that of the summer isotherms. The smallest range is in the west, over the Baltic, but even on the Baltic coast it is as much as 36°. Similarly on the coasts of the Arctic and Pacific Oceans, the Black Sea, the Caspian Sea, and Lake Baikal, the range is notably less than inland. In the interior away from sea influence the range increases from 36° in the west to 65° in the east of European Russia. Almost all Siberia except the Pacific littoral has the enormous range of over 70°. Round Verkhoyansk, in almost exactly the same position as the winter cold pole, is found the greatest range on the earth, over 100°. The following table shows more clearly how rapidly the range increases from west to east (see also Fig. 71):

			Mean Temperature.		
			January.	*July.*	*Range.*
			°F.	°F.	°F.
Riga	.	.	24	64	40
Moscow	.	.	14	66	52
Kasan	.	.	8	68	60
Tobolsk	.	.	—3	64	67
Tomsk	.	.	—3	64	67
Yakutsk	.	.	—46	66	112

Where the range is so great it is evident that the change from month to month must be very rapid, especially in spring and autumn. At Verkhoyansk the mean temperature drops 40° from October to November. This is an extreme case, but even at Moscow, in the west, there is a change of 15° from March to April.

Almost all the world over outside the Tropics, autumn is warmer than spring, especially in maritime climates, although

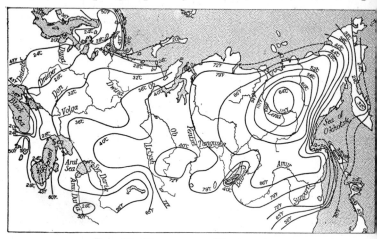

Fig. 70. Mean range of temperature.

the altitude of the sun is greater in spring than in autumn. The air temperature lags behind the sun owing to such causes as a snow-covering to be melted, wet ground to be dried, or, most important of all, the presence of a body of water with its conservative thermal tendency. The ordinary rule holds good in most of the Russian lands, especially on the coasts of the Baltic and Black Seas, but Turan and the steppes of south-west Siberia are anomalous in having spring warmer than autumn:

	Mean Temperature.	
	April.	October.
	°F.	°F.
Tashkent	58	54
Petro-Alexandrowsk . . .	58	52

Thus here the curve of air temperature follows closely that of insolation; there is little 'lag'. It has been pointed out also

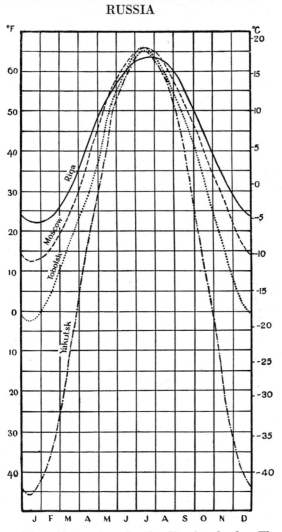

Fig. 71. Mean temperature in the Russian lands. The summer temperatures at the four stations are almost the same. The difference in range is due to the colder winters in the east.

that, owing to the absence of trees, the winter winds are strong and the snow, never very deep, is swept away, so that the spring rise in temperature with the increasing power of the sun is not delayed by the diverting of energy to melt snow or dry the ground, and in the absence of any large body of water the air temperature follows closely the sun, whose altitude is greater in April than in October. The same peculiarity is found at most stations in the interior of eastern Siberia, but on the coast of the Pacific the usual excess of heat in autumn is strongly marked:

	Mean Temperature.	
	April.	October.
	°F.	°F.
Verkhoyansk (interior) . .	8	6
Okhotsk (coast) . . .	21	28

It is interesting to compare the temperature of the deserts of Turan with that of the Tarim Basin on the other side of the Pamirs, for the most part at a considerably greater altitude:

		Mean Temperature.		
	Altitude.	Jan.	July.	Range.
	Feet.	°F.	°F.	°F.
Turan.				
Petro-Alexandrowsk .	295	23	82	60
Samarkand . . .	2,362	32	77	45
E. Turkistan.				
Lukchun . . .	−50	13	90	77
Kashgar . . .	4,255	22	80	58

Both deserts are of the same general type, with cold winters and hot summers, but East Turkistan has considerably colder winters, somewhat warmer summers, and greater range of temperature.

Freezing of rivers and coasts. During winter even large rivers are frozen over in nearly all Russia. The duration of the ice (Fig. 72) is a most important element in the life of the people. In the south-west the Dniester and the middle Vistula are ice-bound for over 70 days in an average year. In the centre, including the middle and upper Volga, the period is 150 days, and in northern Russia over 200 days. The 120-day and the 160-day lines divide European Russia roughly into three equal parts, a southern where the rivers are frozen for less than 4 months, a central with 4 to 5½ months, and a northern with from 5½ to 7 months. In the whole of Siberia the rivers are frozen for at least 5 months, and in the extreme north running water is to be seen only for 3 months in the year. Many rivers and lakes are frozen to the bottom. The air temperature is below freezing-point for 10 to 20 days longer than the period during which the rivers are frozen, so that a general idea of the duration of the frost may be obtained from Fig. 72.

Russia labours under another serious disadvantage in the freezing-up of her ports, even on the Black Sea, the north-west shores of which, exposed to the cold north-east winds

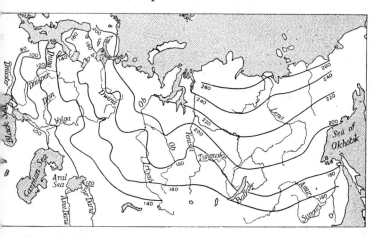

FIG. 72. Lines showing the mean number of days the rivers are ice-bound each year.

from the steppes, are ice-bound during January and February and on into March, a period of about 70 days. The Sea of Azov is frozen right across in mid-winter, and the shores are bordered with ice for a period of 80 days in the west, and over 100 days in the north-east. The northern half of the Caspian Sea is frozen near the coasts every winter, the ice remaining for some 100 days in the north. On the Baltic Sea Libau on the open coast is occasionally free of ice throughout the winter, but the east half of the Gulf of Riga is blocked for 130 days, the shores of the Gulf of Finland for 140 to 150 days, from early November till the beginning of April. The eastern half of this gulf is frozen over completely for about 3 months. In the Gulf of Bothnia the conditions are still worse, for the northern part freezes up in the middle of October and is not open again till the middle of May, after

210 days; the gulf is sometimes frozen almost across even as far south as the Åland Islands (Fig. 73).

With regard to the north coast of European Russia it is an interesting fact that the part which lies farthest north is least obstructed by ice. This is the Murman coast, between Varanger Fiord and the White Sea, which derives such benefit from the Atlantic Drift that in some years there is no fixed ice, and only in the coldest years has the coast been ice-bound for as much as 5 months In the war of 1914–18 Alexandrovsk on this coast usefully supplemented Archangel, which is 300 miles farther south, as a winter port on the Arctic shores of Russia The coast east of the White Sea, being farther from the Atlantic warmth, has ice for 8 months in an average year. Similarly in the

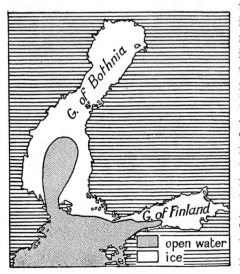

FIG. 73. The ice in the Gulf of Bothnia on 1 March 1905.

White Sea, the northern portion, thanks to the warm drift, is not frozen longer than Onega Bay, the most remote arm of this sea 200 miles south, the average duration of the ice being 200 days. The Gulf of Archangel freezes in the end of October and remains blocked for 140 days. The port of Archangel is closed for 190 days.

The north coast of Siberia is ice-bound most of the year for the permanent ice-cover of the Arctic Ocean almost reaches Nova Zemlya and the coast of the Taimyr Peninsula, and it surrounds the northern islands of the New Siberian group Vladivostok harbour is frozen from the middle of December till the beginning of April. Nikolaievsk at the mouth of the Amur is blocked for 220 days.

The Amur at Blagoveschensk begins to freeze in the

beginning of September, and is frost-bound by the end of
October. The ice in midwinter exceeds 5 feet in thickness.

Lake Baikal begins to freeze in November, but is not completely frozen over till the end of December. It remains
frozen for 4½ months, and the ice is sometimes 9 feet thick.
Sledges are the usual conveyance for crossing the lake during
the 3 winter months. The ice begins to melt at the end of
April.

Precipitation. As might be expected in a country of monotonous relief the amount of precipitation is very uniform.
In a wide belt extending through central Russia and south
Siberia the rainfall is moderate, about 20 inches in European
Russia, and over 20 inches in the extreme east where it is
brought by the south-east monsoon; the central part of this
belt, from the Urals to the Amur, has about 15 inches. North
of this central belt there is considerably less, under 8 inches
in the tundra owing to the cold. South of it also the rainfall
is deficient owing to the dry north-east winds which blow
throughout the year. The driest region includes the deserts
of Kara Kum and Kisil Kum, which have less than 4 inches,
and between them and the central belt are the steppes with
from 8 to 15 inches. Even the coast of the Black Sea between
the mouth of the Dniester and the Crimea has only about
12 inches. But the coast farther east, at the foot of the
Caucasus, has abundant rainfall, over 60 inches in many
parts, and is the rainiest part of Russia. The rain is of the
Mediterranean type, associated with winter depressions on
the Black Sea, which give south and south-east winds on
this coast with heavy rainfall; but the north-west coast of the
Black Sea has prevailing north-east winds from the steppes,
and the precipitation is scanty.

Over most of Russia summer is the rainiest season (Figs.
39 and 74), for in winter the outblowing winds from the continental high pressures hinder the ingress of moisture. But
in summer vapour comes in from both west and east; the
winds from the Arctic Ocean, however, are cold and their
vapour capacity is increased as they are warmed over the
land, so that but little rain is derived from them. The rainfall
maximum is in the late summer months, July and August,
when the inflow of moist air is strongest, and thunderstorms

are most frequent, for a large proportion of the rain falls in
thunderstorms on summer afternoons. The rainfall of east
Siberia is brought by the south-east monsoon of eastern Asia.
It is almost entirely in summer, mostly in late summer; the
amount decreases towards the north. At Okhotsk the rain
for the most part takes the form of drizzle and mist, and the
total is only 7 inches per annum. Vladivostok has 22 inches.
The extreme west and north of European Russia receive most
rain in autumn from the cyclones of the westerlies which are

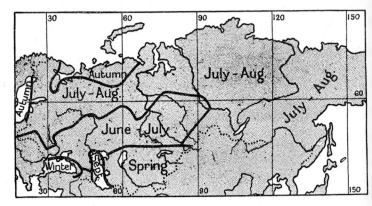

FIG. 74. Period of heaviest precipitation.

then very active, and are not yet kept at bay by the high
pressures which cover the continent in winter.

The region with a winter maximum is very small, including
only the south coast of the Crimea and the east coast of the
Black Sea already referred to as having the heaviest rainfall
in Russia. These small areas are the only representatives in
Russia of the 'Mediterranean' climate, with most of the rain
in autumn and winter, but no season can be called dry. On
the south and west coasts of the Caspian also, and throughout
Turan as far as Lake Balkash, the rainfall is heaviest in the
winter half-year, but the amount is so small and the winters
are so cold that the climate cannot be classed with that of
the Mediterranean shores. The sharp contrast already noted
in the temperature between the north and south of the Crimea
holds equally in respect of rainfall. South of the Yaila Mountains it exceeds 20 inches a year, most of it falling in the

winter, but the steppes on the north have only 12 inches, with the maximum in early summer.

Turan has most of its scant rainfall in March and April. All the months December to May have more than one-twelfth of the yearly total, and the summer months, especially August and September, are particularly dry. The steppes on the north of the desert also have spring rain, with the maximum in May and June, when there are violent thunderstorms with copious downpours, and the rain is so heavy while it lasts that only a small portion of it is able to sink into the ground and so become available for vegetation; most runs off at once and is wasted. The cause of these early summer showers seems to be the rapid heating of the dry ground by the sun while the air some few hundred feet above is still cold, conditions favourable to convectional overturnings and thunderstorms. Later in the summer the heat is equally great, but more evenly distributed, and there is a steadier current of air, so that large temperature differences are less likely to occur.

Though there is a summer maximum nearly everywhere, winter has considerable precipitation, which is practically all in the form of snow from mid-November to March inclusive in European Russia, and during November to April in Siberia; in the far north rain is rare after the beginning of October. The winter snowfall is heaviest in the taiga, where snow 3 feet deep is not uncommon, and the depth is far greater in drifts, for even in winter, despite the high pressures, depressions sometimes make their way far into the continent. The snow lies deepest in the forest, largely on account of the shelter provided by the trees. But there are no permanent snow-fields in Siberia in spite of the intense winter cold, owing to the not very abundant snow being readily melted in the long summer days. In spring, as it melts slowly, the water saturates the ground, and the conditions are ideal for tree growth. The snow covering is very beneficial in another way. In January 1893, there was a layer of loose dry snow, 20 inches deep, at Leningrad, and the temperature on the surface of the snow was −39°, but on the ground under the snow 27°. On a neighbouring piece of ground where there was no snow the temperature was −31° (records quoted by Woeikof). This shows that the snow, being a poor conductor of heat, acts as a most valuable blanket, protecting the ground from excessive cold. Over large tracts in Siberia the soil at a certain depth is permanently frozen, and the thickness of the snow cover is a factor in determining whether or not this permanently frozen layer occurs. In Transbaikalia it is found with a mean air temperature of 25°, for there is little snow; but not at Turukhansk (lat. 66° N., on the River Yenisei), though the mean air temperature is 17°, one reason being that the surface is covered with abundant snow throughout the winter. On the steppes south of the taiga there is much less snow, and what falls is often swept away by the strong north-east winds, so that even at Krasnoyarsk the snow is often not deep enough for sledges to be used. There is here an instructive instance of the interaction of climate and vegetation. The trees of the taiga provide shelter, and therefore snow lies deep for a long period, keeping the ground warm, and providing moisture when it melts in spring. But the steppes are treeless and windy, snow does not lie, the ground temperature is very low, and there is no water in spring to saturate the earth and enable trees to grow; grasses alone flourish. The animals of the tundra, and also many from the steppes, take refuge in winter in the intermediate forest belt, where they find shelter from the cold winds of the open country as well as a certain amount of food.

When the snow melts in spring the rivers rise in heavy flood. In May the Volga swells to 25 feet above its mean level at Samara, and to 7 feet above the mean at Astrakhan, where the floods have a breadth of 25 miles. The rivers that flow northward are flooded in their upper courses before the ice melts farther north, so that the lower parts of their basins are often inundated, and there are widespread tracts of marsh. The floods of the Amur occur in summer, being due to the heavy summer rains, not in spring, for there is not very much snow in its basin. They are very extensive and often do great damage.

The valleys that open on to the deserts of Turan from the mountains on the east owe their fertility to irrigation from the streams which are fed by the melting of the snow which has collected on the mountains during the winter. Such is the Syr Daria, which waters the luxuriant gardens of Ferghana all summer. The streams that descend from Khorasan and Afghanistan are flooded in spring but almost dry up in summer, since the snow is less abundant round their sources.

Cloudiness. Cloud and rainfall do not necessarily have the same annual period. Nearly all European Russia has more rain in summer than in winter, but winter is the cloudiest season, with $\frac{6}{10}$ to $\frac{8}{10}$ of the sky covered, as much as on the cloudy western seaboard of Europe, and as much as in south Russia where winter is the rainiest season. In western Siberia also winter is cloudiest, with about $\frac{6}{10}$, but eastern Siberia

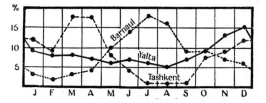

FIG. 75. Mean rainfall (monthly percentage of annual total). Barnaul represents the taiga régime, maximum in late summer; Tashkent the steppe régime, maximum in spring; Yalta the Mediterranean régime, maximum in winter.

receives most cloud as well as most rain from the south-east monsoon. The clearest skies are found in the steppes, and especially in the deserts which are almost cloudless in summer (cloud round Bokhara only $\frac{1}{10}$).

It may be found useful in conclusion to sum up briefly the main features of the climate of Russia by describing in a few words its chief climatic divisions (Fig. 76). Where isotherms are used as boundaries it must be remembered that they denote sea-level temperatures. Hills introduce complications which are not considered.

1. The tundra is characterized not so much by its cold winters—those of central Siberia are far colder—as by its cool summers. The mean July temperature is less than 50° and the 50° isotherm may be used as the boundary of the region. The ground is frozen hard most of the year, and at a few feet below the surface it is frozen permanently. The surface thaws for a month or two in summer, but is then waterlogged, except on south-facing slopes. The precipitation is small, but the air is damp and raw.

2. This is an extensive region which has its rainfall maximum in late summer, but no season is without precipitation; there is much snow in winter. Winter is very cold, the thermometer rarely rising above freezing-point, but summer is warm, the mean July temperature exceeding 50°.

Subdivisions according to temperature are necessary; first according to the winter cold, which becomes more intense

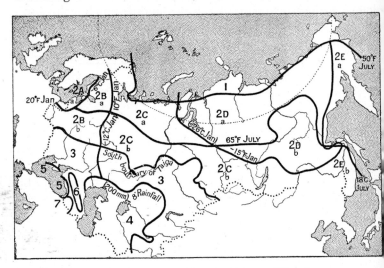

FIG. 76. The major climatic regions of Russia.

eastward into Siberia, and secondly according to the summer heat, which increases from north to south. But the differences in the intensity of the winter cold, great as they are, are probably of no very great importance for plant life where the January mean is below 10° F.

The 65° isotherm for July, which has a generally east to west trend, separates a northern subdivision, (a), with mean July temperature between 50° and 65°, and a southern, (b), with July temperature above 65°.

2 (A). The Baltic coast has a mild winter, the January mean over 20°, and a somewhat cool summer, the July mean being under 65°; the warmer subdivision (b) does not appear here. The rainfall exceeds 20 inches per annum and autumn is the rainiest season. The depressions of the westerlies exercise an important control on the weather.

2 (B). West-central Russia with colder winters.

2 (C). East Russia and west Siberia have very cold winters indeed, the January mean being 10° in the west, −15° in the east. Rainfall is 20 inches per annum on the west of the Urals, only 8 to 16 inches on the east. The northern sub-division (*a*) has less rain than (*b*).

2 (D). Central Siberia has the coldest winters known any-where, and an extreme range of temperature. The air is dry and clear in winter, and the sky is much less cloudy than in 2 (c). The rainfall is decidedly low, from 8 to 12 inches.

2 (E). The east coast is distinguished chiefly by its damp, cloudy, cool summer with much fog and drizzle. Winter is cold, but less so than in the interior. There are almost constant north-west winds, strongest where there is no mountain shelter; Nikolaievsk is 5° colder in January than Aian, almost 4° of latitude farther north, owing to the winds which sweep down the Amur valley. The sky is very clear and there is hardly any rain. Autumn is the driest and most pleasant season. The Amur basin has very heavy rain in summer and the ground is waterlogged; the winters, owing to the strong wind, are more trying than in the far interior of Siberia, and altogether the climate is much less healthy and agreeable.

3. The boundary between this division and 2 is the line separating the taiga from the steppes. In the steppes the rainfall is from 8 to 16 inches, which is not much when the dry air and the heat of summer are taken into account. The rainy season is spring and early summer, and the rain falls in heavy thunderstorms, so that the run-off is excessive, and most of the water is lost to vegetation, only the surface of the soil being moistened. The prevailing winds are north-east, dry and strong throughout the year; in winter they often blow with gale force as the Buran. Nearly all the snow is swept away by the wind and the ground is left bare, exposed to the full rigour of the winter frost, which is very severe. Summer is hot, and spring is as warm as, or warmer than autumn. Thus all factors combine to make a climate very un-favourable to tree-growth, and grass is the natural vegetation.

We may subdivide 3 into a western division with a mean January temperature above 10°, and an eastern with a mean January temperature below 10°.

4. Towards the south the rainfall becomes still less, and 4 is the region with less than 8 inches of rain per annum. There is only very poor grass on its margins, surrounding the bare sand-dunes of the deserts of Turan where the rainfall is less than 4 inches. The winters are very cold for the latitude, with a mean temperature far below freezing-point except in the extreme south. The summers are very hot indeed, the July mean being over 85° in the south. The air is very dry and the sky almost cloudless.

5. The south of the Crimea has mild, rainy winters (mean January temperature above freezing-point) and hot sunny dry summers; the vegetation is of the true Mediterranean type. The eastern shores of the Black Sea have far more rain, which is excessive all the year.

6. The Caucasus climate is of the usual mountain type.

7. Includes high plateau, with very cold winters but hot summers.

STATISTICS

MEAN TEMPERATURE (°F.)

INDIA, CEYLON, AND BURMA

Station.	Alt. Feet.	Jan.	Feb.	Mar.	Apr.	May.	June.	July.	Aug.	Sept.	Oct.	Nov.	Dec.	Year.	Range.
Colombo	24	79.0	79.7	80.6	81.5	82.1	80.4	80.0	80.5	80.4	79.3	79.5	79.2	80.2	3.1
Trincomalee	99	78.2	79.2	80.4	83.3	84.8	83.8	83.1	83.5	82.8	80.7	79.5	77.7	81.4	7.1
Calicut	27	77.8	79.8	81.6	83.6	83.1	78.5	76.7	77.4	78.3	79.1	79.5	78.3	79.3	6.9
Bombay	37	74.5	74.8	78.0	82.1	84.6	82.4	79.5	79.4	79.4	80.7	79.3	76.4	79.3	10.1
Poona	1,846	69.8	73.9	80.1	83.9	83.8	78.7	74.9	73.7	74.4	76.2	72.5	68.9	75.9	15.0
Bangalore	3,021	67.5	72.0	76.7	79.9	78.5	74.0	72.0	71.8	71.8	71.8	69.6	67.5	72.8	12.4
Madras	22	75.3	76.6	79.5	84.1	88.7	88.4	85.7	84.5	83.9	80.8	77.9	75.7	81.8	13.4
Akyab	20	69.5	72.8	79.2	83.4	85.0	82.2	81.3	81.1	82.1	81.6	77.5	71.7	78.9	15.5
Rangoon	18	74.7	77.3	81.2	85.0	82.2	79.5	78.8	78.7	79.1	80.0	78.3	75.6	79.2	10.3
Mandalay	250	68.8	73.8	82.1	89.2	88.5	85.4	85.2	84.7	83.5	82.5	75.9	69.5	80.8	20.4
Calcutta	21	65.2	70.3	79.3	85.0	85.7	84.5	83.0	82.4	82.6	80.0	72.4	65.3	77.9	20.5
Patna	183	60.8	65.3	76.9	86.2	88.0	86.4	83.5	83.1	83.3	79.5	70.1	62.2	77.1	27.2
Benares	267	60.0	65.3	76.6	86.8	91.3	89.4	84.1	83.1	83.0	77.9	67.8	60.2	77.2	31.3
Allahabad	309	59.5	64.9	76.8	87.6	92.5	90.8	84.5	83.2	83.0	77.6	67.5	59.8	77.3	33.0
Cawnpore	416	58.8	63.9	74.9	87.0	92.6	90.9	85.6	83.0	83.4	77.4	67.8	59.9	77.1	33.8
Delhi	718	57.9	62.2	74.1	86.2	91.7	92.2	86.4	84.5	83.9	78.5	67.6	59.6	77.1	34.3
Jaipur	1,431	59.9	64.2	74.9	86.3	91.6	90.6	84.7	82.3	82.4	77.9	68.9	61.5	77.1	31.7
Hoshangabad	1,006	65.6	70.3	80.3	89.6	93.2	87.6	79.6	78.3	79.4	76.9	70.6	65.3	78.1	27.9
Pachmarhi	3,528	57.0	62.4	73.8	81.7	84.3	77.9	71.8	69.5	70.5	67.7	62.0	57.3	69.7	27.3
Lahore	702	53.0	57.3	69.0	80.9	88.9	93.0	89.1	87.1	84.8	75.7	63.2	54.6	74.7	40.0
Mooltan	420	55.6	59.8	71.6	82.0	91.4	94.9	92.7	90.4	88.0	78.6	67.1	57.7	77.5	39.3
Jacobabad	186	57.3	62.4	74.5	85.5	94.2	97.7	95.0	91.6	88.8	79.2	67.5	58.9	79.3	40.4
Karachi	13	65.3	68.4	75.0	80.6	84.7	86.8	84.3	82.4	82.0	80.0	74.0	67.4	77.6	21.5
Peshawar	1,113	49.7	53.3	63.3	73.5	84.0	91.2	90.3	87.6	82.1	71.4	59.1	51.1	71.4	41.5

MEAN TEMPERATURE (°F.), *continued*

INDIA, CEYLON, AND BURMA *(continued)*

Station.	Alt. Feet.	Jan.	Feb.	Mar.	Apr.	May.	June.	July.	Aug.	Sept.	Oct.	Nov.	Dec.	Year.	Range.
Darjeeling	7,376	40.1	41.6	49.7	56.2	58.3	59.9	61.5	60.9	59.4	55.2	47.8	41.8	52.7	21.4
Simla	7,232	38.8	40.6	51.5	59.3	66.0	66.9	64.3	62.8	60.9	56.7	50.1	43.4	55.1	28.1
Srinagar	5,204	30.7	33.0	45.1	55.7	63.9	69.9	73.0	70.8	64.0	53.2	44.0	36.3	53.3	42.3
Leh	11,503	17.3	18.8	30.9	42.9	49.8	57.8	62.6	61.0	53.7	42.7	32.1	22.1	40.9	45.3

CHINA, MANCHUKUO, ANNAM

Station.	Alt. Feet.	Jan.	Feb.	Mar.	Apr.	May.	June.	July.	Aug.	Sept.	Oct.	Nov.	Dec.	Year.	Range.
Charbin	525	−1.7	5.4	24.1	42.3	55.9	66.0	72.1	69.4	57.9	40.1	21.2	3.2	37.9	73.8
Mukden	144	9.0	14.2	28.4	47.1	60.1	70.7	75.9	73.9	62.1	47.8	30.7	14.7	44.6	66.9
Peking	131	23.2	27.7	38.8	55.4	67.6	75.6	77.5	76.1	66.7	54.5	38.3	27.0	52.3	54.3
Shanghai	33	37.8	39.4	46.0	56.2	65.5	73.4	80.4	80.3	73.0	63.5	52.0	42.1	60.4	42.6
Hankow	118	39.6	41.5	48.2	61.2	70.9	77.9	83.0	83.3	74.8	65.1	53.1	42.6	61.9	43.7
Chengtu	1,509	43.9	45.0	53.2	62.6	75.7	75.7	79.2	77.7	70.3	63.1	54.0	46.6	61.9	35.3
Hong Kong	108	59.7	57.7	63.0	70.3	76.8	80.6	81.7	81.1	80.2	76.1	69.1	62.6	71.6	24.0
Hué	23	69.1	67.5	74.1	80.2	83.3	85.1	84.2	85.1	81.3	77.7	73.0	70.3	77.7	17.6

JAPAN

Station.	Alt. Feet.	Jan.	Feb.	Mar.	Apr.	May.	June.	July.	Aug.	Sept.	Oct.	Nov.	Dec.	Year.	Range.
Taihoku (Formosa)	30	60.3	57.2	62.4	69.3	74.8	79.9	82.2	81.9	79.2	73.9	67.3	62.1	70.9	25.0
Kagoshima	394	44.6	44.6	51.1	59.5	65.3	71.1	78.1	79.5	75.2	66.2	56.7	47.8	61.5	34.9
Nagasaki	436	42.3	42.6	48.4	57.6	64.2	70.7	77.9	79.9	74.3	64.4	54.7	45.9	60.3	37.6
Osaka	20	39.0	39.4	45.3	56.1	63.7	71.8	78.6	81.3	74.1	62.2	51.8	43.0	59.0	42.3
Tokio	69	37.4	38.8	44.4	54.5	61.9	68.9	75.6	77.7	71.4	60.4	50.5	41.4	56.8	40.3
Niigata	85	34.5	34.3	39.9	50.2	58.6	66.7	74.1	77.7	70.3	59.2	48.9	39.4	54.5	43.4
Sapporo	56	20.3	22.1	28.9	41.4	50.7	58.5	65.8	69.3	60.6	48.9	37.2	26.2	44.2	49.0

SOUTH-EAST ASIA AND THE EAST INDIES

Station.	Alt. Feet.	Jan.	Feb.	Mar.	Apr.	May.	June.	July.	Aug.	Sept.	Oct.	Nov.	Dec.	Year.	Range.
Penang	23	79·7	80·1	81·3	81·7	81·5	80·6	80·2	79·9	79·5	79·7	79·2	78·8	80·2	2·9
Singapore	10	77·9	78·4	79·3	79·9	80·6	79·9	80·2	79·7	79·5	79·7	79·0	78·3	79·3	2·7
Manila	46	76·6	77·5	80·0	82·6	83·1	82·0	80·6	80·6	80·2	79·9	78·4	77·2	79·9	6·5
Sandakan (British N. Borneo)	98	79·8	80·1	81·1	82·3	82·6	81·7	81·8	81·8	81·7	81·5	80·8	80·1	81·3	2·8
Batavia	23	77·9	77·9	78·8	79·5	79·7	79·2	78·7	79·0	79·7	79·8	79·3	78·4	79·0	1·9
Amboina (Moluccas)	40	80·8	81·0	80·6	79·3	79·3	78·4	77·4	77·7	78·1	79·2	80·4	80·8	79·3	3·6
Port Moresby (Papua)	126	82·2	81·5	81·5	80·5	79·2	79·2	78·1	77·7	78·4	79·6	81·3	82·5	80·3	4·8
SOUTH-WEST ASIA															
Aden	94	76·3	77·1	79·5	83·3	87·1	89·4	87·9	86·5	87·9	83·8	79·7	77·2	82·9	13·1
Jask	13	67·4	68·3	73·1	79·5	85·4	89·7	90·7	89·2	87·1	83·1	76·1	70·2	79·9	23·3
Basra	26	52·1	56·8	64·9	74·5	84·5	90·5	93·0	92·6	87·6	78·1	66·7	55·5	74·9	40·9
Baghdad	220	48·9	53·8	61·2	70·5	81·0	90·0	94·4	94·4	88·0	77·9	63·1	52·6	73·0	45·5
Mosul	870	40·2	45·6	53·1	61·4	77·7	84·4	90·5	89·4	82·0	70·6	61·1	45·4	66·8	50·3
Teheran	4,002	33·6	42·3	48·1	61·3	71·3	80·0	84·9	83·2	77·4	65·8	51·3	41·7	61·7	51·3
Kabul	6,250	30·7	35·7	46·7	58·9	68·0	73·2	76·6	75·5	68·8	58·3	50·8	40·4	57·0	45·9
Quetta	5,500	39·6	41·1	51·1	59·5	67·1	74·2	77·8	75·0	66·6	55·6	47·4	42·2	58·1	38·2
Beirut	111	56·5	57·7	61·2	66·0	71·8	77·7	82·0	83·1	80·8	76·1	67·3	60·6	70·0	26·6
Tiberias	−653	54·7	58·5	61·9	68·9	77·2	82·4	85·8	86·9	84·4	80·1	68·7	60·4	72·5	32·2
Jerusalem	2,456	44·8	47·5	54·8	59·0	66·6	70·3	73·2	73·2	70·0	66·2	56·3	49·1	60·6	28·4
THE HEART OF ASIA															
Kashgar	4,255	21·8	33·6	46·5	60·9	69·6	77·0	79·7	76·2	68·9	55·5	39·9	25·6	54·6	57·9
Lukchun	−50	13·2	26·9	45·4	66·2	75·4	85·4	90·5	85·4	73·7	55·4	32·9	20·9	56·0	77·3
Urga	3,800	−15·2	−4·4	13·0	33·7	47·5	59·0	63·5	59·0	47·4	28·7	7·9	−7·5	27·7	78·7

MEAN TEMPERATURE (°F.), continued

RUSSIA, ETC.

Station.	Alt. Feet.	Jan.	Feb.	Mar.	Apr.	May.	June.	July.	Aug.	Sept.	Oct.	Nov.	Dec.	Year.	Range.
Mariehamn	30	27·5	25·3	27·5	35·2	44·4	54·0	59·5	57·9	51·1	43·0	35·6	30·0	40·9	34·2
Leningrad	30	18·3	18·1	24·6	37·0	49·1	58·3	63·5	59·9	51·1	40·5	30·4	22·1	39·4	45·4
Riga	50	24·3	25·2	30·0	40·8	52·5	60·1	63·5	61·0	53·4	43·3	34·3	27·5	43·0	39·7
Archangel	50	8·1	9·7	17·4	30·0	41·4	52·7	59·5	55·2	45·7	33·8	21·4	12·2	32·2	51·4
Kola	33	11·3	11·1	17·4	29·1	38·1	47·7	54·5	51·3	42·6	31·5	20·5	13·3	30·7	43·4
Moscow	480	13·6	16·7	24·6	39·4	54·9	61·5	65·7	61·7	51·4	39·9	27·9	18·5	39·7	52·1
Kasan	250	7·5	11·3	20·8	38·3	55·4	63·3	67·8	63·3	51·8	38·1	23·9	13·5	37·9	60·3
Warsaw	390	25·9	28·6	34·9	45·0	56·1	61·9	64·8	62·8	55·6	46·0	36·0	29·8	45·6	38·9
Kiev	590	21·2	23·5	31·1	44·2	58·3	63·3	64·8	64·8	56·1	45·1	33·3	25·7	44·4	45·5
Kursk	690	15·3	18·0	26·1	41·5	56·5	62·8	66·9	64·0	53·6	42·3	29·5	20·5	41·4	51·6
Saratov	295	11·5	14·9	23·9	41·0	58·6	67·1	72·1	68·9	57·4	43·3	28·9	17·6	42·1	60·6
Orenburg	360	4·3	7·7	18·5	39·2	58·6	67·5	71·6	67·5	55·4	39·6	23·7	12·2	38·8	67·3
Odessa	210	26·4	29·1	36·5	47·1	60·3	67·8	72·7	71·2	62·2	52·8	40·3	32·2	49·9	46·3
Astrakhan	−50	19·2	22·8	32·7	47·8	63·7	72·7	77·4	73·8	62·6	49·5	36·0	26·6	48·6	58·2
Yalta	135	38·7	39·2	43·3	50·7	61·0	68·9	75·4	74·8	66·2	57·6	47·8	43·0	55·6	36·7
Batum	20	43·3	44·1	47·3	52·2	60·4	68·2	73·4	73·6	68·0	61·5	53·6	48·4	57·8	30·3
Baku	0	38·1	39·4	43·5	50·9	62·8	71·6	77·4	77·5	70·7	61·9	51·4	44·1	57·0	39·4
Tiflis	1,350	32·2	36·5	44·1	52·5	62·2	69·6	75·6	76·3	67·5	57·0	45·0	37·2	54·6	44·1
Kars	5,725	9·0	13·3	23·9	38·5	49·3	56·5	63·0	64·2	55·8	45·1	31·3	18·3	39·0	55·2
Petro-Alexandrowsk	295	22·8	28·8	42·1	57·6	70·9	78·8	82·4	78·3	67·3	52·3	39·6	29·7	54·2	59·6
Samarkand	2,362	31·6	36·3	46·0	56·8	66·2	74·1	76·6	73·6	65·3	53·4	45·3	37·6	55·2	45·0
Tashkent	1,610	29·7	34·5	45·9	57·9	67·8	76·5	80·2	76·3	66·4	53·8	44·6	36·5	55·8	50·5
Pamirski Post	11,985	1·0	5·4	19·8	32·9	42·6	49·8	56·3	55·6	46·0	32·4	18·9	3·9	30·4	55·3
Irgis	360	4·1	6·8	19·2	42·8	62·2	72·7	77·2	73·0	59·9	42·8	25·2	11·7	41·5	73·1
Semipalatinsk	590	3·2	3·6	14·2	37·4	57·6	67·5	71·2	67·3	55·6	38·3	20·5	9·1	37·0	68·0
Barnaul	480	0·3	2·5	13·5	33·6	51·6	62·8	66·7	62·2	51·1	34·5	16·7	5·7	33·4	66·4

RUSSIA, ETC. (continued)

Station.	Alt. Feet.	Jan.	Feb.	Mar.	Apr.	May.	June.	July.	Aug.	Sept.	Oct.	Nov.	Dec.	Year.	Range.
Tobolsk	340	−2·7	3·9	15·6	32·2	48·2	59·2	64·0	59·7	48·7	31·6	13·8	2·8	31·5	66·7
Beresov	100	−10·5	−1·1	8·8	22·5	36·5	50·5	60·3	55·4	43·2	25·9	5·7	−4·9	24·4	70·8
Tomsk	390	−2·9	2·1	12·9	30·2	46·6	59·0	64·0	59·2	48·4	31·8	12·7	1·6	30·6	66·6
Irkutsk	1,610	−5·6	−1·3	13·5	32·7	46·4	57·9	63·0	58·8	46·2	31·5	12·7	−0·8	29·7	68·6
Yakutsk	330	−46·3	−31·5	−8·0	17·8	42·1	59·9	66·2	58·1	42·8	17·6	−18·4	−40·0	13·3	112·5
Verkhoyansk	330	−58·2	−47·7	−22·4	8·4	34·7	53·6	59·2	51·4	36·0	5·7	−34·2	−51·7	3·0	117·4
Okhotsk	30	−13·4	−4·9	5·9	21·2	32·5	41·7	53·1	54·5	46·6	27·9	4·3	−7·4	21·7	67·9
Blagoveshchensk	440	−11·6	−0·6	14·9	36·3	50·7	63·3	70·2	65·7	53·8	34·5	11·5	−6·9	31·8	81·8
Vladivostok	50	7·3	13·8	26·4	39·9	49·1	56·5	64·6	69·1	61·7	48·7	31·1	14·7	40·3	61·8

MEAN RAINFALL (inches)

INDIA, CEYLON, AND BURMA

Station.	Alt. Feet.	Jan.	Feb.	Mar.	Apr.	May.	June.	July.	Aug.	Sept.	Oct.	Nov.	Dec.	Year.
Colombo	25	3·5	1·9	4·5	7·8	13·0	7·7	6·5	3·0	5·9	13·1	11·0	5·2	83·1
Trincomalee	110	6·6	2·1	1·6	2·0	2·4	1·3	2·0	4·1	4·5	8·2	13·9	14·4	63·1
Calicut	27	0·3	0·2	0·6	3·2	9·5	35·0	29·8	15·3	8·4	10·3	4·9	1·1	118·6
Bombay	37	0·1	0	0·1	0	0·7	20·6	27·3	16·0	11·8	2·4	0·4	0	79·4
Poona	1,846	0·1	0·1	0·1	0·6	1·4	5·4	7·2	3·7	5·1	4·0	1·1	0·2	28·9
Bangalore	3,021	0·2	0·3	0·6	1·2	4·5	3·0	4·1	5·8	7·4	6·2	2·4	0·4	36·0
Madras	22	1·1	0·3	0·3	0·6	1·8	2·0	3·8	4·5	4·9	11·2	13·6	5·4	49·6
Tuticorin	30	1·1	0·6	1·0	1·6	0·9	0·2	0·1	0·3	0·6	5·3	7·1	3·2	21·9
Akyab	20	0·1	0·2	0·5	2·1	14·0	46·9	54·8	45·2	22·6	10·9	5·5	0·8	203·4
Rangoon	18	0·2	0·2	0·3	1·6	12·0	18·0	21·4	19·9	15·3	6·9	2·8	0·4	99·0
Mandalay	250	0·1	0·1	0·2	1·1	5·8	5·5	3·3	4·6	5·7	4·7	1·6	0·4	33·2
Calcutta	21	0·4	1·1	1·4	2·0	5·0	11·2	12·1	11·5	9·0	4·3	0·5	0·2	58·8
Dacca	35	0·3	1·2	2·6	5·4	9·8	13·6	12·8	13·1	9·8	4·6	0·8	0·2	74·2

MEAN RAINFALL (inches), *continued*

INDIA, CEYLON, AND BURMA (continued)

Station.	Alt. Feet.	Jan.	Feb.	Mar.	Apr.	May.	June.	July.	Aug.	Sept.	Oct.	Nov.	Dec.	Year.
Cherrapunji	4,309	0.7	2.1	11.7	30.8	46.2	96.8	98.2	76.5	46.1	16.7	1.9	0.2	427.8
Shillong	4,920	0.4	0.8	1.9	4.7	10.1	16.2	13.4	13.0	12.8	6.4	1.2	0.3	81.1
Gopalpur	21	0.3	0.6	0.5	0.8	1.9	5.6	6.1	7.3	7.3	8.5	3.7	0.7	43.3
Raipur	970	0.4	0.7	0.7	0.7	1.0	9.5	14.3	13.3	7.4	2.0	0.4	0.2	50.4
Patna	183	0.6	0.7	0.4	0.3	1.7	7.9	11.6	12.8	8.4	2.6	0.2	0.1	47.3
Benares	267	0.7	0.6	0.4	0.2	0.6	4.8	12.1	11.6	7.1	2.1	0.2	0.2	40.6
Allahabad	309	0.7	0.5	0.3	0.1	0.3	4.5	11.4	11.1	6.0	2.2	0.2	0.2	37.5
Cawnpore	416	0.6	0.5	0.3	0.2	0.4	3.1	9.7	10.2	5.5	1.2	0.2	0.3	32.1
Delhi	718	1.0	0.6	0.5	0.4	0.7	2.9	7.6	7.0	4.7	0.5	0.1	0.4	26.2
Jaipur (Rajputana)	1,431	0.4	0.3	0.4	0.2	0.6	2.6	8.3	7.3	3.2	0.3	0.1	0.3	24.0
Lahore	702	0.9	1.0	0.8	0.5	0.7	1.4	5.1	4.7	2.3	0.3	0.1	0.4	18.1
Mooltan	420	0.4	0.3	0.4	0.3	0.3	0.5	1.9	1.7	0.6	0.1	0.1	0.2	6.8
Jacobabad	186	0.3	0.3	0.3	0.2	0.1	0.2	1.0	1.1	0.3	0	0.1	0.1	4.0
Karachi	13	0.5	0.5	0.4	0.2	0.1	0.9	2.9	1.5	0.5	0	0.1	0.1	7.6
Peshawar	1,164	1.7	1.5	2.0	1.5	0.7	0.5	2.2	3.3	1.2	0.3	0.4	0.6	15.9
Darjeeling	7,376	0.6	1.1	1.8	3.8	8.7	24.9	32.3	26.1	18.4	4.5	0.8	0.2	122.7
Simla	7,232	2.5	2.7	2.7	2.3	2.8	7.2	17.0	17.4	5.9	1.0	0.5	1.0	63.1
Srinagar	5,204	2.7	2.8	3.6	3.8	2.3	1.5	2.2	2.3	1.6	1.2	0.4	1.5	25.7
Chitral	5,486	1.2	1.6	3.2	3.9	0.7	0.3	0.1	0.2	0.2	0.7	0.3	0.9	13.3
Leh	11,503	0.4	0.3	0.3	0.2	0.2	0.2	0.5	0.5	0.3	0.2	0	0.2	3.2

CHINA, MANCHUKUO, ANNAM

Station.	Alt. Feet.	Jan.	Feb.	Mar.	Apr.	May.	June.	July.	Aug.	Sept.	Oct.	Nov.	Dec.	Year.
Mukden	144	0.2	0.2	0.8	1.1	2.2	3.4	6.3	6.1	3.3	1.6	1.1	0.2	26.4
Peking	131	0.1	0.2	0.2	0.6	1.4	3.0	9.4	6.3	2.6	0.6	0.3	0.1	24.9
Hankow	118	1.8	1.9	3.8	6.0	6.5	9.6	7.1	3.8	2.8	3.2	1.9	1.1	49.6
Shanghai	23	2.0	2.3	3.5	3.7	3.5	7.3	6.0	5.7	4.4	3.2	2.1	1.4	45.1

CHINA, MANCHUKUO, ANNAM (continued)

Station.	Alt. Feet.	Jan.	Feb.	Mar.	Apr.	May.	June.	July.	Aug.	Sept.	Oct.	Nov.	Dec.	Year.
Ichang	167	0·8	1·2	2·1	4·0	4·8	6·1	8·3	6·7	4·0	3·3	1·4	0·6	43·1
Chungking	750	0·6	0·8	1·4	4·0	5·5	7·1	5·6	5·1	5·8	4·5	2·0	0·9	43·4
Swatow	13	1·4	2·5	3·1	5·6	9·0	7·8	7·8	8·4	5·5	2·9	1·6	1·5	59·7
Hong Kong	108	1·3	1·6	2·7	5·4	11·7	15·9	13·8	14·1	9·8	4·9	1·9	1·1	84·3
Hué	23	4·0	4·8	1·8	2·4	3·6	2·8	3·4	4·0	16·2	26·3	22·4	10·2	102·0

JAPAN

Station.	Alt. Feet.	Jan.	Feb.	Mar.	Apr.	May.	June.	July.	Aug.	Sept.	Oct.	Nov.	Dec.	Year.
Kagoshima	394	3·5	3·3	6·1	9·1	9·6	13·9	11·2	7·4	8·7	5·1	3·7	3·5	84·7
Nagasaki	436	3·1	3·5	5·2	8·0	7·3	13·5	9·3	7·2	8·6	4·6	3·3	3·3	76·9
Kochi	138	2·2	3·6	7·4	12·3	12·1	13·9	13·0	10·6	15·7	9·5	4·9	3·2	108·5
Okayama	20	1·5	1·6	3·2	4·0	4·4	5·8	6·4	3·8	5·5	3·7	2·2	1·4	43·8
Tokio	69	2·2	2·8	4·4	4·9	5·7	6·5	5·3	5·7	8·7	7·4	4·2	2·1	59·9
Ishinomaki	148	1·5	1·9	2·9	3·7	4·1	4·5	5·9	5·1	6·9	5·0	2·3	2·0	45·7
Kanazawa	95	10·8	6·8	6·2	6·7	6·1	6·6	8·2	7·1	8·8	7·5	10·5	14·4	99·7
Niigata	84	7·7	4·9	4·1	4·2	3·7	5·2	6·2	5·2	7·4	5·7	7·2	9·1	70·6
Hakodate	10	2·2	2·2	2·6	2·8	3·2	3·6	5·0	5·2	6·7	4·6	3·7	3·0	44·7

SOUTH-EAST ASIA AND THE EAST INDIES

Station.	Alt. Feet.	Jan.	Feb.	Mar.	Apr.	May.	June.	July.	Aug.	Sept.	Oct.	Nov.	Dec.	Year.
Penang	23	3·7	3·1	4·6	7·0	10·6	7·8	8·2	12·6	16·4	16·3	12·0	4·9	107·2
Singapore	10	9·7	7·1	7·3	7·8	6·5	7·0	6·7	7·8	6·9	7·9	10·1	10·4	95·1
Manila	46	0·8	0·4	0·8	1·3	4·4	9·3	17·3	16·0	14·3	6·7	5·2	3·0	79·6
Sandakan (British N. Borneo)	98	18·5	9·6	8·1	4·1	5·9	7·3	6·5	8·1	9·4	10·0	14·7	17·7	119·7
Batavia	23	13·0	12·8	7·8	5·2	4·0	3·7	2·6	1·7	2·9	4·5	5·5	8·5	72·1
Amboina (Moluccas)	40	5·1	4·6	5·2	11·3	19·8	24·6	23·1	15·9	9·1	6·2	4·4	5·4	134·8
Port Moresby (Papua)	126	7·5	9·2	6·8	3·3	3·0	0·8	1·0	0·8	1·4	0·8	2·0	4·2	40·8

MEAN RAINFALL (inches), *continued*

SOUTH-WEST ASIA

Station.	Alt. Feet.	Jan.	Feb.	Mar.	Apr.	May.	June.	July.	Aug.	Sept.	Oct.	Nov.	Dec.	Year.
Smyrna	66	2·8	2·6	3·2	1·1	0·9	0·4	0	0·4	0·5	0·8	3·4	3·7	19·8
Sivas	4,200	2·1	1·7	1·4	2·3	3·0	1·1	0·4	0·1	0·7	1·2	1·9	0·9	16·9
Beirut	111	7·3	5·7	3·9	2·2	0·8	0·1	0	0	0·3	2·1	5·3	7·5	35·5
Jaffa	67	5·0	3·5	2·3	0·3	0·1	0	0	0	0·2	0·8	3·0	4·0	19·7
Jerusalem	2,460	6·3	4·6	3·5	1·5	0·3	0	0	0	0	0·4	2·5	5·7	24·8
Aden	94	0·3	0·2	0·5	0·2	0·1	0·1	0	0·1	0·1	0·1	0·1	0·1	1·8
Mosul	870	2·8	2·9	2·4	2·4	0·5	0	0	0	0	0·6	2·8	2·2	16·7
Baghdad	220	1·2	1·3	1·3	0·9	0·2	0	0	0	0	0·1	0·7	1·2	7·1
Basra	26	1·4	1·1	1·1	0·5	0·3	0	0	0	0·1	0·1	0·7	1·2	6·4
Teheran	3,800	1·7	1·1	2·0	1·4	0·6	0·1	0·2	0	0·1	0·3	0·9	1·2	9·5
Quetta	5,500	2·1	2·1	1·8	1·1	0·3	0·2	0·5	0·6	0·1	0·1	0·3	0·8	10·0
Jidda	20	0·9	0	0	0	0	0	0	0	0	0	1·6	0·6	3·1
Jask	13	1·1	0·9	0·8	0·2	0	0·1	0	0	0	0·1	0·3	1·1	4·5

THE HEART OF ASIA

Station.	Alt. Feet.	Jan.	Feb.	Mar.	Apr.	May.	June.	July.	Aug.	Sept.	Oct.	Nov.	Dec.	Year.
Kashgar	4,003	0·2	0·2	0·6	0·8	1·0	0·2	0	0·6	0·6	0	0	0·2	4·0

RUSSIA, ETC.

Station.	Alt. Feet.	Jan.	Feb.	Mar.	Apr.	May.	June.	July.	Aug.	Sept.	Oct.	Nov.	Dec.	Year.
Leningrad	30	0·9	0·8	0·9	0·9	1·7	1·8	2·7	2·7	2·0	1·7	1·4	1·2	18·8
Riga	50	1·3	1·3	1·1	1·5	1·6	2·5	3·5	3·3	2·0	1·9	2·0	1·6	23·9
Archangel	50	0·9	0·7	0·8	0·7	1·2	1·8	2·4	2·4	2·2	1·6	1·2	0·9	16·8
Kola	33	0·3	0·3	0·2	0·3	0·6	0·7	1·4	1·3	1·0	0·8	0·6	0·3	7·8
Moscow	480	1·1	0·9	1·2	1·5	2·0	2·2	2·8	2·9	2·2	1·4	1·6	1·5	21·0
Kasan	250	0·5	0·4	0·6	0·9	1·6	2·2	2·4	2·4	1·6	1·1	1·0	0·7	15·4

RUSSIA, ETC. *(continued)*

Station.	Alt. Feet.	Jan.	Feb.	Mar.	Apr.	May.	June.	July.	Aug.	Sept.	Oct.	Nov.	Dec.	Year.
Warsaw	390	1·2	1·1	1·3	1·5	1·9	2·7	3·0	3·1	1·9	1·7	1·5	1·4	22·3
Posen	217	1·1	0·9	1·3	1·4	2·2	1·9	3·0	2·1	1·8	1·4	1·3	1·4	20·0
Kiev	590	1·1	0·8	1·5	1·7	1·7	2·4	3·0	2·4	1·7	1·7	1·5	1·5	21·1
Simferopol	853	1·2	1·1	1·4	1·3	1·5	2·2	2·0	1·3	1·5	1·1	1·3	1·6	17·5
Saratov	295	0·9	0·8	0·7	1·1	1·1	1·5	1·7	1·3	1·2	1·5	1·4	1·6	14·9
Orenburg	360	1·1	0·8	1·0	0·9	1·4	2·0	1·7	1·3	1·3	1·2	1·2	1·2	15·2
Odessa	210	0·9	0·7	1·1	1·1	1·3	2·3	2·1	1·2	1·4	1·1	1·3	1·3	16·1
Astrakhan	−50	0·5	0·3	0·4	0·5	0·6	0·7	0·5	0·5	0·5	0·4	0·4	0·5	5·9
Yalta	135	1·8	1·6	1·6	1·3	1·1	1·5	1·3	0·9	1·4	1·7	2·0	3·0	19·9
Batum	30	10·2	6·0	6·2	5·0	2·8	5·9	6·0	8·2	11·9	8·8	12·2	10·0	93·3
Baku	0	1·3	0·9	0·8	0·8	0·6	0·3	0·2	0·2	0·8	1·2	1·2	1·2	9·5
Tiflis	1,350	0·6	0·8	1·1	2·1	2·9	2·7	2·1	1·6	2·0	1·3	1·1	0·8	19·1
Kars	5,717	0·7	0·7	1·1	1·7	2·7	1·9	1·7	1·3	1·1	1·3	1·2	0·8	16·3
Krasnovodsk	−66	0·5	0·6	0·7	1·0	0·5	0·6	0·2	0·3	0·3	0·5	0·6	0·5	6·3
Petro-Alexandrowsk	295	0·2	0·4	0·5	0·6	0·2	0	0·1	0·1	0	0·1	0·1	0·1	2·4
Merv	755	1·8	1·4	2·1	1·2	0·1	0	0	0	0	0·4	0·1	0·4	7·5
Tashkent	1,610	1·8	1·4	2·6	2·6	1·1	0·5	0·1	0·1	0·2	1·1	1·4	1·7	14·6
Irgis	360	0·6	0·3	0·5	0·7	0·8	0·9	0·6	0·4	0·5	0·5	0·4	0·7	6·9
Semipalatinsk	590	0·5	0·2	0·4	0·4	0·8	0·9	1·1	0·4	0·6	0·6	0·6	0·8	7·3
Barnaul	480	0·8	0·6	0·6	0·6	1·3	1·7	2·2	1·8	1·1	1·3	1·1	1·1	14·2
Tobolsk	340	0·7	0·6	0·7	0·8	1·3	2·7	3·5	3·2	1·5	1·4	1·3	0·9	18·6
Beresov	100	1·0	0·6	0·8	1·3	1·6	2·2	3·4	2·3	2·3	1·1	1·3	0·5	18·4
Tomsk	390	1·1	0·8	0·8	0·7	1·5	2·7	3·0	2·3	1·4	2·4	1·4	1·9	19·9
Irkutsk	1,610	0·6	0·5	0·4	0·6	1·2	2·3	2·9	2·4	1·6	0·7	0·6	0·8	14·5
Yakutsk	330	0·9	0·2	0·4	0·6	1·1	2·1	1·7	2·6	1·2	1·4	0·6	0·9	13·7
Verkhoyansk	330	0·2	0·1	0	0·1	0·2	0·5	1·2	0·9	0·2	0·2	0·2	0·2	3·9
Okhotsk	30	0·1	0·1	0·1	0·2	0·5	1·1	0·5	1·8	2·1	0·7	0·2	0·2	7·5
Vladivostok	50	0·3	0·3	0·6	1·2	2·0	2·8	3·0	4·3	4·4	1·8	1·1	0·5	22·4

Q

PART IV

EUROPE (EXCLUDING RUSSIA)

CHAPTER XXVII

GENERAL FEATURES

EUROPE is essentially a peninsula of Asia, wide in the east, narrowing towards the west. On the north of the main peninsula, which includes Russia and Central Europe, are Scandinavia and Jutland, which may be considered as secondary peninsulas, and the island group of Britain; similarly Spain, Italy, and Greece are secondary peninsulas on the south. We may look at the matter from the other point of view, and note how the seas work their way far into the land, dispensing marine influences widely. On the north the North Sea and the Baltic are continued by the Gulfs of Bothnia and Finland, while the White Sea extends south-west from the Arctic as if striving to make a continuous waterway to the Gulf of Finland, over the great lakes of north-west Russia. In the Mediterranean Sea with its annexes the Adriatic, the Aegean, the Black Sea, and the Caspian, South Europe has an equally valuable series of enclosed seas to ameliorate its climate. The seas are not only extensive, but are also remarkably warm for the latitude, since the waters of the hot Gulf Stream are wafted across the Atlantic by the prevailing westerlies, and are still so warm when they reach Europe that the winters are extremely mild.

The absence of a mountain range along the west coast is another fact to which Europe owes great climatic advantages. Such a barrier exists in North America, with the result that the mountains themselves near the ocean receive from the westerlies a superfluity of rainfall for which man can find little use, while the country to leeward suffers from aridity and great extremes of temperature. In Europe the most accentuated lines of relief, the Pyrenees, the Alps, the Carpathians, and the Caucasus have a west–east trend, and on crossing them from north to south we have in many parts a sudden transition from the Central European climate to the Mediterranean. There are, it is true, isolated groups of mountains facing the westerlies on the stormy seaboards of the British Isles and Norway, but in spite of the great local increase in rainfall, they are not sufficiently high and continuous to bring about a serious deficiency of rainfall, or very extreme temperatures, in their lee. As a result it is exceptional to find sharp divides of climate in going from west to east; there is a gradual transition from the oceanic seaboard to the continental east, and such climatic boundaries as are chosen are generally arbitrary.

The ubiquity and warmth of the sea, then, and the trend of the main feature lines give Europe a remarkably favourable climate, with very mild winters, warm but not too hot summers, very small range of temperature for the latitude, and abundant and well-distributed rainfall. In proportion to its size, Europe has a far larger area with a climate which may be described as thoroughly suitable for the highest human development than any other continent, and even if Russia is included, there is only one small tract of useless arid desert, that lying north of the Caspian Sea; the cold tundra fringe in the north is but narrow. Many useful crops flourish in considerably higher latitudes in Europe than elsewhere. Of the ordinary products of temperate latitudes, barley is profitably grown beyond 70° N. in Norway, and rye almost as far north in Sweden. Wheat and the vine have their farthest poleward extension in Europe. Subtropical fruits find unusually favourable conditions in the Mediterranean lands; the orange and the lemon grow there even beyond lat. 44° N., and the groves of date-palms at Elche in south-east Spain are famous. Nowhere else do these fruits ripen so far from the Equator.

Pressure. The main movements of the atmosphere are dominated by three great pressure systems, the Icelandic low pressures, the Azores high pressures, and the alternating high and low pressures, of winter and summer respectively, over Asia (Figs. 4 and 34).

It has been pointed out in Chapter II that there is a tendency to low atmospheric pressures round the globe, lying along about lat. 60° N. and S. The Icelandic low-pressure system and the corresponding Aleutian system of the North

Fig. 77. Key map, showi

position of places mentioned in the text.

Pacific are the cores of lowest pressure over the abnormally warm oceans. They are especially deep and extensive in winter when the temperature contrast between land and sea is greatest, and the air is collected in extensive anticyclones over the very cold continental masses. In the Icelandic system the cold dry air from the high-pressure systems of Greenland and the polar regions meets the warm air from the subtropics and tropics, and the interaction of the contrasted air masses is seen in the clouded skies, heavy rain, and sudden

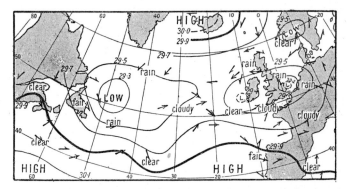

FIG. 78. Irregularities of pressure over the North Atlantic, 7 a.m., 26 August 1912. (Weekly Weather Report, Meteorological Office.)

changes of wind, temperature, and weather, in the numerous deep depressions which move generally from south-west to north-east (Fig. 78).

Some meteorologists consider that the depressions themselves are the direct result of the conflict of the opposed air masses, and they have called the belt of conflict the Polar Front, assigning as its mean position the tract between the Bermudas and the English Channel. Depressions are generally deepest while passing south of Iceland, where consequently the mean barometric pressure is lowest. A tongue of low pressure projects to the north-east beyond the north of Norway, the significance of which will be pointed out later. The depressions are the immediate cause of most of the storms of wind and rain in North and Central Europe. The seas to the north-west of Europe, stormy at all times, are in winter one of the wildest regions on the face of the Earth.

In summer the low-pressure system still persists over the Icelandic region, but its intensity is less and the surrounding gradients are very much weaker than in winter, and the depressions which pass from west to east are neither so numerous nor so vigorous. Their percentage frequency over the North Atlantic month by month is computed by Angot to be:

Jan.	.	20	Apr.	.	5	July	.	2	Oct.	.	6
Feb.	.	17	May	.	2	Aug.	.	3	Nov.	.	13
Mar.	.	11	June	.	2	Sept.	.	2	Dec.	.	17

The high-pressure system which is centred in the neighbourhood of the Azores belongs to the subtropical high-pressure belt of the north hemisphere. The pressure is highest in summer, and the centre of the system is then farthest north, about lat. 35°. It appears on the maps as a great stationary anticyclone, not only covering the Atlantic Ocean, but extending far over West and Central Europe, and the west of the Mediterranean Sea. The intensity of the anticyclone in summer is doubtless due to the fact that the great land masses are then hot, and the normal subtropical belt of high pressure is replaced over them by the low pressures which give rise to the summer monsoon. The air which is unable to remain over the heated continents collects over the cooler Atlantic and Pacific Oceans, where, consequently, there are extensive anticyclones.

In winter, the Azores high pressures are much less intense, and indeed they appear not as a fully developed anticyclone but merely as a band of high pressure, crossing the Atlantic about lat. 30° N., and connecting the great anticyclones over Asia and North America. The straight line joining the centres of the Atlantic and the Asiatic high pressures passes over the Mediterranean Sea. But that sea is warm, and the air over it is moist, and therefore it is conducive to low-pressure conditions. The result is interesting. The high-pressure 'bridge' connecting the Atlantic and Asia divides, one branch following the axis of Central Europe, the other lying over North Africa, and the Mediterranean region is left between them as a 'lake' of low pressure (Fig. 4). The Black Sea and the Caspian are for the same reason regions of lower pressure than the surrounding lands. The lowest mean pressures over the Mediterranean are less than 30·0 inches, over the Black Sea about 30·1, and over the Caspian less than 30·2. The readings over these seas thus become higher towards the great Asiatic anticyclone. West-central Europe, therefore, is a region of high pressure in both summer and winter, but the Mediterranean has high-pressure conditions in summer, low-pressure in winter. Just as the Icelandic low-pressure system is not, strictly speaking, permanent, so the North Atlantic anticyclone is liable to considerable variations from the average in respect of intensity and position, and sometimes it is temporarily replaced by low pressures.

The pressure conditions over Asia, the third of the great systems which control the climate of Europe, have already been described in the chapters on that continent. In winter, the high pressures of Asia are continued west over south Russia, Rumania, the Alps, south-central France, and the Iberian Peninsula. In summer, Asia is a region of low pressure, but a tongue of high pressure projects from the Atlantic over the centre of Europe towards Siberia. The surrounding pressure gradient is less steep than in winter and its axis is somewhat farther north, running from the south of the Bay of Biscay over the Vosges and south Germany, to die out in central Russia. The high-pressure ridge of the centre of Europe has been called the barometric backbone of the continent, and it is of fundamental importance in separating the north European climate, with its prevailing moist westerly winds and cloudy skies, from that of the sunny Mediterranean.

Prevailing winds. In North-west and North Europe, and also in most of Central Europe, the prevailing winds blow from the west ('variable westerlies'), south-west in winter, north-west and west in summer. Their direction is controlled by the Azores high-pressure and the Iceland low-pressure systems. In winter the dominant control is the latter, which extends far south, but its centre is well to the north-west of Europe, and Northern Europe is swept by south-westerly winds. In summer, the Azores system spreads farther north, and the low pressures over Southern Asia exert some control, more and more dominant towards the east, so that the prevailing winds are north-west. These north-westerly winds of summer, blowing more directly into the middle of the

Continent, have been described by some writers as the summer monsoon of Europe, but the term seems to be hardly suitable. The strong westerly winds of winter blow straight from the warm ocean, which is then a more important source of heat to West Europe than the direct rays of the sun, and they give the mild, moist, cloudy climate of West and North Europe. The extension of the Icelandic low pressures in a tongue to the north-east carries the warm oceanic conditions far east over Scandinavia and north Russia.

In most of Central Europe the prevailing winds are westerly, but their force and constancy become less towards the high-pressure axis of the continent. They are often interrupted, especially in the valleys of the Alps, by spells of almost calm weather in winter under the domination of extensive anti-cyclones which are much more frequent here than in North-west Europe, and at such times the weather is cold and dry. In summer the prevailing winds are north-west, controlled by the low pressures of Asia. In South-east Europe the winds are north-west on the western shores of the Black Sea, and north-east in the steppes of south-east Russia, the main control here also being the great low-pressure system of Asia.

The European countries bordering the Mediterranean have the high pressures of the 'barometric backbone' on their north throughout the year and consequently the winds are northerly, north-east, north, or north-west according to the lie of land and sea. In summer they are strong and constant, but in winter the frequent depressions which appear over the Mediterranean give variable winds and rainy weather. The north coast of Africa being south of these depressions has prevailing westerly and south-westerly winds in winter, but strong northerly winds in summer. The circulation over the Mediterranean Sea itself is described in Chapter XXXI. The local relief and the trend of the coastline may give a strong set to the winds, which masks the general direction; Vienna has a strong preponderance of winds from west and south-east, Toulouse from north-west and south-east, Gibraltar from east and west. In general the winds are much stronger in the winter half-year, in most parts in winter and early spring, than in summer.

Temperature. It is not intended to give here an account of the climatic elements of the continent as a whole, except pressure and winds, for they will be more conveniently described in the sections devoted to the separate climatic regions. But it will be useful to glance at the general distribution of temperature, which presents many features of interest. The most notable characteristic is its great equability. Along most of the west coast of the continent the difference between the mean temperature of the warmest and coldest months is less than 20°, a remarkably small range for the latitude. The range increases towards the east, but in almost all Europe, excluding Russia, it is below 40°, and only in central Russia reaches 50°, which may be regarded as an average range for countries in these latitudes.

The summer isotherms (Fig. 79) have a normal course, running generally from west to east, but bending somewhat poleward as they go farther inland. Very little of Europe has a mean temperature below 50° in July, and the barren tundra lands are of small extent. At the other extreme, very small areas have a mean July temperature above 80° F., the 80° isotherms enclosing only the Mediterranean peninsulas. Thus Europe is not enervated by excessive tropical heat in summer, for though in all the Mediterranean lands summer means are high, exceeding 70° for three months, and in the south of Greece for five months, yet the air is dry and the climate healthy.

The isotherms for January are much more striking, owing to their marked tendency to run from north to south. The 40° isotherm illustrates this. Running north-east over the ocean it makes a sharp curve in the neighbourhood of the Shetland Islands, and comes due south along the west of Scotland, England, and France; in the south of France it bends towards the east, reaches the head of the Adriatic Sea, and turns south and south-east again over the Balkan Peninsula to the Aegean Sea near Salonika, and then north-east to the Black Sea. In the Shetlands it is 20° of latitude north of its southernmost position over the Aegean. Equally anomalous is the course of the 30° isotherm from Iceland, far to the north-east beyond 70° N. lat., thence south-west along the Norwegian coast, and south through Jutland and Central Europe till it reaches the Danube, where it swings round to

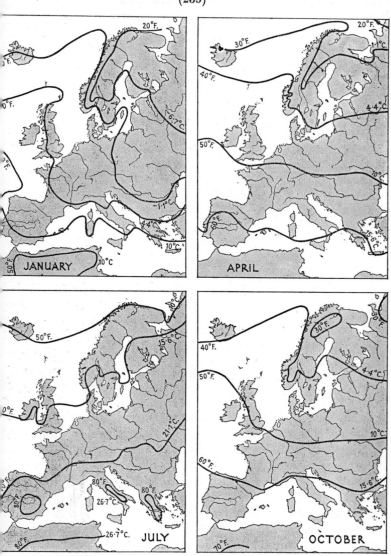

FIG. 79. Mean temperature.

the north-east. There is a difference of almost 30° of latitude, 2,000 miles, between its extreme north and south points.

There are two main factors involved in the north–south trend of the winter isotherms. The first is that the central core of the European peninsula is cold, like all land masses in temperate latitudes at this season; the second, that the north, and especially the north-west, of Europe is abnormally warm, and owes its heat to the warm North Atlantic Ocean from which the prevailing winds blow. The second point is

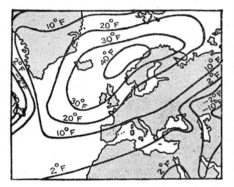

much the more important. The air over the ocean, west of Norway, is more than 40° warmer than the average for the latitude, the greatest 'anomaly' (see p. 3) of temperature known (Fig. 80). The very favourable winter temperatures of North-west Europe are due to the remarkably warm surface-water of the ocean, and this in turn is a result of the shape of the Atlantic

FIG. 80. Lines of equal 'anomaly of temperature' in January. The greatest excess amounts to more than 30° north-west of the British Isles.

basin. For thanks to the fortunate accident that Cape St. Roque, the easternmost point of Brazil, projects into the ocean some few degrees south of the Equator, not only the north equatorial current, but also about half of the south equatorial current, are turned into the North Atlantic Ocean, at the expense of the South Atlantic. In consequence the 'Gulf Stream' is especially voluminous, and the warm water is wafted on towards Europe by the prevailing westerly winds, the wide opening into the Arctic Ocean between Europe and Iceland giving it free entry far north round Norway and along the Russian coast. The open sea in these parts is never frozen, in striking contrast to the seas north of America. Thus the advantages which result everywhere in temperate latitudes in winter from oceanic winds are specially great in North-west Europe. The temperatures of the Norwegian

coast are considerably higher than those of the west coast of
North America in the same latitude.

The coldest part of Europe in January is the extreme north-
east of Russia, with a temperature below 0°. The warmest
parts are the tips of the Mediterranean peninsulas, marked
off by the 50° isotherm, the line which is found in the extreme

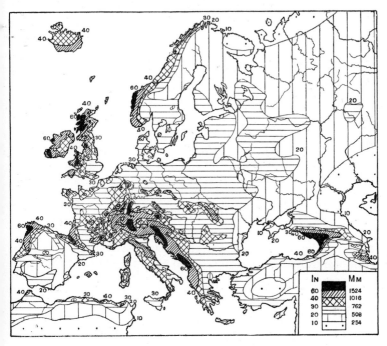

FIG. 81. Mean annual rainfall. (Herbertson.)

north of Russia in July. The south-west of the British Isles
has a mean temperature in January almost as high as the
French and Italian Rivieras. In most of West and North-west
Europe, and on the Mediterranean coasts, no month has a
mean temperature below 32°, in the west of Germany the
mean temperature is below 32° for one month, in the east of
Germany for four months.

If on the same map the isotherms of 32° for January and
70° for July are drawn, Europe is divided into four thermal
provinces, which have mean temperatures above or below 32°

in January, and above or below 70° in July, respectively.
These are (1) the north-west, with mild winters and cool
summers, (2) the north-east, with cold winters and cool summers, (3) the south-west with mild winters and hot summers,
(4) the south-east, with cold winters and hot summers.

The range of temperature increases inland, and especially
towards the east, owing to the greater winter cold and, in a
lesser degree, the greater summer heat. The following stations,
situated in almost the same latitude, show this:

| | | Mean Temperature °F. | | |
Station.	Altitude in Feet.	Warmest month.	Coldest month.	Range.
Nantes . . .	131	65	40	25
Basel	909	66	32	34
Vienna . . .	656	67	29	38
Debreczin . . .	459	71	25	46

There will be frequent occasion to refer in later chapters
to the general principles that the farther east we go the colder
are the winters, and the greater is the range of temperature.

Figs. 81 and 82 show the distribution of rainfall.

The continent may be divided into four major climate
regions (Fig. 83). East Europe has been described already
(Chapter XXVI). Descriptions of the other three follow.

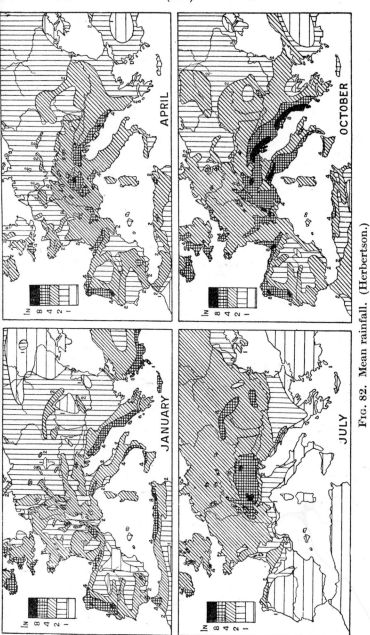

Fig. 82. Mean rainfall. (Herbertson.)

CHAPTER XXVIII

NORTH-WEST EUROPE

THE prevailing winds in winter are south-west, not only in North-west Europe but also in north Russia, owing to the extension of the Icelandic low-pressure system to the north-east. The frequent strong winds and many gales that rage round the coasts have already been mentioned; their fury added to the coolness of the summers is unfavourable to tree growth, and on the most exposed coasts, as in the Orkney and Färoe Islands, there are no trees at all except in sheltered spots. In summer the Azores high-pressure system extends farther to the north-east and the prevailing winds are west to north-west, much lighter in force than in winter, and gales are rare.

Temperature. In the last chapter one of the most important facts to which Western Europe owes its open winters, the main peculiarity of its climate, was considered, viz. the remarkable warmth of the surface water of the North Atlantic Ocean. It was seen that the mean air temperature in January over the ocean west of Norway is more than 40° above the average for the latitude. The excess becomes less towards the east, and in central Russia the continental deficit begins. The mean temperature in January at Thorshavn, Färoe Islands, is 38°, and severe frost is unknown; at Yakutsk, in the same latitude in eastern Siberia, the mean is –46°. Comparing the east and west shores of the Atlantic, we find a mean of 39° in January in the Orkney Islands, –6° at Hebron, Labrador, in the same latitude. The open sea on the northwest and most of the north of Europe is never frozen, even in the severest winters.

The mean January temperature in North-west Europe is above (or only very little below) 32° F.; in Spain, the warmest part of the continent, it exceeds 50°, and in the west of France and the British Isles it exceeds 40°. The 32° isotherm for January skirts the coasts of Norway and Jutland, its abnormal course showing that the temperature decreases from west to east, rather than from south to north; the south-west of Ireland has the same mean temperature as Nice and Rome.

It becomes rapidly colder towards the east. At Brest, the mean January temperature is 43°, at Paris 37°, so that in a distance of 310 miles from the coast the mean temperature

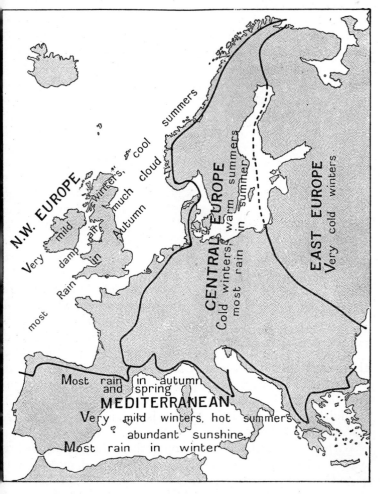

FIG. 83. The major climatic regions of Europe.

falls 6°, and Paris is colder than Thorshavn, which is 850 miles nearer the Pole. The west coast of the British Isles is much warmer than the interior and the east coast, the January mean at Valencia being 44°, at London 39°. Similarly in Norway (Fig. 84), the heads of the longest fiords are as much as 10° colder than the open coasts, and their farthest recesses are often frozen over for some time in winter, but on the open coast ice is unknown even beyond the Arctic circle. The mean January temperature is 34° at Bergen, 24° at Oslo, which has comparatively severe winters with a mean temperature below 32° for four months, since it is at the

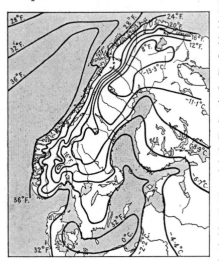

head of a fiord which runs far into the land, and is in the lee of the land-mass of Norway. Christiansund on the open west coast of Norway is warmer than Hamburg, which is about 700 miles farther south but some distance up the estuary of the Elbe.

No month of the year has a mean temperature below 32° except in the north of Norway. Here the duration of the cold period increases rapidly towards the north, and inside the Arctic circle

Fig. 84. Mean temperature in January (after Graarud and Irgens, and Wallén).

there are four months with a mean temperature below, but only a little below, freezing-point. At altitudes above 2,000 feet the conditions become more rigorous, and the highest summits even in the British Isles have at least one month with a mean below 32°.

With regard to the lowest temperatures that occur, on the west coast of Spain and Portugal frost even at night is the exception, and on the extreme west coasts of France and the British Isles frost is rare. At Paris frost must be expected on half the nights during the three winter months. In the neighbourhood of London the thermometer remains above freezing-point on January nights rather more often than it falls below it, and the temperature is very rarely below 15°. On the coast of Norway frost is more frequent, but is very rarely severe except in the north. The extreme readings that have been recorded are:

	Abs. min.	Abs. max.
Paris	−11°	100°
Greenwich (London) . .	4°	100°
Valencia	20°	81°
Scilly Isles (St. Mary's) .	25°	82°

To sum up, the winters of North-west Europe near sea-level are 'open', mild and windy, cloudy damp and rainy—conditions brought from the windward ocean. Frost occurs, but in an average season it is neither severe nor continuous; snow is most frequent in late winter and early spring, but is rarely of serious practical importance. The conditions are most open in the south, where in the mildest seasons frost may hardly occur at all; farther north it is much more stormy, and in hard winters there are spells of two or three weeks of severe frost, 'imported' to the coastal belt from the frozen interior of North and Central Europe.

The mildness of the winters of the south-west coasts of the British Isles and the west coast of Brittany finds expression in the vegetation. The strawberry tree (arbutus) flourishes in the woods of Killarney, the myrtle, fuchsia, and laurel grow well, and even the lemon tree will live, given a little shelter, in South Devon, recalling the flora of the Mediterranean lands. Snow is sufficiently rare in most of north-west Europe to be a topic of conversation when it lies more than a few days, but in the more mountainous parts it is often deep and lasting, and Ben Nevis is snow-capped from mid-October till July. At Aberdeen the ground is snow-covered for 34 days in an average year, and this is the highest figure for a station at sea-level; Oxford has 17 days.

The summers are cool, cooler on the coasts than in the interior, which shows that at this season the sea is a cooling agent in spite of the North Atlantic Drift. The mean temperature in July ranges from about 70° in Portugal to 50° in the north of Norway. The interior is warmer than the coasts, but not nearly so much warmer in summer as it is colder in winter, the mean July temperature being only slightly higher at Paris than at Brest, and London being only 4° warmer than Valencia. The highest temperature ever recorded at Paris is

100°, and Greenwich has the same record. Only the north of Scandinavia is liable to have frost in every month of the year near sea-level; here even the midnight sun cannot ensure immunity. In most of North-west Europe the three summer months at least are always free of frost.

Autumn is warm as compared with spring, a common feature of a maritime climate; the mean temperature at Valencia in April is 48°, and in October 51°.

Rainfall (Figs. 81 and 82). The rainfall is everywhere abundant, and in the mountains excessive, in all seasons except spring. Rain is frequent even on the plains, the number of days with rain ranging in the British Isles from 160 in the south-east to 240 in the north-west. The driest tracts are the Paris and Garonne basins, the Low Countries and north Germany, and the east of the British Isles, with from 20 to 30 inches of rain a year. Even low hills have a heavier rainfall than the plains, and the Pyrenees, the Central Plateau of France and the Highlands of Brittany, show their influence very clearly on the rainfall map. But especially heavy is the rainfall of the rugged western seaboard of the British Isles, notably in south-west Ireland, the Highlands of Scotland, the Lake District, and the Welsh mountains. The last has the heaviest rainfall in North-west Europe; it is indeed one of the heaviest in the whole continent, and takes a high place among the rainfall totals of the world, for at Styehead Pass, Cumberland, the mean is 170 inches in the year, and round Snowdon as much as 200 inches. There is an extraordinarily rapid diminution from west to east in the British Isles; Ben Nevis has 171 inches in the year, Nairn, 70 miles to the east, only 25 inches. Similarly in Norway the western slope of the Highlands has about 100 inches a year, Bergen has 81 inches, the head of the Sogne Fiord, 100 miles from the open coast and well 'shadowed' by high land, only 30 inches.

The copious rainfall of the west coasts is due to the mountains which rise in the course of the prevailing westerlies. The warm sea over which the winds have blown has provided an abundant store of moisture, which the frequent pressure-irregularities assist in condensing. Fortunately the mountain barrier is neither so high nor so continuous that the lowlands beyond are in danger of drought in normal years, though a succession of dry seasons usually causes considerable inconvenience.

The rainfall shows no strongly marked periodicity, being abundant in all seasons, but in most of North-west Europe spring is the driest season, and autumn the wettest, since cyclonic activity is then greatest, and the sea is warmest relatively to the land. Thorshavn (see p. 247) has a pure oceanic régime; the winter half-year is rainiest with 63 per cent. of the year's total, and of the four seasons winter and autumn have most rain, summer and spring least; January is the rainiest month, June the driest. These facts have evidently a close connexion with the monthly frequency of depressions over the North Atlantic (p. 231); most rain falls in the most stormy months. The west coasts of Norway, the British Isles, and France (Bergen, Valencia, and Brest), have much the same rainfall curve as Thorshavn.

To leeward of the western seaboard there is a change, summer becoming rainier at the expense of winter. In the British Isles (Oxford, London, Edinburgh), spring is still the driest season as at Valencia, but winter has almost the same percentage of the year's total rainfall as spring. The summer maximum is highest in the east, the excess of summer over spring at Edinburgh being equal to the excess of winter over spring in the west.

Over most of the east midlands and the east coast of Great Britain as far north as Forfar, and in the east of Ireland, the summer percentage is so much increased as to become the maximum of the year, but the autumn figure follows close behind; the summer excess is greatest in East Anglia. On the east coast north of Dundee autumn and winter are the wettest seasons, the oceanic régime dominating the whole of north Scotland. There is little difference in the winter and summer half-years, but it is interesting from a theoretical point of view that the summer half-year is the rainier in much of the midlands, and on the east coast except in the extreme north. Thus the east of the British Isles has a continental rather than an oceanic rainfall régime.

The mean monthly rainfall shows everywhere two maxima, one in autumn or winter, generally in October, the other in late summer, generally in August. Almost everywhere the autumn or winter maximum is the chief, and is due to the same causes that produce a mid-winter maximum on the ocean, viz. cyclonic activity and the relative excess of warmth in the sea (Valencia, Fig. 85). As autumn runs on into winter the land cools rapidly, and the cold, together with the resulting tendency to high atmospheric pressure, prevents the rainfall increasing inland beyond the October figure in spite of the increasing storminess over the ocean. The late summer monthly maximum is the main one only in a small part of the east of Great Britain (Cambridge, Fig. 85) and of Ireland.

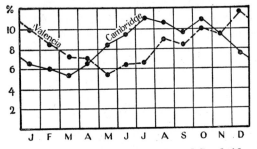

Fig. 85. Mean monthly rainfall at Valencia and Cambridge (percentage of yearly total).

This is a continental characteristic, and it will be considered more fully in describing the rainfall of Central Europe, where it is more prominent. September is a comparatively dry month, coming between the rainier months of late summer and autumn.

Spring is the driest season everywhere in the British Isles, April and May the driest months. The sea is then coolest relatively to the land, so that the vapour-capacity of air blowing from the sea is increased over the land and the air tends to become drier rather than to give up moisture. Moreover there is a greater tendency in spring than in other seasons for anticyclones to take up a position to the north of the British Isles, giving dry north-east and east winds.

In France there is a similar transition from the oceanic type of the west coast (Brest) with seasonal percentages much the same as in the west of Ireland, to the more continental régime of the interior and east, with more rain in the summer than in the winter half-year. By far the greater part of the country conforms to this latter type, for the oceanic régime is found only in a narrow coastal strip. In the north interior of France (Paris) summer is slightly rainier than autumn. In the centre (Clermont-Ferrand) and east (Lyon) summer is wettest, with twice as much rain as winter. But in the more continental as in the oceanic division, October is in most places the wettest month (June at Clermont), and there is a secondary maximum in early summer, June or July. Thus the interior of France shows an interesting transition from the pure oceanic type of the west coast, with an autumn maximum and more rain in the winter than in the summer half-year, to the continental type in which summer is the rainiest season and the summer half-year is rainier than the winter.

SEASONAL DISTRIBUTION OF RAINFALL IN NORTH-WEST EUROPE
(PERCENTAGES OF THE YEARLY TOTAL)

	Winter.	Spring.	Summer.	Autumn.	Winter Half-year.	Summer Half-year.
Thorshavn .	33	21	*16*	30	63	37
Bergen .	29	*18*	21	**32**	58	42
Valencia .	31	*20*	21	28	58	42
Oxford .	24	*21*	**28**	27	51	49
London (Camden Sq.)	24	*21*	27	28	52	48
Edinburgh .	22	*20*	**31**	27	48	52
Brest . .	29	19	*19*	**33**	59	41
Paris . .	*20*	23	29	28	46	54
Lyon . .	*15*	25	30	30	41	59
Clermont-Ferrand	*16*	26	**32**	26	38	62
Brussels .	22	*21*	**30**	27	48	52
Emden .	22	*20*	**31**	27	48	52
Hamburg .	*21*	22	**33**	24	45	55

Brussels on the south coast of the North Sea has almost exactly the same régime as Edinburgh. Emden and Hamburg are very similar but the summer maximum is more pronounced.

In North-west Europe, then, the oceanic type of rainfall with its maximum in winter is confined to a very narrow coastal strip (Fig. 86). Immediately inland the winters become drier and the summers rainier. But, as already stated, there is no marked periodicity in the rainfall, which is abundant in all seasons; even in the driest years serious drought is rare. With a warm ocean lying close to windward the air is always damp, especially in winter, and evaporation is slow, the mean annual evaporation from a water surface being only 16 inches

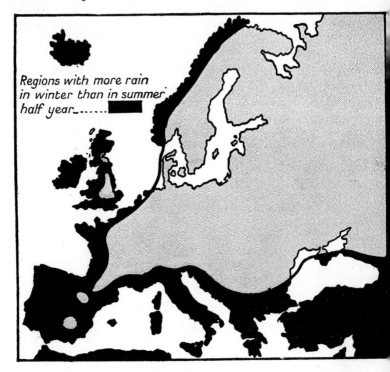

Regions with more rain in winter than in summer half year_____

FIG. 86.

at Camden Square, London. It is not lack of water as in the savanna lands, but the cold of winter, that determines the resting-time for plant life.

The skies of North-west Europe are very cloudy, indeed this is one of the cloudiest regions on the earth. In the south of England on the average of the year $\frac{7}{10}$ of the sky is clouded; in September alone the cloud covering decreases to $\frac{6}{10}$. Sunshine is scanty, notably in the extreme north of Scotland which projects towards the most frequented cyclone tracks of the North Atlantic and sees the sun for only 1,200 hours in the year and for less than an hour a day in winter. On the south coast of England the mean annual total is 1,700 hours, but even this record represents a land of dull skies. The winters of the south-west of Ireland are as mild as those of Italy, but the sunshine records warn us against attempting to put the two places in the same climate category; for at Valencia there are only 1,442 hours of sunshine in the year, 31 per cent. of the total number of hours during which the sun is above the horizon, at Rome 2,362 hours, 55 per cent. of the total possible. North-west Europe is often cloudy and rainy and does not see the sun for days and even weeks together, but Rome is in the favoured Mediterranean region, where the rainfall may be heavy but is usually of short duration, and there is rarely a day on which the sun does not shine.

CHAPTER XXIX

CENTRAL EUROPE

CENTRAL EUROPE is the transition region between the oceanic north-west of Europe and continental Russia. The prevailing winds over most of the area are westerly all the year, but are neither so constant in direction nor so strong as in the north-west, and on many a winter day, while the shores of Britain are swept by gales bringing heavy rain and abnormal warmth from the western ocean, Germany is enjoying the cold, crisp, calm air of an anticyclone, or, it may be, shivers in the grip of bitterly cold east winds, often full of snow, which sweep across from Russia. The change is great indeed when mild westerlies from the ocean regain the upper hand over these harsh continental conditions.

It has been seen that the high-pressure belt, the 'wind-divide' of the continent, lies over the Alps in winter, somewhat farther north in summer. North Switzerland and all Germany have prevailing west winds, Hungary, Rumania, and the Balkan Peninsula have north and north-west winds, dry and piercing in winter like the winds in the steppes of south Russia.

The winter temperature decreases towards the east rather than the north, as already explained. In the western half of Germany long-continued frost and snow are much less frequent than in the east where they are the usual conditions. In the Scandinavian Peninsula the highland barrier which rises steeply from the west coast effects the change from oceanic to continental conditions within a few miles; the Norwegian coast has remarkably mild winters, and snow is only a temporary interruption of the humid and rainy conditions, but in the interior of the peninsula the cold is severe, and at Sveg, in a valley bottom in central Sweden, the temperature has fallen to $-56°$. Especially on the highlands of southern Norway snow lies deep and crisp from November to April, and above 6,000 feet throughout the year. The depth and the duration of the snow decrease towards the lower and drier east; the ground is snow-covered from November to February inclusive round Stockholm and from November to March in the middle of the peninsula in that latitude. In higher latitudes the snow lies longer, for six months at Haparanda, and throughout the year on the highlands of north Sweden above 3,500 feet. The whole of Finland except the coastal strip bears a white carpet from early November till late April. In Scania the average duration is only one month, and in Denmark the winter often passes without the ground being snow-covered for any appreciable time.

The highlands of the south of Norway show a strong inversion of temperature in calm weather in winter:

Station.	Alt. ft.	Mean temp. for Jan.	Mean min. temp. for year.	Absolute min. temp.
Röros (in bottom of upper Glommen Valley) . .	2,100	12·9	−34°	−60°
Finse (on snow-covered plateau) .	4,100	16·5	−20°	—

The east coast is warmer than the interior owing to the effect of the Baltic Sea, but is much colder than the west coast. Below are given the mean temperatures at typical series of stations. The first series lies across the south of the peninsula: Karlstad has a higher temperature than might have been expected from its position in the interior, and this is doubtless due to the large lake Wener lying to windward. In the second series, Karesuando, which is situated on the frontier of Sweden and Russia in lat. 68·30° N., is remarkably cold by comparison with Skomvaer in the extreme south of the Lofoten Islands. Haparanda, on the north shore of the Gulf of Bothnia, shows that the ice-bound sea has but little ameliorating influence, for it is only 6° warmer than Karesuando which is 1,050 feet higher.

Station.	Altitude in Feet.	MEAN TEMPERATURE		Range. °F.
		Coldest month. °F.	Warmest month. °F.	
Skudesnaes . . .	16	34	58	24
Oslo	82	24	63	39
Karlstad . . .	180	25	62	37
Stockholm . . .	148	26	62	36
Skomvaer . . .	66	31	51	20
Karesuando . . .	1,083	6	53	47
Haparanda . . .	33	11	59	48

On the west coast, south of Christiansund, no month has a
mean temperature below 32°, but in the interior the mean
monthly temperature is below 32° for 6 months of the year.

The following table, compiled from data given by Wallén,
shows the lengthening of the winter from south to north in
Sweden, and illustrates the conditions in the high latitudes of
Europe generally:

	Mean last date with mean temp.		*Mean number of days with mean temp. below 32°*
Station.	*below 32°*	*above 32°*	
Malmö (Lund), 55·42 N. .	Mar. 4	Dec. 23	71
Stockholm, 59·41 N. .	Mar. 27	Nov. 27	120
Hernosand, 62·38 N. .	Apr. 7	Nov. 10	148
Storlien, 63·19 N. . .	Apr. 29	Oct. 24	187
Haparanda, 65·50 N. .	Apr. 25	Oct. 23	184
Karesuando, 68·27 N. .	May 10	Oct. 6	216

In Russia and Finland, except on the Baltic coast, frost
occasionally occurs north of lat. 60° N. even in July.

East of the Elbe temperatures below zero occur in most
winters, and there is at least 1 month, in east Germany at
least 3 months, with a mean temperature below 32°. All the
rivers of Germany are frozen in part of their courses in winter.
The Rhine is ice-bound at Köln for 21 days in an average
winter, and in the severe winter of 1829–30 no less than 220
miles out of the 270 miles between Mannheim and Holland
were frozen; in December 1879, 170 miles were frozen. The
Oder is frozen for 80 days on an average, the Memel at Tilsit
for 134 days. Even the lower Danube is blocked by ice for
37 days. The Saône (east France) is closed to navigation
for 15 days. The rivers and the smaller lakes are frozen for
about 130 days in the south of Sweden, 230 days in the
north. Germany's North Sea coasts are never frozen, but
ice-breakers are required to keep the harbour of Hamburg
open. Her Baltic shores have more severe winters, and,
though the open coast is rarely frozen, the harbours are ice-
bound every year, Lübeck for 32 days, Swinemünde for 20
days, Stettin for 61 days, the inner harbour of Memel for
142 days. The whole of the Swedish coast may be blocked,
but this is exceptional on the south and west coasts. In the

Gulf of Bothnia shipping is held up in an average year from November to May inclusive. In most winters there is enough drift ice in all parts of the Baltic to impede navigation, and the passages on the east of Denmark are more or less blocked; in these narrow sounds the duration of the ice is more variable than in the open Baltic, and may even exceed 4 months. The west coast of Denmark is always open. Ice is not unknown in Oslo Fiord, but it is never a serious obstacle.

In summer the interior of the continent is warmer than the coasts, the isotherms curving poleward as they cross from west to east. In July the Arctic coast of Finland has a mean temperature just above 50° and the extreme south of Central Europe in the north of Italy and Greece has 80°, sharing the hot summers of the adjacent Mediterranean lands. In Scandinavia Oslo has the warmest summers, being sheltered from the open sea behind the wide plateau of south Norway, and it has recorded 95°. The limit of cultivation of the vine trends north with the isotherms to its farthest north, lat. 52°, on the Elbe, east of which the limit falls again towards the south, since, though the summers are warmer, they are too short for grapes to ripen satisfactorily, and autumn is not so warm in east as in west Europe. Spring, however, is slightly warmer in the east, the maritime influence in Western Europe checking the rise of temperature, and the Baltic shores have especially raw cold weather in spring. The very long summer days in the interior of the far north of Sweden, where the mean sunshine record for June is 12 hours a day, sometimes give remarkably high temperatures, and 99° has been recorded at Jockmock on the Arctic Circle. The hottest part of Central Europe in summer includes Hungary and Rumania, the mean July temperature being 74° at Szegedin, 73° at Bucharest. These steppe lands are exceedingly hot on summer days.

	Jan.		July.			
	Mean daily max.	Mean daily min.	Mean daily max.	Mean daily min.	Abs. max.	Abs. min.
Berlin . .	34	26	75	58	99	−13
Vienna . .	36	25	77	59	102	−14
Bucharest .	33	19	85	61	105	−23

The land rises on the whole from the flats on the coast o the North Sea to the foot of the Alps, and this rise neutralize the effect on temperature of the more southern latitude i summer. Thus Berlin, 164 feet above the sea, has a mean Jul temperature of 66°, Munich, 1,740 feet above the sea, 64° A special section (p. 258) is devoted to the modification introduced by the Alps.

Rainfall. The mean annual rainfall in the plains is prac tically the same everywhere, between 20 and 30 inches. I is well distributed over the year; summer has most, bu there is no true dry season. An instructive picture of th rainfall régimes is presented by 'sections' of the rainfall o the continent from west to east, and from south to north The first section is from Brittany to Rumania:

Station.	*Rainfall. Percentage of Yearly Total.*						Rainiest month.	Driest month.
	Winter.	*Spring.*	*Summer.*	*Autumn.*	*Winter Half-year.*	*Summer Half-year.*		
Brest .	29	19	*19*	**33**	59	41	Oct.	May
Paris .	*20*	23	**29**	28	46	54	Oct., June	Feb.
Karlsruhe.	*19*	23	**32**	26	44	56	June, Oct.	Feb.
Munich .	*13*	24	**39**	24	31	69	June, July	Feb.
Salzburg .	*14*	23	**42**	21	30	70	July	Jan.
Klagenfurt	*13*	23	**35**	29	37	63	July	Feb.
Budapest .	*18*	**28**	**28**	26	44	56	June, May, Oct.	Feb.
Szegedin .	*19*	26	**31**	24	42	58	June, Oct.	Feb.
Bucharest	*17*	25	**35**	23	39	61	June, Nov.	Feb.
Sulina .	*19*	23	28	**30**	45	55	June, Sept.	Feb.

In Brittany most rain falls in autumn and winter—a oceanic régime. At Paris the maximum comes in summer but autumn has almost the same percentage, and the summe half-year receives more rain than the winter half; October i the wettest month but there is a secondary maximum i June; this is typical of most of France, but in the south-eas the secondary maximum is in May. Entering Germany, a Karlsruhe we find the continental régime, with a pronounce summer maximum; the rainiest month is June, but th secondary maximum in October shows that the oceanic influence is not yet completely lost. Munich and Salzburg have a more accentuated continental régime, and there is no secondary maximum in October. In Austria and Hungary a new tendency appears, spring becoming more rainy at the expense of summer. In most of Hungary and Rumania more than a quarter of the rainfall is received in spring, though summer is the rainiest season, and May and June are the rainiest months; autumn has considerably less rain than spring. At Budapest the rainfall régime is the opposite of that of Brest (Figs. 87 and 88).

The second section runs from the head of the Adriatic to the Baltic. Central Europe is bounded on the south by the Mediterranean region with rainy autumns and dry summers, represented by Fiume, which has most rain in October, least in July, and a secondary maximum in June.

Station.	Rainfall. Percentage of Yearly Total.						Rainiest month.	Driest month.
	Winter.	*Spring.*	*Summer.*	*Autumn.*	*Winter Half-year.*	*Summer Half-year.*		
Fiume	20	23	20	37	54	46	Oct., June	July
Agram	16	24	30	30	44	56	Oct., June	Feb.
Budapest	18	28	28	26	44	56	June, May, Oct.	Feb.
Prague	13	26	38	23	31	69	June	Feb.
Breslau	16	24	38	22	36	64	July	Feb.
Berlin	20	23	33	24	44	56	July	Feb.
Kiel	22	20	31	27	48	52	July, Oct.	April

The Mediterranean régime dies out rapidly as the sea is left behind, and at Karlstadt (Croatia) and Agram there is more rain in summer than in winter, but in all Hungary except Siebenbürgen the Mediterranean influence can be traced in the rise in the rainfall curve in October. The table on p. 256 shows how October becomes relatively drier with distance from the Adriatic, and summer, especially early summer, rainier.

At Budapest early summer is the rainiest season, the régime

of the steppes of Hungary resembling that of south Russia (p. 215). Farther north the maximum is retarded; July is the rainiest month and spring becomes drier, but even on the south coast of the Baltic Sea (Kiel) the winter maximum of North-west Europe does not occur. In almost all Sweden the maximum comes still later, in August, and there is a slight secondary maximum in October.

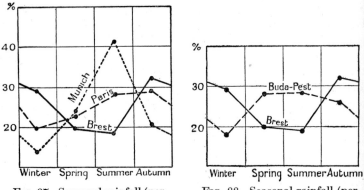

FIG. 87. Seasonal rainfall (percentage of annual total).

FIG. 88. Seasonal rainfall (percentage of annual total).

The two rainfall sections, then, illustrate the facts that in much of France away from the coasts and in the south and west of Germany the rainiest month is June, and that the maximum is still earlier in Hungary and Rumania, where there is a marked early summer maximum as in the steppes of south Russia. February is almost everywhere the driest

PERCENTAGE MONTHLY RAINFALL

Station.	Distance in miles from Adriatic Sea.	January.	February.	March.	April.	May.	June.	July.	August.	September.	October.	November.	December.
Fiume .	0	6	6	8	9	8	8	4	6	11	15	11	8
Karlstadt	55	5	5	7	8	9	11	7	9	10	12	10	7
Agram .	80	5	5	6	8	10	11	9	10	9	12	9	6
Kanizsa	145	4	5	6	9	11	10	10	10	9	11	9	6
Budapest	265	6	5	7	9	11	12	8	8	8	9	8	7

month, and winter is the driest season. In the interior of the continent autumn is drier than spring.

The winter minimum is the result of the high pressures over Central Europe due to the winter cold. The cushion of dense air tends to ward off the depressions which give so much rain to North-west Europe at this season. But in summer pressure is lower, and there is less resistance to the advance of depressions, which, therefore, though neither so numerous nor so deep as in winter, are able to reach Central Europe. The prevailing north-west winds blow from the sea, and, moreover, the air, being warmer, can contain more moisture than in winter and gives more precipitation for a given drop of temperature. The ground is heated by the strong sunshine, and convectional overturnings take place, often with thunderstorms and heavy downpours of rain; in Hungary 61 per cent. of the rain in June falls on days with thunderstorms. Convection might naturally be expected to be most vigorous in the hottest month, July, and it is so in north Central Europe. But in most of the region the heaviest rainfall is in June, so that surface heating alone is not sufficient explanation. The most vigorous convectional overturning takes place not necessarily when the lowest strata of the atmosphere are heated most, but when equilibrium between them and the higher strata is least stable. The instability is probably greatest in the early summer during the midday hours, since the upper air has not yet been much heated, and, indeed, is but little past its minimum temperature for the year, while the air resting on the ground is already greatly warmed. In July the surface air is warmer, but so also is the upper, and convection is less active. It must also be remembered that irregularities of pressure distribution are more frequent in early summer, the season of transition from winter to summer conditions, when barometric gradients are slight, than when the summer circulation is fully established. The rainfall of July and August is of less value for plant life since much is lost by rapid run-off from the hard dry ground, and evaporation is very active in the hot thirsty air.

Though summer is the rainiest season in Central Europe, yet there, as in North-west Europe, the relative humidity is less than in winter, and evaporation more active, a fact which makes the seasonal distribution of moisture more uniform from the point of view of animal and plant life than the monthly rainfall means indicate. In summer, too, the sky is least cloudy, but most of Central, like North-west, Europe can be truly described as cloudy in all seasons. In central and southern Germany the mean cloudiness is about $\frac{8}{10}$ of the sky in December, $\frac{6}{10}$ in July. There is less cloud in the Danube lands, e.g. Budapest $\frac{7}{10}$ in December, $\frac{4}{10}$ in July; Bucharest has the same means.

MEAN DAILY SUNSHINE (HOURS)

	Max. month.	Min. month.	Year.
Berlin	8·2 (June)	1·1 (Dec.)	4·4
Strasburg	7·0 (July)	1·1 (Dec.)	4·1
Nürnberg	6·0 (June, Aug.)	0·9 (Dec.)	3·6

It is only on crossing the Alps that we leave the region of gloomy skies, and enter, quite suddenly, the bright and sunny Mediterranean world.

The Alps

Mountains make their own climates. The Alps offer a particularly tempting field for investigation, since they are the greatest range in Europe, and excellent series of meteorological observations are available. Furthermore the region is often dominated by anticyclonic conditions, under which some of the most interesting peculiarities of mountain climate occur.

Temperature. On an average the air is 1° F. cooler for every 300 feet increase of altitude. But this is merely a mean value, derived from very diverse figures, and it will rarely be found to hold good in practice if simultaneous readings are taken at different heights on a mountain side. The actual vertical 'gradient' of temperature depends on the time of day, the season of the year, the state of the weather, and especially on the topography. In the Alpine region major topographical types are (i) wide open plains as the Swiss Foreland, 1,200 to 2,500 feet above the sea, which belong climatically to the plains of Central Europe rather than to the Alps (e.g. Basel and Geneva), (ii) narrow valleys, deep and steep-sided ravines between some of the highest ranges in Europe, with climatic peculiarities which vary according as they open to the north

or the south, the east or the west (Altdorf and Klagenfurt),
(iii) upland valleys (Andermatt and Davos), (iv) the mountain
summits (Säntis). The mean temperature and rainfall of the
typical stations are given on pages 295 and 300.

In many cases the topography has more influence than the
absolute altitude of the station. Below are given the mean
temperatures at Lucerne, situated almost on the Swiss Foreland, the Rigi, an isolated mountain summit overlooking
Lucerne from some 4,500 feet above, and Bevers, a station
in the valley-bottom of the Upper Engadine, a deep trench
bounded by lofty mountain ranges. Bevers has approximately
the same altitude as the Rigi, but the topography is in
complete contrast.

MEAN TEMPERATURE, °F.

Station.	Alt. Feet.	July.			January.			Range. July–Jan.
		Mean for month.	7 a.m.	1 p.m.	Mean for month.	7 a.m.	1 p.m.	
Lucerne	1,480	65	62	71	30	27	32	35
Rigi	5,860	50	49	52	24	22	25	26
Bevers	5,610	53	48	62	14	8	22	39
Difference.								
Lucerne–Rigi		15	13	19	6	5	7	
Rigi–Bevers		−3	1	−10	10	14	3	

The atmosphere is heated in the daytime in two ways, by the
passage through it of the direct rays of the sun, and by
conduction from the earth which is heated by those rays.
Pure air is unable to absorb much of the insolation directly,
but the presence of dust and moisture particles increases the
absorption, and as dust and moisture are most abundant in
the lowest layers those layers are most heated. But the second
way is much more effective, and the heat will be greatest in
valley-bottoms where the air rests on concave slopes which
provide the greatest area of contact. The pointed summits
and convex slopes of highlands, on the other hand, present
but small areas as sources of heat to the air around them.
The movement of the air is another factor, for at the higher
levels there is usually a strong wind, and the air cannot be

warmed so much during its short contact with the warm rocks as the calmer strata below. The nocturnal cooling of the air is due chiefly to contact with the ground which loses its heat through radiation into space, and therefore the concave valleys will be almost as effective in cooling the air at night as in warming it by day. Moreover, cool air is denser than warm, and the coldest air tends to drain downwards from all the slopes around and to collect in the bottoms, where it forms stagnant 'lakes', in which the temperature is sometimes lower than on the mountain tops. Such 'inversions of temperature' are most frequent during calm anticyclonic weather. It is true that owing to the clearer and less dense blanket of air the sun's rays at great elevations are very powerful, and the rocks on the mountain tops become very hot by day; they also lose their heat very rapidly at night. But the other influences outweigh this in controlling the shade temperature of the air.

Valleys, then, are especially warm as compared with the summits on summer days, and especially cold on winter nights, as is illustrated by the means given above for Lucerne and Rigi; the Rigi is 19° colder than Lucerne at 1 p.m. in July, only 5° colder in the morning in January. The Rigi and Bevers present a very striking contrast. The two stations are at almost the same altitude, but in January the valley station is 14° colder than the summit in the morning, in July 10° warmer during the heat of the day. The range of temperature is therefore least on the Rigi, greatest at Bevers. The lowest reading ever actually recorded in Switzerland, −31°, was taken at Bevers. The Rigi can show nothing below −9°, and even on the Säntis, a summit station 8,200 feet above the sea, the absolute minimum is only −15°. On the summit of Mont Blanc −45° has been recorded. The mean winter temperature is, as a rule, higher well up the sides of a valley than in the bottom, and this is one of the reasons that mountain villages are so often built at some height above the valley floor. Thus the Brünig Pass (3,315 feet above the sea) is somewhat warmer in winter than Meiringen (1,985 feet) which lies below it in the Haslital.

'It is especially in November, December, and the first half of January that the higher stations enjoy the greatest advantages, that is to say when the days are shortest. At that season a gloomy pall of fog often enshrouds the lowlands of the Swiss Foreland for a week together, and penetrates into the mountain valleys to an altitude of about 2,500 feet. If we ascend we rise out of the damp, cold, dark, sunless winter and come out suddenly into a wonderland of sunshine and beauty. The landscape is full of light, the air is mild and dry and exceedingly bracing, and we enjoy to the full a warm climate only comparable with that of Alpine summits of more than 6,500 feet on clear calm summer days. The sudden change in the meteorological conditions which is experienced above the fog surface is astonishing, and in particular the transparency and dryness of the air, together with the bright light, are at first almost overpowering' (MAURER).

Temperature inversions are especially notable during anticyclonic conditions as the following example shows:

	Altitude.	*Temperature at 7 a.m.* °F. 1881.		
Station.	Feet.	Dec. 25.	Dec. 26.	Dec. 27.
Altdorf . . .	1,480	20	19	23
Rigi . . .	5,863	13	27	35
St. Gothard Pass .	6,877	−2	24	30

On 25 December 1881, the weather was cyclonic, and the wind strong, and the St. Gothard was 22° colder than Altdorf. But the change to an anticyclonic calm on the 26th brought about an extraordinary inversion of temperature. The Rigi was 8° warmer than the valley station, the St. Gothard 5° warmer; the temperature at the St. Gothard had risen 26° in 24 hours. The inversion still continued on the 27th. During such calms the coldest air drains slowly downward and collects in the bottoms, but the strong winds associated with depressions mix the strata, and as the air is driven up the mountain sides and down again into the valleys, the adiabatic temperature changes are predominant, and the lowest temperatures are found at the greatest altitudes.

The severest winter cold is felt in the valley bottoms of the eastern Alps, which are shut off from western influences, and are more frequently subject to anticyclonic conditions. The basins of Klagenfurt and Graz have especially extreme temperatures, with strong temperature inversion. At Graz (altitude 1,200 feet) the mean temperature in January is 26°, in July 65°, and the mean annual extremes are 85° and 4°. The following series given by Hann illustrates the conditions at Klagenfurt, in the bottom of a wide enclosed basin, and at other stations situated at increasing heights on the side of the mountains which enclose the basin on the east:

	Altitude. Feet.	Mean Temp. January. °F.		Altitude. Feet.	Mean Temp. January. °F.
Klagenfurt .	1,444	20	Lolling .	2,755	27
Eberstein .	1,870	24	Do. .	3,610	29
Hüttenberg .	2,560	26	Stelzing .	4,625	25

The higher stations are warmer up to 3,610 feet, above which there is a decrease of temperature with increasing elevation. The figures given are the mean January temperatures. The following is an interesting example of the extreme cases of inversion which may occur. The Obir is a mountain summit which looks down on Klagenfurt from the south-east, and the fortnight referred to was one of abnormally high atmospheric pressure with calm air over all Central Europe, when the cold was unusually severe.

16–28 December 1879.

	Altitude. Feet.	Mean Temp. °F.	Mean Cloud (tenths of the sky covered).
Klagenfurt . .	1,444	3	3
Obir . . .	6,695	24	2

The poljes of the eastern and the Dinaric Alps similarly collect lakes of extremely cold air on calm winter nights. It may be considered a general rule that the valley-bottoms are relatively coldest, as compared with the summits, in the coldest winters in Central Europe, relatively warmest in the mildest winters, since cold winters are the result of anticyclonic, mild open winters of cyclonic conditions.

Valleys with a wide opening allow the cold air which gravitates into them to drain away, and they are not so cold as enclosed basins. Such valleys opening towards the north-west of the Alps are indeed abnormally warm in winter. Altdorf, in the deep Reuss Valley just before it opens on to the Lake of Lucerne, and Lucerne at the other end of the

same lake, on the Swiss Foreland, at the same altitude make
an interesting comparison—

| | Altitude. Feet. | MEAN TEMPERATURE | | |
		January. °F.	July. °F.	Range. °F.
Altdorf . .	1,480	32	64	32
Lucerne . .	1,480	30	65	35

The greater warmth at Altdorf in January is partly due to the
better drainage of the cold air, but chiefly to the abnormally
warm föhn wind which it enjoys. This is a wind which has
crossed the ranges on its journey from the south, and is
heated and dried by compression as it descends the northern
valleys sometimes with gale force, and it causes remarkably
large and sudden rises of temperature and decreases of
humidity at the valley stations. On Christmas morning 1870
Trogen, near St. Gall, recorded a temperature of −1°, and the
valley was full of cold foggy stagnant air. But a change set
in about noon. A depression had appeared to the north of
the Alps, and air was drawn in towards it from the south,
across the mountains. It blew as a föhn at Trogen, raising
the temperature to 41°, a rise of 42° in 24 hours. In the
Reuss valley föhn winds blow on an average 48 days per
annum, March, April, and May having most, and they have a
very appreciable effect in raising the mean temperature of the
winter months. The pronounced föhn effect is lost when
the wind passes beyond the narrow valleys (Fig. 89). The
upper Rhine, the Reuss, and the upper Aar have been well
called climatic oases in winter owing to their frequent föhn
winds. The Rhône Valley above Martigny as far as Sion is
especially dry and warm, and the vegetation is reminiscent
of subtropical types, but the very warm summers are chiefly
responsible for this.

The southern valleys of the Alps are the warmest, owing to
their latitude, their southern exposure and sunny skies, and
the föhn influence on northerly winds that may have crossed
the mountains from Central Europe; the winter winds, however, usually originate in the high pressures which normally
lie over the Alps themselves. Many Alpine valleys have their
characteristic local winds which blow by day or by night, but
space does not admit of a description here. The means for

Lugano and Basel, at the same altitude on opposite sides of the Alps, are:

	Altitude. Feet.	MEAN TEMPERATURE	
		January. °F.	July. °F.
Basel . . .	909	32	66
Lugano . . .	902	34	71

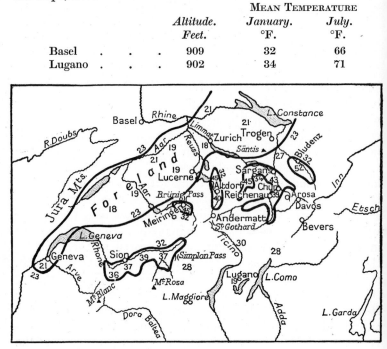

Fig. 89. Temperature (°F.) during a föhn wind 13 January 1898, 1 p.m., corrected to 500 metres above sea-level.

An important local influence in a system with an east–west trend like the Alps is exposure, for the south-facing slopes enjoy a great advantage, especially in the winter half-year, an advantage which has visible expression in both the natural vegetation and the agriculture and settlements of man. The contrast between the upper north-facing slopes, the Schatten-seite, still deep in snow, and the bare southern slopes, the Sonnenseite, which are already warm in the bright and almost vertical rays of the midday sun strikes any one who makes his way through the mountains in spring.

Cloudiness and Humidity. The valley-bottoms in the Alps are dampest and foggiest (or cloudiest) in winter, especially at night when the air that is chilled by radiation to its saturation point drains down from the slopes. The mountain summits on the other hand are clear in winter, but are often hidden in thick cloud during the heat of summer days, when the air movement is upwards in all the valleys, and the masses of vapour condense as the ascending currents cool by expansion. The curves of relative humidity at Zürich and on the Säntis illustrate these changes (Fig. 90). For the same reasons summer is the sunniest season in the valleys, winter on the summits. On the Säntis the sunniest hour of the day in August is 9 to 10 a.m., just before the heavy mountain clouds form.

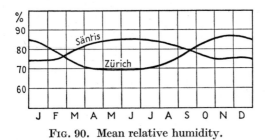

Fig. 90. Mean relative humidity.

Hence, to find a bright sunny climate, we must ascend from the valleys in winter and return to them again in summer.

The driest air is found in different situations under different meteorological conditions. Some of the lowest humidities in the deep northern valleys occur with strong föhn winds. The air is then often so dry that villages have been burnt down owing to the wooden chalets easily catching fire. On the other hand during the temperature inversions of anticyclonic weather the mountain tops are not only warm but also remarkably dry and sunny, owing partly to the warming and drying by compression of the air which is descending from the higher strata of the anticyclone. At such times the summits offer great climatic attractions to invalids requiring bright invigorating air, and sunshine rich in ultra-violet radiation. But equal advantages in a more accessible form are available in certain elevated valleys, as at Arosa and Davos. These resorts are indeed cold in winter, like other valley stations, and the range of temperature from day to night is very great. Davos has the greatest range recorded in Switzerland, and some of the lowest temperatures, lower than the Säntis, and eclipsed only by Bevers and Andermatt.

	Altitude. Feet.	*7 a.m.* °F.	*1 p.m.* °F.	Difference, *1 p.m.–7 a.m.* °F.
Lucerne . .	1,480	27	32	5
Davos . . .	5,121	13	27	14
Säntis . . .	8,202	14	16	2

MEAN TEMPERATURE. JANUARY

But though Davos is cold it is rarely subject to the chilly wet fogs which often fill the lower valleys in winter, and the cold is of that dry variety which invigorates. It is especially the clear sunny skies which make the Davos winter climate famous, for there is only half as much cloud as at Lucerne, and twice as much sunshine. The snow-clad valley enjoys clear deep-blue skies, crisp calm invigorating air, and long hours of sunshine which has the merit of containing a notably higher proportion of radiation of short wavelength, owing to the absence of moisture and dust particles in the rarefied air, advantages which are prized by many seekers after health. But in summer Davos shares the cloudy skies and moist air of the mountain tops, and has less sunshine than the lower valleys.

The following table shows the relative advantages of the Säntis summit, Davos, Chur in the deep Upper Rhine valley below Davos, and Bern and Zürich:

	Altitude. Feet.	Cloud (tenths). Jan.	July.	Sunshine (hours per day). Jan.	July.	Relative Humidity Per cent. Jan.	July.
Säntis .	8,202	5	7	3·9	5·3	75	85
Davos .	5,121	4	5	3·2	6·7	84	80
Chur .	2,001	5	5	—	—	90	70
Bern .	1,877	8	5	1·9	8·3	85	71
Zürich .	1,542	8	5	1·4	7·7	88	74

The difference in temperature between the north and south sides of the Alps has already been mentioned. The south side is favoured in the other climatic factors also:

	Sunshine (hours per day).		Cloud (tenths).		Rainfall.			
					January.		July.	
					Amt.	No. of days.	Amt.	No. of days.
	Jan.	July.	Jan.	July.	In.		In.	
Basel . .	1·9	7·2	7	6	1·5	10	3·5	13
Lugano .	4·1	9·4	4	4	2·5	7	6·6	11

Basel and Lugano represent not merely the two sides of a mountain range but two different regions, cloudy Central Europe and the bright Mediterranean.

Rainfall. The rainfall in the Alpine lands is far heavier than on the lowlands on both sides, but it is not nearly so heavy as on lesser mountains situated near the sea. The valleys have much less rain than the ranges which bound them, and the valley lines stand out plainly on the rainfall map. In Switzerland the rainiest districts are the mountain groups which include the St. Gothard and the Säntis, the latter with 96 inches per annum, Sargans in the bottom of the Rhine valley at the foot of the mountain only 50 inches, little more than half as much. The Upper Rhône valley, with less than 24 inches, is the driest part of Switzerland and is as dry as the plains of south Germany and north Lombardy. In the eastern Alps the north and south ranges have the heaviest rainfall, over 60 inches, and the interior valleys least. The smallest totals, about 30 inches, are in the great longitudinal valleys of the rivers Inn, Salzach, and Enns, which are not only deep but lie in the heart of the Alpine system. The Engadine has a notably dry continental climate, with clear skies and relatively extreme temperatures. In the north and centre of the Alps summer is the rainiest season both on the summits and in the valleys, July being the wettest month at most stations. In the eastern Alps the maximum comes somewhat later, in August, and the minimum is in February. At most stations autumn has most rain, and summer almost as much; winter has least, though the amount is still considerable. October is the rainiest month.

On the Säntis summit all the precipitation in the months November to April inclusive is in the form of snow, and only in July and August is rain more frequent than snow. At Davos rain is practically never seen from November to

March, and there are occasional snowfalls even in June and August; in July alone is all the precipitation rain. In the lower valleys, at Altdorf for example, it never snows from the beginning of May till the end of September; in December, January, and February snow is as frequent as rain. A depth of 20 to 25 feet of snow is not uncommon in the higher valleys such as the Engadine in winter, and 45 feet has been measured on the Säntis. Snow covers the ground in an average year for a fortnight at Geneva, a month at Basel, 6 weeks at Altdorf, over 6 months in the Upper Engadine, and for 10 months on the Säntis. The lower limit of perpetual snow is estimated at about 9,000 feet above the sea in the western Alps, 10,500 feet in the drier interior ranges. Most of the road passes are blocked from November till the end of May in an average year. Deciduous trees and agriculture generally extend up the valley sides to about 4,500 feet; then comes a zone of coniferous forests to about 5,500 feet, separated by grass slopes (alps) and bare rock from the perpetual snows.

CHAPTER XXX

THE MEDITERRANEAN LANDS

THE Mediterranean basin, which has seen the rise of so many of the great civilizations of the world, will always command special attention. The physical aspects of its geography are of no less fascinating interest than the human. The Mediterranean climate, in spite of great local differences, possesses an essential unity and individuality among the climates of Europe, and it has produced a very characteristic type of vegetation. The environment was highly favourable for the early development of civilization, and the wide extension of the inland seas, and the climate to which they give rise, has always been one of the great natural advantages of Europe.

The Mediterranean climate has three main characteristics. (i) Most of the rain falls in the winter half-year, and there is drought, more or less complete, in summer. The periodicity is much stronger than in the rest of Europe but the period of marked drought is not more than 3 months in most of the region. (ii) The winters are not only rainy, but very mild; the coldest month has a mean temperature above 40°, and in much of the region above 50°. Summer is very hot as well as dry, the mean July temperature exceeding 70°, and in Africa 85°. Fig. 91 shows that in winter the south-west of the British Isles is as warm as Italy, but the course of the July isotherm of 70° excludes Britain from the Mediterranean climate province. On the other hand, vast areas in the south-east of Europe are as warm as Italy in summer, but the winters are long, cold, and dry. Perhaps the best indication of the actual extension of the Mediterranean climate is given by the distribution of the olive-tree, one of the most characteristic elements in the Mediterranean vegetation (Fig. 92). (iii) The bright sunny skies—almost cloudless in summer, and far less cloudy even in winter than the skies of North Europe—are an essential feature in the climate of the Mediterranean, and probably one of far-reaching influence on human development. The hot sunny weather is ideal for ripening the fruits for which the region is famous.

The general conditions are described on p. 231. They are

simplest in summer, when the air movement is controlled by the extension of the North Atlantic anticyclone over Western Europe and the great low-pressure system covering south Asia and the Sahara. North-west and west winds set in in May and continue almost constant in direction during the summer months except for prominent land and sea breezes on the coasts; they are strong, sometimes reaching gale force. There are many local variations in the wind direction, such as the north winds of the Aegean Sea (the

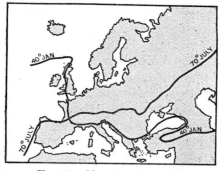

Etesiae of the ancient Greeks, now called by the Turkish name Meltemi); the north-east winds which blow fairly strongly and steadily on the western half of the north African coast, under the control of the Saharan low pressures, reinforced by the effect of the strongly heated land adjacent to the

FIG. 91. Mean temperature.

cooler sea; the almost constant north winds of Egypt which not only blow on the coast, here again reinforced by the sea-breeze effect, but far up the Nile to the Sudan; the west winds of the Levant; and the monsoonal indraft into Anatolia and Iberia. The region is akin to the Sahara in summer. The sky is almost as cloudless, and the sunshine almost as abundant, but the wide expanse of sea prevents the parching heat and drought of the Sahara being realized to the full. Temperature, however, is high, highest in the south and east, lower near the Atlantic. Everywhere the heat of summer-days increases rapidly with distance from the coasts. The following description of the summer weather in Greece is given by Philippson:

'Day after day the sun pours down its fierce rays on the thirsty earth from a deep-blue sky, in which only occasionally is a little white cloud seen. Very rarely there is a passing shower of rain which evaporates at once. The direct rays of the sun are very powerful, and objects exposed to them are heated to an astonishing degree. In the shade the air temperature reaches 105° at times, but the temperature of the sand on the dunes of Phalerum may rise to 160°. When it is calm the heated air vibrates over the parched land, at other times the north wind carries thick clouds of dust over the plains in great whirls. Distant islands and promontories appear to float high above the surface of the sea in mirages. Most rivers and streams dry up, grasses and herbs wither, and the harvest is gathered in early in the season. The ground cracks, and lies naked to the glare of the sun. The landscape,

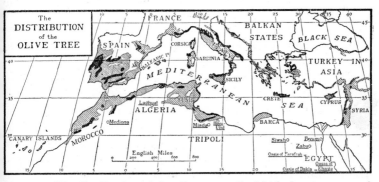

FIG. 92. The distribution of the olive tree; the black denotes areas of most intensive cultivation.

which in spring was gay with waving fields of corn or the green shimmer of sprouting vegetation, now shows the harsh colours of the desert, and the vineyards and maize fields and irrigated gardens alone preserve their bright verdure. In the midday hours all life seems to stop, men and animals drag themselves to shady places to rest, and only the shrill monotonous noise of the cicada fills the air, like the sound of a gigantic rattle. However, the dryness of the air and the resulting rapid evaporation make the heat bearable, provided that there is protection from the direct rays of the sun. The heat is intense, but not sultry. Moreover, the air is almost always in rapid movement owing to the Etesian winds or the sea-breeze. The heat is far more oppressive in the sheltered valleys and the basins of the interior, or in moist artificially irrigated agricultural districts, than on the coasts, though even the interior, at any rate at the foot of the higher mountains, is not without a regular air movement. By day the wind blows up the mountains, but hardly has the sun set before the first puffs of the cool wind descend from the heights, so that in the neighbourhood of mountains some protection against chill is necessary in the evenings. At night there is everywhere rapid radiation, but nevertheless it is always quite warm, and dew is rare. Nothing is more magnificent than a summer night on the coast of Greece, when the land-breeze wafts down cool fragrant air, and the stars sparkle with a fire never seen in our latitudes. The natives sleep in the open air in order to avoid the musty air and the insects of their houses. Summer is also the time of the brightest light, and the most glorious play of colour, especially in the evenings. Every line in the landscape, even at a great distance, is sharply cut, and every tint in the ground shows up brightly since there is little vegetation to hide it.'

But if the Mediterranean lands recall the Sahara in summer, which continues till mid-September, in winter there is a close resemblance to north-west European conditions. The pressure distribution is neither so regular nor so constant as in summer. Speaking generally, the Mediterranean is a region of low pressure between the high-pressure belts which cover Central Europe and North Africa, the low pressure being the result of the warmth and humidity over the sea. But the Iberian, Italian, and Balkan peninsulas introduce irregularities, since those lands, narrow as they are, give rise to tongues of somewhat high pressure, separating the lower pressures over the western Mediterranean, Adriatic, and Aegean Seas, though the difference in pressure is hardly sufficient to show itself on maps of isobars. In terms of the daily weather, there is a tendency for barometric depressions to form or deepen, and to remain more or less stationary, in the winter months over these seas, with the result that on the west coasts of the peninsulas the winds are frequently from the south, warm and rainy, while the east coasts experience dry and cool north winds, and everywhere sudden changes of wind and weather are liable to occur. South-west winds may bring very heavy rain, and, in the northern Mediterranean, north-west winds much snow.

Many depressions come from the Atlantic (Fig. 93, tracks 1, 2, and 3), often as secondaries, but others spring up over the warm Mediterranean itself, especially in the Gulf of Genoa, the Adriatic, and the Cyprus region, and in these same areas there is a strong tendency for depressions which have come from the Atlantic to deepen. The frequency on each track varies with the seasons. In general depressions are numerous in the winter half-year, few in summer; in the eastern basin they are almost unknown from May to September, and summer is a season of unbroken fine dry weather, blue skies, great heat, no rain; but in the western basin occasional disturbances cause more varied conditions. Track 3 seems to be followed especially in winter, the tracks over the Gulf of Genoa and the Adriatic in autumn, winter, and spring; in the Gulf of

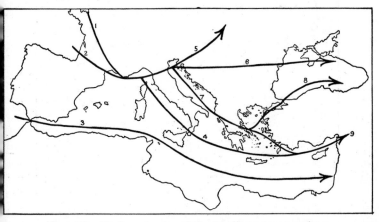

Fig. 93. Cyclone tracks of the Mediterranean region.

Genoa cyclonic activity is more vigorous in autumn and spring than in winter. Of the tracks that diverge from the Gulf of Venice, 5 is followed mostly in spring, 6 especially in spring and summer, this giving the spring and early summer rains to the steppes of the Lower Danube. The continental block of Asia Minor frequently causes depressions approaching from the Adriatic to divide into two systems, one following path 8 over the Sea of Marmora into the Black Sea, the other path 9 to the Cyprus region and the coast of Syria. Both these tracks are followed most frequently in winter, but very frequently in spring also; in autumn depressions are as numerous on track 8 as in spring, but much less frequent on track 9, and hence the autumn rains on which agriculture in Syria is largely dependent are liable to be late or deficient (WEICKMANN).

The winds in winter are variable, as in the westerlies. But

since the depressions tend to remain over the sea the prevailing winds blow from the surrounding lands. Thus round
the western basin the winds are south-west on the Algerian
coast, south-east to east on the west side of Italy, north in
France, north-west in Spain. Similarly round the eastern
basin there are south-west winds on the coast of Egypt,

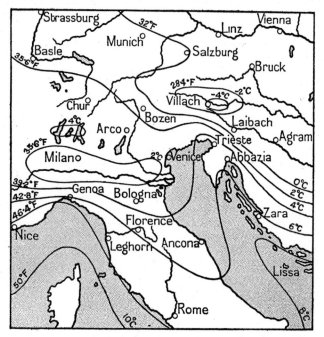

FIG. 94. Mean temperature in January.

south-east to east in Palestine and Syria, north in Asia Minor.
The Black Sea and the Adriatic also have their own cyclonic
circulations. Greece and the Aegean have especially variable
winds owing to their position between the main low-pressure
systems over the western and eastern basins, but the prevailing direction in the Aegean is north.

The isotherms for January (Fig. 94) show the influence of
the pressure and wind systems on the temperature, the lines
bending south over the east of Italy, and then northward
again towards Dalmatia. Leghorn, on the west coast of Italy,
has a mean January temperature of 45°, Ancona in the same

latitude on the east coast 42°, and Florence in the interior is cooler than both, with 41°. Similarly in Greece, Zante has 53°, Athens 48°, and the interior basins are much cooler than the coasts, as Larissa with 42°, Volo with 45°. Still more striking than the temperature difference is the difference in the rainfall. The mountains that rise steeply from the east coast of the Adriatic are one of the wettest regions of the continent; Crkvice, 3,600 feet above the sea, overlooking the Bocche di Cattaro, has the heaviest rainfall recorded on the mainland of Europe, 183 inches a year, while the opposite shore of the Adriatic has only 20 inches. The east coasts of Greece have about half as much rain as the west coasts, and the eastern parts of Spain are very much drier than the Portuguese coast, where the Serra da Estrella was formerly thought to be the rainiest part of Europe.

It is the waters of the Mediterranean Sea which maintain the winter heat and moisture and hence the low atmospheric pressure to which the maritime winter conditions are due. Thus the Mediterranean climate is the gift of the Mediterranean Sea, and is only found on its shores. Towards the interior of the Iberian or Balkan peninsulas the climate becomes more continental. The mountain chains which enclose the Mediterranean are sharp climatic divides.

The Mediterranean is a windy region for the latitude both in summer and winter.

'On the islands of the Greek Archipelago the north winds blow with such force in summer that in many places trees cannot grow on the high ground. In the summer storms the wind remains constant in direction, and does not veer as it does in northern Europe. Such a storm on the Mediterranean is a magnificent sight, and a striking one for those who are accustomed to associate dark skies, driving clouds, and showers of rain with the idea of a storm. Here the sky is deep-blue, and the sea appears indigo, almost black, and the waves roll along with silver crests from which the wind tears shreds of foam. But in winter also there are frequent storms in the Mediterranean, and then the winds are changeable, and the weather is overcast and rainy. Small vessels are much more afraid of the veering winds of the winter storms than of the Etesian winds of summer, which are constant in direction, but often so strong that it is impossible to sail northward against them' (PHILIPPSON).

The strong winds of summer are due to a temporary steepening of the normal barometric gradient; those of winter are the inflow into the depressions which then follow one another from west to east along the Mediterranean basin.

Local winds, irregular in their time of occurrence, are prominent round the Mediterranean. The Mistral, the 'masterful' north wind, often swoops down in winter in violent gusts over the usually warm littoral between the mouth of the Ebro and Genoa, and is an especially unwelcome visitor in the lower course of the Rhone below Donzère, where the trees bear the mark of its violence in their permanent set towards the south-east, gardens are often surrounded by a thick screen of cypress for shelter, and the humbler dwellings have openings for doors and windows only on their south-east sides. Such is the force of the Mistral that trains have been overturned by it on the Rhone delta, and a local proverb classes the Mistral with the flooding propensities of the torrential Durance, and the Parlement, as the three scourges of Provence. During a Mistral the sky is often cloudless, but the wind is very cold and dry, often considerably below freezing-point, and is keenly felt by both the human and plant inhabitants of a coast which usually enjoys less rigorous conditions.

The Mistral blows when there is a deep depression over the Gulf of Genoa, and an anticyclone over the west of Europe. On the north and west sides of the depression the wind sweeps down from the Central Plateau of France, the Cevennes, and the Alps, all very cold and often snow-covered in winter, and the Rhone valley perhaps acts as a funnel for the cold flood. Thus the Mistral is a descending wind. All descending winds are warmed by compression, but the air that feeds the Mistral is so cold before its descent, that, in spite of the heat acquired by compression, its temperature is still about the freezing-point when it reaches the Mediterranean coast.

A similar wind blows in winter at the head of the Adriatic Sea, and indeed along the whole Dalmatian coast from Trieste to Albania, and is known as the Bora (*boreas*, the north wind). As in the case of Provence a warm sea is here in close proximity to a cold land, the thermal gradient being one of the steepest in Europe (Fig. 94). During the days preceding the

Bora abnormally cold air has been stagnating in the valleys
of the Karst plateau and Dinaric Alps, probably during an
anticyclonic calm. A depression appears over the Adriatic,
and the icy wind rushes to the Dalmatian coast in irresistible
blasts of a speed at times of 100 m.p.h.; the sky is usually
clear, and the air very dry, when the Bora blows. Cold dry
winds with a clear sky are also a feature of the winter climate
on the northern shores of the Aegean Sea; they blow especially
from the cold interior down the Vardar valley, whence their
name Vardarac.

In the middle and south of the Mediterranean basin winds
sometimes blow whose qualities are the opposite of those of
the characteristic local winds of the north. They may all be
grouped under the name sirocco (or scirocco), and they owe
their characteristics to their origin in the hot deserts of north
Africa and Arabia. As a depression passes along the Mediterranean the winds on its front may be derived from the desert
hundreds of miles to the south or south-east, and they are abnormally hot and dry, and often carry dust and fine sand. They
are most felt in spring when depressions are numerous and
there is a large difference in temperature between the Mediterranean and the deserts. Generally the sirocco starts pro-
gressively later from the west to the east of the basin as the
disturbance which causes it moves eastward, appearing in
the Levant four or five days later than in Algeria. After
blowing one or two days, or occasionally longer, the sirocco
is replaced by the cooler northerly wind in rear of the depression. Such a prominent feature of the weather has naturally received local names, in south-east Spain leveche, in
Algeria sirocco, in Tunis chili, in Tripoli gibli, in Egypt
khamsin, in Palestine and Syria sirocco. The high temperature and low humidity continue through the night as well as
the day, and in extreme cases much damage may be done to
vegetation.

These desert winds may blow as far as the middle or even
the north of the Mediterranean Sea. In crossing the sea they
are somewhat cooled and pick up a great deal of moisture,
and on the coasts of Italy and the Aegean (where they are
called garbi) they are damp, warm and depressing, and give
very heavy rain which may contain red dust from the

Sahara. The brisk cool Tramontana, blowing from the north when the depression has passed on, comes as a welcome change. Sometimes while the moist and muggy sirocco is blowing in Italy and the Adriatic, the cold dry mistral is sweeping over the Rhone delta, the depression which is the cause of both winds lying over the Tyrrhenian Sea. If the sirocco descends from mountains its heat and dryness are intensified by compression. This is the case on the north coast of Sicily where the highest temperature ever recorded at Palermo, 114°, occurred during a sirocco, and 95° may be exceeded even in the midnight hours. The very high temperatures with south-east winds on the Syrian coast have a similar cause. The frequency of siroccos depends on that of the depressions which cause them. In the western Mediterranean they occur on about fifty days each year, distributed over all seasons, but in the Levant they are rather less frequent, and are associated especially with winter and spring; from June to October they are very rare, since depressions are almost absent from the east Mediterranean in summer. During the dry sirocco of north Sicily

'the air is misty, the sky yellowish to leaden, filled with heavy vapours, through which the sun can be seen only as a pale disc if at all. Man feels languid and oppressed, and disinclined for mental activity, and animals also suffer from these hot dry winds. Every one stays at home as much as possible and does nothing. When the sirocco is specially hot, its scorching breath does great injury to the vegetation; the leaves of the trees curl up and fall off in a few days, and if the sirocco sets in when the olive trees and vines are in blossom, a whole year's harvest may be lost. It is usually heralded by a mist which rises over the southern horizon and overspreads the sky' (FISCHER).

Rainfall. The rainfall in the Mediterranean basin varies very much in amount from place to place. There are large variations from year to year, especially in autumn, and droughts are a serious menace. The heaviest rainfall of the continent, 183 inches per annum, is recorded on the east coast of the Adriatic Sea, one of the smallest totals, 10 inches, in the south of Spain. The rainfall is distinguished from that of the rest of Europe not only by its periodicity, but also by the small number of days on which it falls. St. Malo and Nice have approximately the same mean annual rainfall, but at St. Malo it is distributed over 189 days, at Nice only 81 days. In most of the Mediterranean the number of rainy days is larger than on the Riviera, being 80 to 110 days in Italy, but even the highest figures are far less than in the rest of Europe. The dry summers of course contribute largely to this, but the rainy winter months also have fewer rainy days than in the north. Thus at Nice in October there is a mean rainfall of 6 inches, but it all falls on 10 days; the wettest month at Naples is November, with 5 inches, falling on 13 days. We may compare Portland Bill with 4 inches in October, and 17 rainy days. The rainfall in the winter months is much larger in amount in much of the Mediterranean than in most of North Europe, but it falls more heavily, on fewer days, and in fewer hours on those days. Records up to 8 inches in a day, often in thunderstorms, are not uncommon even in the drier areas. The intensity of the rainfall, especially in the mountains, is a most important feature, one result of which is very destructive floods in the rivers, whose beds, dry, wide, and gravel-strewn in summer, often become filled in a few hours in winter by swollen torrents. The steep mountain slopes, which improvident man has deforested, are rapidly swept bare of their soil-covering, and the white limestone rock is left to glare in the dazzling sunshine which soon follows. The week-long palls of cloud, which are common in North Europe, are almost unknown in the south. There are 2,316 hours of sunshine a year at Montpellier, twice as much as in the north of the British Isles, and still more in the southern parts of the Mediterranean. The following table shows the advantage enjoyed over northern Europe:

MEAN SUNSHINE (HOURS)

	Year.	Month with maximum.	Month with minimum.
Oxford	1,473	May 193	Dec. 43
Berlin	1,614	June 247	Dec. 34
Rome	2,362	July 348	Dec. 107
Athens	2,655	July 364	Dec. 108

In the middle and south of the Mediterranean basin ordinary fog is much less frequent than in North and Central Europe, but dust as thick as fog is liable to be carried over the Levant waters from the desert.

Eastward from the Azores, over the Mediterranean, Black Sea, and Caspian, and as far as Lake Balkash and Afghanistan, most of the rain falls in the winter half-year. In general the rains begin in the middle of September and set in with full vigour in October, but there are considerable differences in the annual distribution in different parts. The simplest régime is in the south and east of the Mediterranean, where

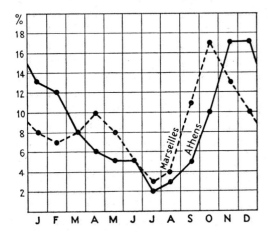

FIG. 95. Monthly rainfall (percentage of yearly total) at Athens and Marseilles.

early winter is the rainiest period, December or November being the rainiest month; summer is practically rainless, one or more months being rainless, with hardly even an occasional thunderstorm. Such are the conditions at Athens (Fig. 95), where in 46 years July was rainless 13 times and August 17 times. Sicily has a similar curve. The dry season becomes shorter towards the north and west—Tripoli has 7 dry months, Malta and Sicily 4, Naples 3, Rome 2, the Gulf of Genoa 1.

In most of Mediterranean Europe, except the south of Spain, Italy, and Greece, there are two rainfall maxima in the year, the chief in autumn, which is essentially the wet season, and a secondary one in spring. Summer is the dry season, but no month can be called rainless, though July is almost so in many parts (Marseilles, Fig. 95). The line separating these two rainfall types cuts off the south-east of Spain,

runs between Sardinia and Corsica, crosses Italy a little north
of Sicily, and the Balkan Peninsula from Corfu to Euboea.

The Spanish Meseta has another régime. There are two
maxima, in late spring and autumn, but the spring maximum
is the higher, and the summer half-year has more rain than
the winter half (Albacete, Fig. 96), which really marks off the
Meseta climate from the true Mediterranean type; the rainfall
maximum in May is associated with a maximum of thunder-

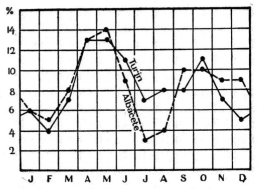

FIG. 96. Monthly rainfall (percentage of yearly total) at
Albacete and Turin.

storm activity. A similar régime, but with least rain in
winter is found in the Po plains (Turin, Fig. 96), the Maritsa
Valley in Bulgaria, and the interior of Georgia (HELLMANN).

The summer drought, which is liable to be more prolonged
and intense than the normal, necessitates various devices in
the plant world for resisting excessive evaporation; thickened
stems, thick bark, thorns, waxy coatings, small leaves,
growths of hair, are characteristic. Succulents have found a
congenial habitat. Summer is the resting time, not winter as
in the rest of Europe.

'At the end of April rain showers become rarer and rarer, the sun
pours down its fiery rays more and more vertically, the ground
becomes dry and hard and cracks open or the soil powders to
dust. Plants die away, and grey and yellow tints take the place
of the glorious blooms, which are now dried up and fallen to dust
on the ground. August and September are the months with fewest
flowers, the landscape is parched and lifeless, only the cicada is

heard among the grey olive trees. The land, which in December
gloried in a green carpet of wheat fields, now recalls a desolate
sun-burnt steppe over which hangs the calina, the peculiar heat
haze of the south. So Nature continues to sleep till the rains of
autumn rouse her to new life, and the seeds spring up which were
scattered by the short-lived annuals, grasses, and shrubs before
they died. The woody bushes put forth new shoots, and the sap
begins to circulate in the tubers and bulbs, which have been pro-
tected in the hot ground by their numerous coats.'

In the southern Mediterranean lands plant-life continues
very active throughout the winter, but on the northern shores
the cold at mid-winter is sufficient to check growth, and there
is another and greater outburst of energy in spring. The most
luxuriant vegetation requires heat and moisture at the same
time, but in the Mediterranean the hot season is rainless and
most of the plant growth has to be effected in a comparatively
cool season. The natural vegetation is forest, but the trees
are of less noble proportions than in both Central Europe to
the north and the tropics to the south, where the growing
season is the hottest time of the year. The typical Mediterranean trees are evergreen, so that they are able to continue
their slow growth even in summer whenever there may chance
to be water, and they commonly have very long roots which
enable them to get water from great depths in the ground.
To the absence of rain in the hot season the region owes its
healthiness and considerable immunity from endemic diseases.
But where there is much standing water, as in the deltas of
the rivers, the coastal marshes, and lake basins, mosquitoes
find an excellent breeding-ground, and malaria is so rampant
that many such spots have had to be abandoned by man.

Humidity. The air is much drier than in North Europe.
Curiously enough, some of the districts with the greatest rainfall have the lowest relative humidity. Genoa, with an annual
rainfall of 52 inches, has an average humidity of only 62 per
cent., and occasionally readings as low as 8 per cent. are
recorded. Similarly dry air is a feature of all the Italian and
French Riviera, and is doubtless due to the descending currents from the mountains to windward. The mean monthly
relative humidity at Montpellier ranges from 55 per cent. in
July to 82 per cent. in January, at Rome from 53 per cent.

in July to 74 per cent. in December, at Athens from 46 per cent. in August to 75 per cent. in December. In Greece readings as low as 5 per cent. are sometimes recorded.

Temperature. The main features have already been mentioned. The western sides of the peninsulas are warmer than the eastern in winter, and in general the east of the Mediterranean region is by far the warmest part in summer and the

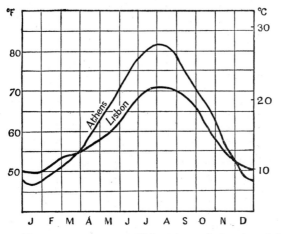

Fig. 97. Mean temperature at Lisbon (oceanic type) and Athens (interior).

coolest in winter (Fig. 97). The following statistics illustrate both these points:

MEAN TEMPERATURE

		Warmest Month.	Coolest Month.	Range.
		°F.	°F.	°F.
Lisbon (west coast)	. .	71	50	21
Valencia (east coast)	. .	75	49	26
Zante (west coast) .	. .	80	53	27
Athens (east coast) .	. .	80	48	32

Frost occurs on all the Mediterranean coasts except on the smaller islands in the south, such as Malta. The following table shows that, except on the southern coasts, the thermometer falls well below freezing-point in an average year, especially in the neighbourhood of the Rhone delta, which is subject to the Mistral, the north-east of the Adriatic, and the north of the Aegean, which experience similar cold winds. Much lower readings are liable to occur in the interior of the peninsulas.

	Mean lowest Temperature in the Year.	Absolute lowest on record.	Mean highest Temperature in the Year.	Absolute highest on record.
	°F.	°F.	°F.	°F.
Valencia	31	19	99	109
Marseilles	21	11	92	100
Nice	28	15	91	93
Rome	27	16	95	99
Naples	31	24	92	99
Palermo	34	29	103	114
Trieste	23	14	94	99
Salonika	21	14	97	102
Athens	29	20	100	107

Owing to the power of the sun's rays, both direct and reflected from the sea, and the strong winds, there are great local differences in climate according to exposure to the one and shelter from the other. The Riviera is specially favoured, and has a mean January temperature only 5° lower than the Algerian coast 500 miles farther south. Leaving the shelter of the mountains round the Gulf of Genoa we must go south along the west coast of Italy as far as Naples to find again a mean temperature equal to that of Cannes. The Alps provide a similar shelter for the Italian lakes, the Dinaric Alps for the Adriatic coast, and the Yaila Mountains for the south coast of the Crimea, and the chief winter resorts of the Mediterranean are situated either in these sheltered positions in the north or else very far south.

Autumn is everywhere considerably warmer than spring, a true maritime feature. The moist heat of October is often more oppressive than the hotter but drier weather of July.

Snow is very rare in the south of Italy and Greece near sea-level, but is not uncommon in the north of Italy, especially in the Po plains and the Apennines, where it is occasionally deep enough to hold up railroad traffic. Very few of the mountains that overlook the Mediterranean Sea are high enough to have a cap of snow most of the year, and the

Great Atlas and the Sierra Nevada alone retain a few patches of snow throughout the summer.

Main climatic subdivisions.

The Iberian Peninsula (Fig. 98) is large enough to develop a tendency to a continental climate. In winter, owing to the cold, there is high atmospheric pressure with outflowing winds, the cold 'Norte' of eastern Spain, but in the heat of summer pressure is low, and the wind blows inward on the east coast as the hot, dry and dusty solano or levêche (Fig. 99); thus there is a monsoonal change of wind. A change of wind only, however, not of weather, for the summer season of inblowing winds is a period of bright sunshine and almost unbroken drought, since the air becomes more and more heated as it blows over the hot land, and therefore has its vapour-capacity increased; being heated, it rises, but

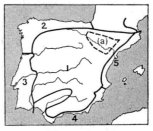

Fig. 98. The major climatic regions of the Iberian Peninsula.

is carried away in the outflow in the higher strata of the atmosphere before it is cooled to dew-point by expansion.

1. (Fig. 98.) The Meseta is different in many respects from the coasts. In spite of the altitude the mean summer temperature is higher in New Castile than on both east and west coasts. The days are especially hot on the plateau, but when the sun sets temperature falls rapidly, and the mean daily range is 30° in July. The range from summer to winter is also very great, and the winters are far colder than on the coasts. Long spells of frost with temperatures as low as 15° are not uncommon, so that even at Madrid skating is sometimes possible, and in the mountains and plains of Old Castile traffic is often seriously impeded by snowstorms.

				MEAN TEMPERATURE		
				Coldest Month.	Warmest Month.	Range.
				°F.	°F.	°F.
Lisbon	.	.	.	50	71	21
Madrid	.	.	.	40	77	37

In summer there is very active evaporation and almost complete drought, broken only by an occasional thunderstorm, and the fierce heat burns up the vegetation. Without irrigation the landscape is semi-desert, brown and grey are

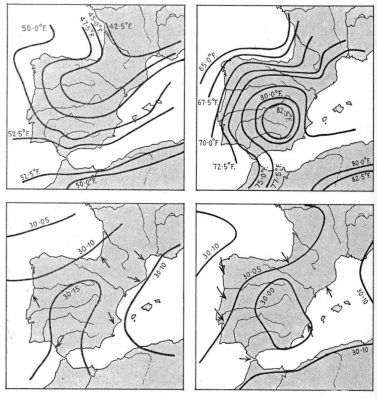

January   *July*

FIG. 99. Pressure, winds, and temperature over the Iberian Peninsula (after Gorczinski).

the dominant colours, and dust is everywhere—the parched ground is thickly covered, and the air is hazy with minute dust particles which have been swept up by the strong winds. The haze is known as the 'calina', and is probably due to irregular refraction of the light as well as to dust. The view is frequently obscured by the dismal grey calina in all the south Mediterranean lands.

The high pressures of winter check the ingress of the rain storms of that season, so that February is not much rainier than July. Spring is the rainiest season, and this fact, together with the strong winds and extreme temperatures, favours steppe vegetation.

The Ebro plains (*a*) lie lower, but have about the same temperature as Madrid owing to their more northern position. The rainfall is small and much of the land is steppe.

2. (Fig. 98.) The north coast has a west-European coastal climate, with warm winters and equable temperature, and heavy rainfall, in general more than 50 inches a year. The rainfall is considerable even in summer, owing to the monsoonal indraught meeting the Cantabrian mountains, but the westerlies give much heavier rain in winter.

3. (Fig. 98.) The west coast has the most oceanic variety of Mediterranean climate—cool summers, mild winters, small temperature range, damp air, and abundant rain in the winter half-year. The summer months are almost rainless, but the aridity is much less marked than in the interior and east of the peninsula.

4. (Fig. 98.) The south and south-east coasts are sheltered by the Sierra Nevada, and are especially distinguished by their hot sunny summers. The rainfall is small (maximum in November), but there is good irrigation from the streams fed by the melting snow on the mountains. The most tropical fruits of Europe are grown here, the date-palm ripens its fruit, bananas and sugar-cane are cultivated. The plain of Andalusia in the south is the hottest part of the peninsula and indeed of all Europe, and in summer the heat is excessive. At Seville the mean August temperature is 85° and in an average year the thermometer rises as high as 116°, a figure which approaches the records from the Sahara. The rainfall is scanty, as in most of the rest of the interior of Spain except the mountains, the sunshine is notably abundant throughout the year, and in summer the sky is almost cloudless.

5 (Fig. 98) resembles 4, but is cooler in all seasons, especially in autumn and winter.

Italy. 1. (Fig. 100.) The Po plains are akin to Central Europe rather than the Mediterranean in climate. The summers are almost as hot as in Sicily, but the winters are cold,

very much colder than on the Riviera on the other side of
the Apennines (Fig. 94), for the plains are frequently covered
with cold damp air which has drained down from the mountain valleys. There is a well-marked 'temperature inversion';
the cold air lies on the lowest ground, and it is warmer on
the hillsides. The Italian lakes have rather milder winters,
and lemon groves and olive trees flourish, signs of a Mediterranean climate. When we cross the Alps from the north, we
seem to enter a new world in this mild and sunny region, but
on continuing to descend we return
to the Central European winter at
Milan, where snow often lies for
days, and skating is sometimes possible. Piacenza has the same mean
January temperature as Berlin, and
a far lower one than Skomvær in
the south of the Lofoten Islands.
Even the rapid River Po and the
lagoons round Venice have been
frozen over, but not within living
memory. Venice is somewhat milder
than the plains to the west, owing
to the influence of the sea. The

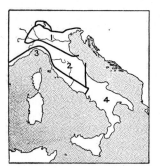

FIG. 100. Major climatic
regions of Italy.

prevailing wind in winter is down the Po to the Adriatic, in
summer it is upstream.

The rainfall is about 30 inches a year over the plain and
about 40 inches along the foot of the surrounding mountains.
It is more evenly distributed over the year than in the rest
of the Mediterranean lands, and, in opposition to the régime
elsewhere, the summer half-year has more rain than the
winter half. The rainiest months are in spring and autumn,
the driest are January and February. The summer rain and
the abundant water for irrigation provided by the mountain
torrents enable large crops of maize and rice to be produced,
here only in Italy.

2. (Fig. 100.) The northern Apennines and the highlands of
Tuscany carry the Central European climate far south. There is
most rain in the winter half-year, but summer is not rainless.
Frost usually occurs even on the coasts of northern Italy every
winter, and the mountains are sometimes buried deep in snow.

3. (Fig. 100.) The Riviera has been described already.

4. (Fig. 100.) South Italy has a very dry and hot summer, even in the mountains. Frost is rare. The climate is typically Mediterranean. There is a single maximum in the rainfall curve about November.

The Balkan Peninsula. 1. (Fig. 101.) The west coast has a Mediterranean climate, with very wet but mild winters, subject, however, to the Bora.

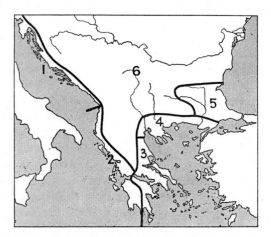

Fig. 101. Major climatic regions of the Balkan Peninsula.

2 (Fig. 101) has a very favourable Mediterranean climate. It is warmer than the Dalmatian coast, especially in winter, when the mean temperature is as much as 10° higher; moreover there is no Bora. The rainfall is 30 to 40 inches a year, with a single maximum in winter; summer is almost but not quite rainless. Zante has one of the highest sunshine records in Greece, 3,107 hours.

3 (Fig. 101) differs from 2 in being an east-coast region. The rainfall is considerably less, 20 to 30 inches a year, and the land is very dry and dusty through long summer months; by comparison western Greece is a land of running waters. The winters are much cooler—mean January temperature at Athens 48°, at Zante 53°—and in enclosed basins at a distance from the sea keen frosts occur, zero readings having been recorded in Thessaly. But on the coasts of the Peloponesus

frost is rare. Summer days are very hot and dry at places which are out of reach of the sea-breeze, such as Sparta where the July mean temperature is 82°, and from June to September the temperature rises well over 90° on most days, and may exceed 100°.

4. (Fig 101.) The north coast of the Aegean has a Mediterranean climate, and the olive is a common tree. But the colder winters and the appreciable rainfall in summer mark it as a separate region. An anticyclone often covers the Balkans in winter and a cold northerly wind blows down the valleys to the coast. Under such conditions a reading of 14° F. was once observed at Salonika, and much of the inner gulf had a thin coating of ice. On most January nights the mercury falls nearly to freezing-point and in Macedonia and Thrace even the diurnal maximum may occasionally be below 32°. A good deal of snow is brought by north-east winds in winter.

5 (Fig. 101) has a transition climate between the Mediterranean and the steppes. Most of the rain falls in winter, as in the Mediterranean lands, but there are often bleak north winds from the steppes of south Russia, bringing low temperatures and precluding the typical Mediterranean flora; the olive does not flourish. The northern plains are coldest; Constantinople is somewhat warmer owing to its peninsular position, but a reading of 17° has been noted, and the Bosphorus has been covered with ice, so that the passage from Europe to Asia could be made on foot. The ice, however, had probably drifted from the coasts of the Black Sea and, being compacted in the narrow channel by the current, had frozen into a solid covering.

6 (Fig. 101) must be classed with Central Europe, having rain all the year, with maxima in May and June and October as in south Hungary. The winters are cold for the latitude. The Mediterranean vegetation of the coasts of the Aegean is replaced by the forest trees characteristic of Central Europe. The lower Danube lands have some distinctive winds; the Crivetz blows from the north-east in spring and autumn and brings very variable weather—hot in the hotter months, cold in the cold, sometimes dry, sometimes rainy or snowy; the Austru is essentially a winter wind which blows from the

west, bringing dry and clear and often very cold weather; the Kossava, a cold and dry wind, blows in winter from the south-east down the lower Morava; it is noted for carrying much coarse dust which darkens the atmosphere and may form appreciable deposits.

STATISTICS

MEAN TEMPERATURE (°F.)

NORTH-WEST EUROPE

Station.	Alt. Feet.	Jan.	Feb.	Mar.	Apr.	May.	June.	July.	Aug.	Sept.	Oct.	Nov.	Dec.	Year.	Range.
British Isles.															
Valencia	30	44·4	44·3	45·0	48·0	52·2	56·7	58·8	58·9	56·6	51·5	47·5	45·5	50·8	14·6
Birr	175	39·8	40·6	41·9	46·1	51·3	56·7	58·8	58·1	54·6	47·9	43·1	40·6	48·3	19·0
Dublin	12	42·1	42·5	43·6	47·0	51·8	57·1	60·1	60·0	56·0	50·2	45·8	42·7	49·9	18·0
Scilly	131	45·7	45·3	46·0	48·6	52·5	57·2	60·5	60·8	58·6	53·8	49·8	47·4	52·2	15·5
Dungeness	21	39·3	39·9	41·7	46·1	52·0	57·3	60·9	61·4	58·2	51·7	45·7	41·7	49·7	22·1
London (Kew)	18	38·9	40·1	42·4	47·3	53·4	59·2	62·7	61·6	57·1	49·9	44·0	40·3	49·7	23·8
Oxford	208	38·4	39·7	42·1	47·0	52·8	58·5	61·9	60·9	56·6	49·4	43·5	39·9	49·2	23·5
Cambridge	41	37·6	39·1	41·8	46·7	52·8	58·5	61·9	61·1	56·9	49·4	43·1	38·9	49·0	24·3
Holyhead	15	41·8	41·7	42·7	46·4	50·8	55·8	58·5	58·7	56·4	51·0	46·6	43·4	49·5	17·0
Buxton	987	35·3	36·1	38·2	42·9	48·5	54·4	57·4	56·4	52·3	45·7	40·4	36·6	45·4	22·1
York	56	37·9	39·1	41·5	46·0	51·7	57·6	60·5	59·7	55·6	48·6	43·0	39·0	48·3	22·6
Leith	18	39·1	39·5	41·3	45·4	50·1	55·7	58·6	58·3	54·7	48·5	43·3	39·9	47·9	19·5
Fort William (1884—1903)	171	39·2	38·8	40·4	44·9	49·9	55·4	56·9	56·3	53·2	46·9	43·7	39·9	47·1	18·1
Ben Nevis (1884—1903)	4,406	24·1	23·8	24·0	27·6	33·0	39·7	41·1	40·4	38·0	31·4	28·9	25·2	31·4	17·3
Nairn	82	37·2	37·6	39·5	43·9	48·8	54·2	56·7	56·2	52·7	46·1	41·2	37·6	46·0	19·5
Braemar	1,120	34·3	34·4	36·0	40·7	46·2	52·6	54·8	53·6	49·9	43·5	38·4	34·8	43·3	20·5
Orkney (Deerness)	160	39·0	38·5	39·2	42·3	46·3	50·7	53·5	53·4	51·4	46·9	42·8	40·0	45·3	15·0
France.															
Biarritz	115	45·9	47·7	50·0	54·3	58·8	64·2	68·4	68·9	64·8	59·2	50·9	46·8	56·7	23·0
Pic du Midi	9,383	17·8	18·3	19·2	22·6	28·9	37·0	43·5	43·5	37·8	30·6	23·7	19·6	28·6	25·7

Station.	Alt. Feet	Jan.	Feb.	Mar.	Apr.	May.	June.	July.	Aug.	Sept.	Oct.	Nov.	Dec.	Year.	Range.
Bordeaux	246	40·6	43·2	46·9	53·1	58·3	64·2	68·2	68·2	63·7	55·4	46·9	41·2	54·1	27·6
Nantes	131	39·9	43·5	45·0	49·8	56·5	61·5	64·8	63·5	60·1	52·0	45·7	41·5	52·0	24·9
Paris	164	36·7	39·4	43·2	49·3	56·1	61·7	64·6	63·9	58·5	50·0	42·5	38·1	50·3	27·9
Lille	66	36·0	38·1	41·7	48·4	54·3	60·4	63·5	63·1	58·8	50·5	42·3	36·9	49·5	27·5
Holland and Belgium.															
Brussels	328	34·4	36·1	39·7	46·9	53·2	59·7	63·0	62·2	57·7	49·5	41·2	35·6	48·2	28·6
Utrecht	43	34·2	35·6	39·2	46·4	53·2	59·9	62·6	62·1	57·2	48·9	40·5	35·8	48·0	28·4
Groningen	33	33·4	35·2	38·3	45·0	52·0	58·6	61·7	61·2	56·7	48·6	39·7	35·4	47·1	28·3
Germany.															
Hamburg	82	32·5	33·4	37·4	45·0	52·9	60·1	63·0	61·9	56·5	48·2	38·5	33·6	46·9	31·5
Norway.															
Skudesnæs	16	35·8	34·5	35·8	41·5	47·7	53·8	57·0	57·9	54·3	47·3	40·8	37·0	45·3	23·4
Bergen	66	34·2	33·6	35·4	42·1	48·9	55·0	57·9	57·6	52·7	45·1	38·5	34·7	44·6	24·3
Lärdal	16	29·7	29·5	32·7	42·3	50·9	57·7	60·6	59·2	51·5	42·6	34·9	29·8	43·5	31·1
Ona	33	36·9	35·6	36·1	39·9	44·6	49·5	53·8	54·7	52·0	46·2	40·5	37·6	43·9	19·1
Christiansund	49	34·9	33·6	34·9	39·9	46·0	52·2	55·6	55·8	51·5	44·6	38·1	35·4	43·5	22·2
Trondhjem	33	27·3	26·8	30·0	37·9	45·9	53·4	57·2	56·3	50·0	41·2	32·7	27·5	40·5	30·4
Röros	2,067	12·9	12·4	18·3	28·6	39·2	48·9	52·2	50·7	43·3	32·4	21·0	13·6	31·1	39·8
Skomvær	66	33·8	31·5	32·0	36·0	41·4	46·6	49·8	51·1	47·5	42·4	38·7	36·0	40·6	19·6
Tromsö	49	26·6	25·0	26·6	31·5	38·8	47·3	51·8	51·1	44·8	36·0	30·0	27·1	36·3	26·8
Fruholmen	49	26·4	25·9	26·2	30·4	37·0	43·7	48·9	49·8	44·1	36·5	30·7	27·5	35·6	23·9
Vardö	33	21·7	21·2	23·0	28·9	34·7	42·4	47·5	48·6	43·2	34·7	27·9	23·9	33·1	37·4
Denmark.															
Fanö	16	31·8	31·8	34·7	41·7	50·2	57·4	59·9	59·0	54·0	46·0	38·8	33·6	45·0	28·1

MEAN TEMPERATURE °F.), *continued*

CENTRAL EUROPE

Station.	Alt. Feet.	Jan.	Feb.	Mar.	Apr.	May.	June.	July.	Aug.	Sept.	Oct.	Nov.	Dec.	Year.	Range.
France.															
Clermont-Ferrand	1,280	35.4	38.5	42.8	50.4	55.8	62.2	66.0	64.8	58.6	50.5	42.4	36.1	50.4	30.6
Puy de Dôme	4,823	28.1	28.8	29.7	35.1	40.8	47.8	52.0	51.8	47.8	40.1	34.0	28.8	38.7	23.9
Lyon	574	35.1	38.5	43.9	51.6	57.9	64.4	68.2	66.7	60.9	51.8	42.4	35.2	51.4	33.1
Strasbourg	472	31.5	35.1	41.2	49.3	57.0	63.3	65.7	63.9	57.7	48.4	40.3	34.0	48.9	34.2
Germany.															
Karlsruhe	410	32.9	35.8	41.2	49.5	56.5	63.3	66.2	64.8	58.6	49.5	40.5	34.0	49.5	33.3
Munich	1,739	28.2	31.6	37.8	45.9	54.5	60.9	63.9	62.4	55.9	46.6	37.2	30.7	46.2	35.7
Hanover	180	32.7	33.8	37.6	45.7	53.8	60.3	63.1	61.5	56.3	47.7	38.5	33.8	47.1	30.4
Erfurt	656	30.7	32.7	37.2	45.9	54.1	61.0	63.9	62.4	56.5	47.7	37.8	32.0	46.8	33.2
Brocken	3,756	24.8	24.3	26.2	33.8	41.5	48.4	51.4	50.5	46.0	38.7	29.8	25.2	36.7	27.1
Kiel	16	33.6	33.8	36.7	44.4	51.8	59.5	62.6	61.7	56.5	48.7	39.7	35.2	46.9	29.0
Berlin	164	31.5	33.8	38.8	46.9	57.0	63.5	65.8	64.0	58.1	48.7	39.6	33.8	48.4	34.3
Leipzig	394	30.6	32.2	36.9	45.7	54.5	61.9	64.8	63.0	56.7	47.5	37.4	31.8	46.9	34.2
Stettin	98	30.7	31.6	36.0	45.3	54.0	61.9	65.1	63.5	57.4	47.8	37.8	32.2	46.9	34.4
Königsberg	16	27.0	27.9	32.7	42.6	52.2	59.9	63.3	61.9	55.2	45.9	35.8	29.5	44.6	36.3
Scandinavia.															
Copenhagen	16	32.2	31.8	34.5	41.7	50.7	58.6	61.9	60.6	55.4	47.3	40.1	34.5	45.9	30.1
Göteborg	33	30.7	30.4	33.1	41.7	50.7	59.0	62.2	60.6	54.9	46.0	38.5	32.7	45.0	31.8
Oslo	82	24.4	25.5	30.6	40.5	50.9	60.1	63.1	59.9	52.3	42.3	32.9	26.4	42.4	38.7
Finse	4,022	16.5	16.2	18.0	25.0	33.1	41.5	46.0	44.6	38.8	30.2	22.3	17.2	29.1	29.8
Karlstad	180	25.8	25.5	29.7	38.7	49.1	59.2	62.4	59.9	52.7	43.0	34.2	27.3	42.3	36.9
Stockholm	148	26.6	25.7	28.9	37.8	47.3	57.4	62.1	59.5	52.7	43.0	34.9	28.4	42.1	36.4
Röros	2,067	12.9	12.4	18.3	28.6	39.2	48.9	52.2	50.7	43.3	32.4	21.0	13.6	31.1	39.8
Hernösand	344	20.5	19.9	25.3	34.2	43.0	54.5	59.2	56.8	49.6	39.4	30.4	22.1	37.9	39.3
Haparanda	33	11.7	10.6	16.9	28.6	39.4	52.9	59.0	55.0	46.0	34.5	23.0	14.0	32.5	48.4

CENTRAL EUROPE (continued)

Station.	Alt. Feet.	Jan.	Feb.	Mar.	Apr.	May.	June.	July.	Aug.	Sept.	Oct.	Nov.	Dec.	Year.	Range.
Switzerland.															
Basel	909	31.8	36.0	40.8	49.3	56.1	62.8	66.4	64.6	58.6	48.6	40.6	33.1	49.1	34.6
Geneva	1,329	32.0	35.6	40.8	48.9	55.9	62.8	67.1	64.9	59.2	49.1	40.8	33.6	49.1	35.1
Lucerne	1,480	29.7	33.3	38.7	47.5	54.9	61.5	64.9	62.8	57.4	47.1	38.7	31.3	47.3	35.2
Altdorf	1,480	32.4	35.6	40.6	48.7	55.4	61.2	64.4	63.1	58.3	49.1	40.8	33.4	48.6	32.0
Andermatt	4,741	19.9	23.5	28.0	35.6	43.0	49.5	53.2	51.8	47.3	38.5	29.8	21.7	36.9	33.3
St. Gothard	6,877	18.1	19.2	20.8	27.7	34.3	40.8	46.2	45.7	41.4	32.4	24.6	19.2	30.9	28.1
Sargans	1,663	29.8	34.4	39.9	48.4	55.2	60.8	63.9	62.4	58.1	48.6	39.6	31.1	47.7	34.1
Säntis	8,202	16.5	16.5	18.3	23.7	31.5	37.0	40.5	40.5	36.9	29.8	23.5	18.7	27.7	24.0
Davos	5,121	18.7	22.8	27.3	36.1	44.1	50.4	53.8	52.2	47.1	37.9	29.7	21.0	36.9	35.1
Bevers	5,610	14.2	18.7	24.4	33.3	42.4	49.3	53.2	51.3	45.9	36.3	26.1	16.0	34.4	39.0
Austria, Hungary, &c.															
Innsbruck	1,968	26.1	30.9	38.7	47.8	55.2	61.2	64.0	62.4	57.0	47.8	36.9	27.3	46.2	37.9
Klagenfurt	1,444	20.5	25.9	35.2	47.1	55.8	62.8	65.8	63.9	56.8	46.9	34.5	23.7	45.0	45.3
Graz	1,214	25.9	30.9	37.9	47.8	56.1	62.2	65.3	63.5	57.2	47.8	36.5	27.9	46.6	39.4
Vienna	656	28.9	32.4	39.0	48.9	57.2	63.9	67.3	65.8	59.4	49.6	38.3	30.9	48.6	38.4
Lemberg	1,115	24.3	25.7	33.1	46.0	57.0	63.3	66.4	64.9	57.0	47.3	34.7	26.2	45.5	42.1
Budapest	509	28.2	31.6	39.9	51.1	60.1	66.7	70.3	68.5	61.0	51.1	39.0	30.6	49.8	42.1
Agram	509	30.9	35.1	43.0	52.7	60.6	67.1	70.9	69.4	62.4	53.4	41.9	33.1	51.6	40.0
Debreczin	459	25.2	30.2	38.5	51.1	60.1	67.5	70.9	69.1	61.5	50.9	38.1	28.9	49.3	45.7
Balkan States.															
Belgrade	459	30.4	33.4	44.1	52.3	62.1	67.1	71.2	70.3	63.0	54.5	42.3	35.2	52.2	40.8
Sofia	1,804	28.9	32.7	41.5	50.4	59.2	64.8	68.7	68.2	61.0	51.4	39.9	32.5	50.0	39.8
Uskub	804	29.5	34.2	45.1	53.2	62.1	68.7	73.8	72.1	66.4	57.0	43.0	34.0	53.2	44.3
Bucharest	279	26.2	30.6	41.0	52.2	62.2	68.9	72.3	72.0	63.5	52.9	39.7	30.9	51.1	46.1
Sulina	7	30.6	32.9	39.7	49.3	60.4	68.0	72.1	71.1	63.9	55.0	43.7	35.8	52.0	41.5

MEAN TEMPERATURE (°F), *continued*

THE MEDITERRANEAN LANDS

Station.	Alt. Feet.	Jan.	Feb.	Mar.	Apr.	May.	June.	July.	Aug.	Sept.	Oct.	Nov.	Dec.	Year.	Range.
Spain and Portugal.															
Santiago	886	45.1	47.1	48.9	51.8	56.7	62.2	64.8	66.0	62.4	55.6	50.7	46.4	54.9	20.9
Lisbon	66	50.5	52.2	54.3	57.6	60.3	66.7	70.0	71.1	68.4	62.2	56.5	51.7	60.3	20.6
Gibraltar	49	55.0	55.9	55.9	60.6	64.7	69.5	73.4	74.9	72.0	65.7	60.5	56.1	63.7	19.9
Murcia	197	50.2	53.2	56.3	60.8	66.2	73.0	78.8	78.8	73.4	66.0	58.3	51.6	63.9	28.6
Barcelona	131	46.4	49.5	51.3	55.8	61.7	68.5	73.9	73.4	68.9	61.0	54.0	47.8	59.4	27.5
Burgos	2,920	36.1	39.9	42.8	48.2	53.4	60.3	65.5	66.0	59.9	50.9	42.8	36.9	50.2	29.9
Madrid	2,149	40.3	43.7	47.7	53.8	61.0	69.6	77.2	76.6	67.3	56.1	47.3	41.0	56.8	36.9
Ciudad Real	2,083	41.4	45.7	49.3	54.3	61.2	70.3	77.5	76.6	67.8	56.7	48.9	41.7	57.6	36.1
Seville	66	52.2	55.9	59.5	63.9	69.6	78.1	84.7	84.9	78.1	68.4	60.1	52.9	67.3	32.7
France.															
Montpellier	115	41.0	43.9	48.0	54.5	61.2	67.6	72.9	71.6	65.5	57.0	48.2	42.1	56.1	31.9
Avignon	66	39.4	43.5	49.1	55.8	63.0	70.5	75.4	73.2	66.2	56.7	47.1	40.3	56.7	36.0
Marseilles	246	44.3	46.2	50.0	54.9	61.2	67.5	71.8	70.5	66.4	58.6	51.1	45.7	57.4	27.5
Nice	66	46.4	47.5	50.7	56.5	62.2	69.1	73.8	73.2	68.2	61.0	52.7	47.3	59.4	27.4
Italy.															
Genoa	177	45.5	47.7	51.5	57.6	63.3	70.0	75.4	75.2	70.7	62.1	53.2	47.3	59.9	29.9
Alessandria	322	31.1	36.5	45.1	54.5	61.9	69.6	74.5	73.2	66.0	55.0	43.0	34.7	53.8	43.4
Milan	482	34.3	39.2	46.9	55.2	63.7	70.9	74.8	74.1	66.6	55.6	43.9	39.2	55.2	40.4
Lugano	902	34.4	38.3	44.4	52.5	59.2	66.4	70.7	68.9	63.0	52.7	43.2	36.1	52.5	36.3
Florence	240	40.8	43.9	48.9	56.1	63.1	70.7	76.1	74.8	68.5	58.8	49.3	42.6	57.7	35.3
Rome	164	44.6	46.8	50.9	56.7	64.4	70.9	76.1	75.4	69.6	61.7	52.7	46.4	59.7	31.5
Naples	492	46.8	48.4	51.5	56.8	63.7	70.3	75.6	75.0	69.8	63.1	54.7	48.7	60.4	28.8
Palermo	230	50.5	52.2	54.7	58.6	64.0	70.7	76.3	76.6	73.4	67.3	59.4	53.4	63.1	26.1
Trieste	220	39.4	40.8	45.9	54.3	61.5	69.3	73.4	72.3	66.4	58.1	48.4	41.7	55.9	34.0

THE MEDITERRANEAN LANDS (continued)

Station. Bulkan States.	Alt. Feet.	Jan.	Feb.	Mar.	Apr.	May.	June.	July.	Aug.	Sept.	Oct.	Nov.	Dec.	Year.	Range.
Ragusa	49	47·7	48·9	51·6	57·4	64·6	72·0	77·0	76·6	72·1	65·1	56·1	50·4	61·7	29·3
Corfu	98	50·4	51·1	53·2	59·7	66·4	73·6	78·4	78·6	74·3	67·8	59·4	53·4	63·9	28·2
Athens	351	48·4	49·5	52·2	58·6	66·2	74·3	79·9	79·5	73·4	66·0	57·2	52·2	63·1	31·5
Salonika	7	41·7	44·8	50·2	57·2	66·9	74·3	79·9	78·4	71·6	63·5	52·3	46·0	60·6	38·2
Constantinople	246	40·6	41·0	45·5	52·3	61·0	69·1	73·2	72·5	67·3	61·3	52·5	45·3	56·8	32·2

MEAN RAINFALL (inches)
NORTH-WEST EUROPE

Station. British Isles.	Alt. Feet.	Jan.	Feb.	Mar.	Apr.	May	June	July.	Aug.	Sept.	Oct.	Nov.	Dec.	Year.
Valencia	30	5·5	5·2	4·5	3·7	3·2	3·2	3·8	4·8	4·1	5·6	5·5	6·6	55·6
Dublin	47	2·3	1·9	1·9	1·9	2·0	2·0	2·6	3·0	1·9	2·7	2·7	2·5	27·4
Plymouth	116	3·3	2·9	2·9	2·2	2·1	2·1	2·8	3·0	2·4	3·9	3·6	5·0	36·2
London (Camden Square)	110	1·9	1·7	1·8	1·5	1·8	2·0	2·4	2·2	1·8	2·6	2·4	2·4	24·5
Oxford	208	1·8	1·6	1·6	1·6	1·9	2·2	2·4	2·3	1·7	2·9	2·3	2·5	24·8
Shrewsbury	191	1·9	1·5	1·7	1·5	2·0	2·1	2·3	3·0	1·7	2·9	2·2	2·3	25·2
Buxton	987	4·5	3·7	4·1	2·9	3·1	3·2	3·9	4·4	3·2	4·9	4·7	5·7	48·4
Nottingham	82	1·7	1·5	1·6	1·3	1·8	1·9	2·3	2·4	1·6	2·4	1·8	2·3	22·5
Seathwaite	422	13·3	11·9	11·2	7·4	7·4	6·5	8·5	11·6	9·9	12·0	13·6	16·3	129·5
Newcastle	201	2·0	1·6	2·1	1·6	2·4	2·2	2·6	2·9	2·0	3·2	2·4	2·4	27·2
Glasgow	180	3·3	2·9	2·7	2·1	2·6	2·5	3·1	3·9	3·0	3·4	3·6	4·2	37·2
Edinburgh	227	1·7	1·6	1·9	1·4	2·0	1·9	2·7	3·1	2·0	2·6	2·1	2·2	25·0
Fort William (1891–1903)	171	8·7	6·9	7·2	4·2	3·5	3·5	4·6	6·9	8·2	7·9	7·5	11·3	80·4
Ben Nevis (1891–1903)	4,406	18·7	15·1	17·0	10·2	8·3	7·8	11·3	14·0	16·9	14·8	16·0	21·2	171·3
Nairn	82	2·0	1·8	1·9	1·5	1·8	1·8	2·7	2·4	2·2	2·4	2·4	2·2	24·9

MEAN RAINFALL (inches), *continued*

NORTH-WEST EUROPE (*continued*)

Station.	Alt. Feet.	Jan.	Feb.	Mar.	Apr.	May.	June.	July.	Aug.	Sept.	Oct.	Nov.	Dec.	Year.
France.														
Bayonne	66	3·9	3·3	3·9	3·7	3·3	3·6	2·5	2·9	4·3	5·5	5·4	4·1	46·4
Bordeaux	33	2·5	2·0	2·3	2·5	2·8	2·8	1·9	2·0	2·6	3·6	3·1	2·7	30·7
Brest	217	3·3	2·6	2·0	2·1	1·8	2·0	2·0	2·2	2·8	3·9	3·6	3·4	31·6
Cherbourg	59	3·3	2·4	2·3	1·8	2·0	1·9	2·0	2·4	3·2	4·8	4·1	3·7	34·0
Paris (St. Maur)	164	1·5	1·2	1·6	1·7	2·1	2·3	2·2	2·2	2·0	2·3	1·8	1·7	22·6
Lille	85	2·0	1·6	1·9	1·6	2·2	2·2	2·7	2·4	2·5	3·1	2·4	2·4	27·0
Holland and Belgium.														
Ostend	13	2·0	1·6	1·9	1·5	1·9	1·9	2·2	2·9	2·8	2·6	3·1	2·3	26·8
Brussels	187	2·2	1·9	2·0	1·9	2·3	2·5	2·9	3·0	2·6	2·8	2·5	2·4	28·9
Utrecht	121	2·1	1·7	2·0	1·7	2·0	2·3	3·0	3·3	2·6	2·9	2·4	2·7	28·7
Helder	13	2·0	1·6	1·7	1·3	1·5	1·7	2·2	3·1	2·9	3·5	2·7	2·4	26·8
Germany.														
Emden	26	2·1	1·6	2·0	1·6	2·0	2·4	3·2	3·4	2·4	2·9	2·4	2·5	28·5
Hamburg	85	2·0	1·7	2·1	1·8	2·0	2·4	3·5	3·1	2·2	2·6	2·0	2·2	27·5
Norway.														
Bergen	59	8·5	6·4	5·9	4·1	4·5	3·8	5·8	7·5	8·7	8·9	8·3	8·5	81·0
Christiansund	59	5·1	3·6	3·2	2·4	2·5	2·1	3·1	4·2	5·4	5·7	4·8	4·4	46·5
Trondhjem	33	3·4	2·9	2·2	1·8	1·5	1·7	2·2	3·0	3·3	3·4	3·1	2·6	31·1
CENTRAL EUROPE														
France.														
Clermont-Ferrand	1,273	1·4	1·3	1·7	2·0	2·8	3·2	2·5	2·7	2·8	2·3	1·7	1·3	25·4
Lyon	574	1·5	1·5	1·9	2·4	3·3	3·3	3·0	3·2	3·0	3·9	2·6	1·7	31·3
Grenoble (Éc. Nor.)	712	2·6	2·4	2·3	2·5	3·7	3·5	2·8	3·4	3·3	4·8	3·3	2·7	37·5

CENTRAL EUROPE (continued)

Station.	Alt. Feet.	Jan.	Feb.	Mar.	Apr.	May.	June.	July.	Aug.	Sept.	Oct.	Nov.	Dec.	Year.
France (continued)														
Besançon	1,020	2·8	2·3	3·1	3·2	3·9	4·1	3·9	3·7	4·2	4·7	3·5	3·2	42·5
Metz	581	1·9	1·5	1·8	1·7	2·0	2·7	2·7	2·4	2·2	2·6	2·2	2·2	25·8
Chamonix	3,412	2·3	2·7	2·5	2·6	3·4	4·6	4·6	5·1	4·4	4·4	3·4	3·4	44·1
Germany.														
Köln	184	1·8	1·7	2·0	1·7	2·1	2·8	3·3	2·7	2·1	2·4	2·0	2·3	27·0
Frankfurt a M.	341	1·5	1·3	1·7	1·2	2·0	2·2	2·7	2·3	1·9	2·1	1·7	2·0	22·7
Freudenstadt	2,395	5·1	4·7	5·7	3·9	4·3	4·8	5·1	4·5	4·0	4·6	5·0	6·4	58·0
Nürnberg	1,014	1·1	1·1	1·6	1·4	2·3	2·6	3·1	2·4	2·0	1·7	1·5	1·7	22·9
Munich	1,739	1·6	1·3	1·9	2·8	3·7	4·8	4·7	4·0	3·7	2·3	1·7	1·8	34·3
Münster	197	2·3	1·8	2·4	1·7	2·2	2·8	3·6	3·1	2·3	2·6	2·3	2·8	29·9
Hanover	187	1·7	1·5	2·1	1·6	2·1	2·7	3·3	2·8	1·9	2·0	1·7	1·8	25·2
Kiel	154	2·1	1·7	2·1	1·7	1·8	2·2	3·2	3·1	2·2	2·8	2·3	2·4	27·7
Stettin	85	1·5	1·2	1·6	1·3	1·8	1·9	3·0	2·4	1·8	1·8	1·5	1·7	21·5
Königsberg	26	1·3	1·1	1·0	1·1	1·5	1·9	2·4	2·7	2·4	1·9	1·8	1·6	20·5
Berlin	161	1·5	1·3	1·7	1·4	2·0	2·0	3·1	2·2	1·8	1·8	1·6	1·7	22·2
Leipzig	394	1·4	1·3	2·0	1·6	2·5	2·6	3·7	2·6	2·3	2·0	1·7	1·7	25·3
Breslau	482	1·3	1·0	1·6	1·5	2·4	2·4	3·4	2·8	2·0	1·5	1·5	1·5	22·9
Scandinavia.														
Copenhagen	16	1·3	1·3	1·5	1·3	1·5	1·8	2·3	2·6	1·8	2·1	1·7	1·8	20·7
Oslo	82	1·1	1·1	1·3	1·3	1·7	1·9	2·9	3·5	2·3	2·6	1·9	1·7	23·2
Röros	2,100	1·1	0·9	0·8	0·5	1·0	1·8	2·7	2·8	1·8	1·3	1·0	1·0	16·5
Ostersund	1,010	0·9	0·9	0·9	0·9	1·5	2·0	2·2	3·0	2·0	1·5	0·9	1·2	17·8
Hernosand	49	1·5	1·1	1·5	1·0	1·7	1·7	2·4	3·1	2·7	2·7	2·1	1·7	23·2

MEAN RAINFALL (inches), *continued*

CENTRAL EUROPE (*continued*)

Station.	Alt. Feet.	Jan.	Feb.	Mar.	Apr.	May.	June.	July.	Aug.	Sept.	Oct.	Nov.	Dec.	Year.
Switzerland.														
Basel .	909	1.5	1.5	2.0	2.6	3.2	4.1	3.5	3.4	3.1	3.2	2.4	2.0	32.5
Geneva .	1,329	1.6	1.8	2.1	2.6	3.2	3.0	3.1	3.5	3.1	4.4	3.1	2.2	33.7
Lucerne .	1,480	1.7	2.0	2.8	3.7	4.8	5.8	6.3	6.1	4.4	3.9	2.5	2.3	46.3
Altdorf .	1,480	2.1	2.5	3.1	3.9	4.1	5.3	6.5	6.0	4.6	4.6	3.5	3.3	49.0
Andermatt .	4,741	3.8	4.2	3.5	3.2	3.4	3.5	4.3	4.7	5.5	5.6	3.1	2.9	47.7
Sion .	1,772	1.7	1.8	1.9	1.5	1.7	1.8	2.4	3.0	2.1	2.6	2.3	2.3	25.1
Sargans .	1,663	2.3	2.6	3.1	3.5	4.4	5.6	6.9	6.3	5.2	4.6	2.9	2.9	50.3
Säntis .	8,202	7.1	6.3	7.1	8.6	7.7	10.9	12.0	10.9	8.6	6.7	5.9	8.7	100.3
Davos .	5,121	1.8	2.2	2.2	2.2	2.3	4.0	4.9	5.0	3.7	2.7	2.2	2.5	35.7
Bevers .	5,610	1.4	1.0	1.6	2.2	2.6	3.4	4.3	4.3	4.2	3.5	2.4	1.8	32.7
Danube States.														
Innsbruck .	1,870	1.6	1.4	2.0	2.3	2.9	4.0	4.8	4.2	3.3	2.2	1.9	2.1	32.8
Ischl .	1,532	3.6	3.5	4.6	4.4	5.8	7.4	8.7	8.5	5.6	4.1	3.8	4.7	64.8
Klagenfurt .	1,444	1.5	1.3	2.3	2.6	3.8	4.2	4.8	4.6	4.1	4.2	3.1	2.2	38.7
Vienna .	666	1.5	1.3	1.8	2.0	2.8	2.8	2.8	2.8	1.7	1.9	1.6	1.7	24.5
Budapest .	367	1.5	1.3	1.8	2.4	2.8	3.0	2.1	2.0	2.1	2.5	2.1	1.9	25.9
Agram .	476	1.8	1.7	2.3	2.8	3.5	3.9	3.1	3.3	3.1	4.2	1.9	2.2	35.1
Debreczin .	423	1.5	1.1	1.6	1.7	2.5	3.1	3.1	2.3	1.5	2.4	1.9	1.7	24.5
Szegedin .	312	1.3	1.1	1.4	1.9	2.4	2.6	2.1	1.9	1.6	1.9	1.7	1.5	21.5
Belgrade .	459	1.3	1.2	1.6	2.4	2.8	3.0	2.6	1.9	1.7	2.4	1.9	1.6	24.4
Uskub .	804	1.1	1.5	0.8	2.0	2.2	2.2	1.3	1.6	1.7	2.0	1.9	1.7	20.1
Hermanstadt .	1,345	0.9	1.0	1.6	2.0	3.4	4.5	4.2	3.1	1.3	1.5	1.4	1.1	26.7
Bucharest .	295	1.3	1.1	1.6	1.7	2.5	3.5	2.7	2.0	1.6	1.7	1.6	1.6	23.1
Braila .	98	1.5	0.8	1.2	1.3	1.8	2.6	1.8	1.0	1.1	1.3	1.1	1.1	16.7
Sofia .	1,814	1.5	1.4	1.5	2.0	3.4	3.2	2.7	2.1	1.9	2.4	1.9	1.4	25.9

THE MEDITERRANEAN LANDS

Station.	Alt. Feet.	Jan.	Feb.	Mar.	Apr.	May.	June.	July.	Aug.	Sept.	Oct.	Nov.	Dec.	Year.
Spain and Portugal.														
Santiago	863	7·5	7·0	6·3	5·9	5·0	2·8	2·3	1·9	5·2	6·7	7·0	7·0	65·2
Lisbon	312	3·5	3·4	3·5	2·9	2·0	0·8	0·2	0·2	1·5	3·1	4·5	4·1	29·7
Gibraltar	49	5·1	4·2	4·8	2·7	1·7	0·5	0	0·1	1·4	3·3	6·4	5·5	35·3
Murcia	138	1·2	1·1	1·4	1·4	1·3	0·7	0·2	0·2	1·8	1·9	1·7	1·5	14·5
Barcelona	69	1·4	1·3	1·7	2·0	1·5	1·3	1·1	1·4	3·0	3·0	1·8	1·7	21·2
Valladolid	2,346	1·0	0·9	1·1	1·1	1·6	1·1	0·4	0·4	1·3	1·3	1·4	1·0	12·5
Madrid	2,149	1·3	1·1	1·7	1·9	1·7	1·2	0·5	0·4	1·3	1·8	1·9	1·6	16·4
Seville	98	2·6	2·0	2·6	1·8	1·7	0·6	0	0·1	0·8	2·4	3·1	2·5	20·3
France.														
Montpellier	95	3·1	2·7	2·4	2·3	2·8	1·8	0·9	2·0	3·0	4·1	3·4	2·4	30·9
Avignon	66	1·5	1·5	1·6	2·0	2·4	2·0	1·1	2·0	2·9	3·5	2·6	1·8	25·4
Marseilles (Obs.)	246	1·7	1·5	1·9	2·2	1·7	1·1	0·7	0·8	2·4	3·9	2·8	2·1	22·6
Nice (Éc. Nor.)	59	2·5	2·2	2·7	2·2	2·4	1·6	0·6	0·9	2·4	5·8	4·4	3·1	30·9
Italy.														
Trieste	98	2·2	2·3	2·8	2·9	3·7	4·1	3·7	3·7	4·0	4·7	3·6	3·4	41·8
Milan	482	2·4	2·3	2·7	3·4	4·1	3·3	2·8	3·2	3·5	4·7	4·3	3·0	39·8
Padua	102	2·1	1·9	2·4	3·0	3·4	3·4	2·5	2·6	3·0	3·8	3·3	2·5	33·9
Genoa	177	4·2	4·2	4·1	4·1	3·5	2·8	1·7	2·4	5·0	7·8	7·5	4·8	52·0
Florence	240	2·7	2·5	3·0	3·1	3·1	2·2	1·4	2·4	3·3	4·3	4·0	3·2	34·8
Rome	164	3·2	2·7	2·9	2·6	2·2	1·5	0·7	1·0	2·5	5·0	4·4	3·9	32·7
Naples	489	3·5	2·8	2·9	2·6	2·0	1·3	0·6	1·1	2·8	4·5	4·6	4·4	33·0
Palermo	233	3·9	3·3	2·8	2·6	1·3	0·6	0·3	0·6	1·5	3·9	3·9	4·5	29·5

MEAN RAINFALL (inches), *continued*

THE MEDITERRANEAN LANDS (*continued*)

Balkan Peninsula.

Ragusa . . .	49	6.8	5.0	5.4	4.8	3.5	2.8	1.3	2.6	4.3	7.7	7.8	7.2	59.2
Corfu . . .	98	5.9	6.7	3.4	3.3	2.3	1.3	0.4	0.9	2.9	5.8	6.3	8.3	47.9
Athens . .	351	2.0	1.7	1.2	0.9	0.8	0.7	0.3	0.5	0.7	1.6	2.6	2.6	15.5
Salonika . .	128	1.5	1.4	1.6	1.9	2.4	1.7	1.0	1.2	1.6	2.1	2.7	2.4	21.5
Constantinople .	230	3.4	2.7	2.4	1.7	1.2	1.3	1.1	1.7	2.0	2.5	4.0	4.8	28.9

PART V

NORTH AMERICA (EXCLUDING MEXICO)

CHAPTER XXXI
GENERAL FEATURES

NORTH AMERICA is the second largest of the land masses of
the Earth, but its area is less than half that of Asia. The
continent is compact in form. The only inland sea is Hudson
Bay, a shallow basin, largely ice-covered much of the year.
The Great Lakes are much smaller but they are not completely frozen over in winter, and therefore they have not
less influence on the climate of the continent than Hudson
Bay. On the west coast the continent lacks large indentations,
and thus presents a great contrast to Eurasia, and another
important difference is the trend of the main feature lines.
The Western Mountain system of America runs from north
to south, the mountain ranges of Eurasia from west to east,
and the greater continuity of the former causes them to be
a very important barrier although they are less lofty than
the mountains of Eurasia. Rising steeply from the Pacific
Ocean, and consisting of several parallel ranges and intermont
basins with a width of 500 miles in Canada and as much as
1,000 miles in the States, the system is a formidable rampart
in the way of the prevailing westerly winds, and the highly
complicated topography gives rise to very varied climatic
conditions. On the east the mountains fall sharply to the
Great Plains, in places 6,000 feet above the sea, and the Great
Plains slope gradually down to the vast lowland in the middle
of the continent which includes Hudson Bay, the western
part of the Great Lakes, and the Mississippi valley, and
affords a wide open passage from the frozen wastes of the
north of Canada to the subtropical shores of the Gulf of
Mexico, for there is no transverse barrier. The gently rolling
lowlands are for the most part between sea-level and 2,000
feet; they are highest in the neighbourhood of the international frontier, but it is possible to go from the Barren

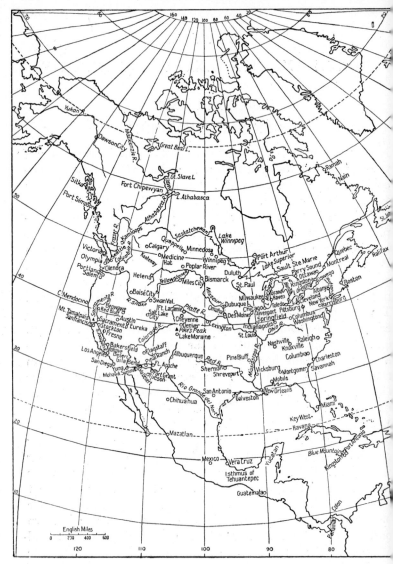

Fig. 102. Key map, showing the position of places mentioned in the text.

Lands to the Gulf without rising above 1,000 feet. The Appalachian system with ranges of 4,000 feet and the heights of northern Quebec and Labrador are much lower and less continuous than the western mountains, and have little effect on the climate of the surrounding country.

The lowlands of Europe, on the other hand, are in the west as well as in the north, and no mountain barrier cuts them off from the ocean, which is able to extend its influence far to the east, assisted by the bordering seas on the north and south of the continent. But the north and south of Eurasia are climatically severed, especially in Asia, by the east–west feature lines of the Tertiary mountain folds, and the elevated plateaux of the heart of the continent.

Oceanic conditions. The North Pacific Drift is a continuation of the Kuro Shio current, the counterpart of the Gulf Stream of the Atlantic Ocean but much less important, owing partly to the less volume of warm water in proportion to the size of the Ocean which the equatorial currents pour into the North Pacific, and partly to the shape of the basin, which is almost enclosed in the north. The air temperature between Japan and British Columbia has a positive anomaly of about 20°, the corresponding region of the North Atlantic about 40° (p. 236). The Drift, wafted from west to east by the westerlies, meets the American coast in the neighbourhood of the mouth of the Columbia River, and divides; one branch flows northward and gives British Columbia its mild winters, the other southward as the cool California current which greatly modifies the climate of the coast, causing low temperatures, scanty rainfall, but much summer fog; it corresponds to the Canaries current off North-west Africa.

On the east coast the cold Labrador current flows southward from Baffin Bay to Newfoundland. Its Arctic water and great masses of ice, much of which does not melt till it reaches the warm Gulf Stream on the Grand Banks, are responsible for the very cool summers of the Labrador coast. The Labrador current can be traced far south as the Cold Wall along Nova Scotia and the United States coast, but here its climatic importance is not great, since it is narrow and is overshadowed by the Gulf Stream. The Gulf Stream, a great current of very warm water, flows near the American coast from the south of Florida to Newfoundland. The direct climatic benefit which America derives from it is not nearly so great as might be expected, since in winter, when a warm

X

current can have most effect in temperate latitudes, the prevailing winds are offshore; even in the coastal belt the rigorous winters are not much tempered by the warm water. In summer the onshore winds blow over it and are hot and moist. When these qualities are specially intense the winds are known as 'hot waves', which are an unpleasant element in the climate of the eastern states. The Gulf of Mexico, the source of part of the Gulf Stream, is always warm, and the air over it is charged with moisture. This explains the heavy rainfall of the south of the United States. In winter the warm damp air over the Gulf is conducive to low-pressure conditions, and hence to the spread of 'cold waves' from the interior of the Continent to its subtropical shores.

CHAPTER XXXII

PRESSURE AND WINDS

IN January (Fig. 103) the subtropical belt of high pressure spreads northward over the cold continent, especially over the western part, and invades the planetary low-pressure belt of temperate latitudes, which it divides into the 'permanent' low-pressure systems of the North Atlantic and North Pacific Oceans. The mean barometric gradient is steepest over the north-west of the continent. The continental high-pressure system is not nearly so intense nor so permanent during the winter as that over Eurasia, since it is constantly liable to modification by the cyclonic activity which is remarkably vigorous over North America; indeed there is an almost unbroken procession of high- and low-pressure systems rather than a stationary high-pressure system. Depressions are probably more numerous than in any other continent. Their speed is about twice as great as in Europe, and the absolute barometric pressure is higher. They almost always alternate with well-developed anticyclones, and in this respect also present a contrast to depressions in north-west Europe. The resulting weather and temperature in North America is extremely variable. Sometimes a single cyclone or anticyclone may dominate the weather from Hudson Bay to the Gulf of Mexico, and owing to the lack of a transverse mountain barrier the winter temperature of north Canada or the summer heat of the Gulf may spread over much of the continent, modified of course with distance, but very perceptible. The St. Lawrence region has perhaps the most variable conditions owing to the convergence there of the most frequented cyclone tracks of the continent.

In winter most of the continent is within the westerlies, which are much modified by the continental influence but not nearly so much as in Asia. In the east of Canada and the United States the prevailing winds are west and north-west, strong and variable, blowing between the high pressures of the interior and the low pressures off south Greenland and Iceland. The Great Plains, being on the east and south of the high pressure, have northerly and westerly winds.

North winds prevail on the shores of the Gulf of Mexico also, but the coast of Texas, especially the western part,

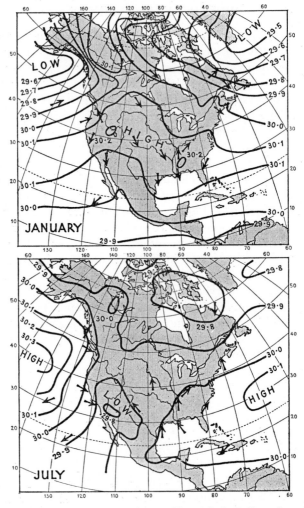

Fig. 103. Mean pressure and prevailing winds (isobars based on Köppen u. Geiger, II. J.).

has variables, and at some stations, Galveston for example, the prevailing direction is south-east in January. The region between the Appalachians, the Mississippi, and the Great Lakes is exceptional in having south-west winds in winter and in summer, caused in winter by a detached high-pressure system over the south-east of the States. But these prevailing winds are much less constant than those of Asia owing to the frequent veering and backing under the influence of the numerous pressure irregularities.

The direction of the wind on the Pacific coast shows that either the western mountain barrier, or the continental high pressures, or both, present an effective obstacle to the westerlies. North of the fortieth parallel the prevailing winds are south and south-west, on the coast of British Columbia south-east, blowing along and somewhat off shore. They are the inflow on the east side of the North Pacific depression (the Aleutian low-pressure system), and correspond to the south-west winds of the British Isles, being like them rainy and mild, stormy, and variable in direction and force. In British Columbia they are confined to the islands and the narrow littoral, since the mountains prevent that great landward extension of oceanic conditions which is such a valuable climatic asset in the case of Europe. The sheltered valleys of the Fraser and Columbia and their tributaries enjoy fine dry weather with only light winds, gales being notably rare here in comparison with the stormy Pacific coast. On the coast of Oregon the winds are variable, south and west being the most frequent directions; in the south of California they become north-west, and finally north in Lower California under the influence of the North Pacific anticyclone; these latter are really trade winds, as are also the easterly winds of south Florida and the Gulf of Mexico.

With the approach of spring the high pressures over the continent become less intense, and in April they have almost disappeared. The isobars for May show the commencement of the summer conditions which culminate in July (Fig. 103). As in the case of Eurasia the land mass is warmer than the sea and pressure is low, the subtropical high pressures being now interrupted by the continent, which is covered by a trough of low pressure connecting the low pressures of the Equatorial and the temperate zones; but the low pressures over North America are neither so deep nor so constant as over Asia. The North Atlantic anticyclone is a prominent feature on the map and spreads over much of the south-east of the States. Still more prominent is the anticyclone which extends far north to cover most of the North Pacific and replaces the Aleutian low-pressure system of winter, so that it dominates the weather of the whole of the west coast of the continent from the south of California to Alaska.

WIND-DIRECTION, PERCENTAGE OF ALL OBSERVATIONS

		N.	NE.	E.	SE.	S.	SW.	W.	NW.	Calms.
Portland	Jan.	7	6	11	19	19	10	6	21	1
(Ore.)	July	10	2	3	8	8	8	6	54	3
San Fran-	Jan.	25	6	5	19	7	9	10	20	0
cisco	July	1	1	0	1	2	53	41	1	0
New York	Jan.	8	13	6	4	6	15	18	30	0
	July	5	9	6	10	19	24	12	16	0
Galveston	Jan.	15	15	13	20	13	7	4	12	0
	July	3	4	5	30	33	18	4	3	0

PREVAILING WINDS

	January.	July.		January.	July.
Los Angeles	NE.	W.	Reno	W.	W.
Key West	NE.	E.	Pikes Peak	W.	SW.
Charleston	N.	SW.	St. Paul	NW.	SE.
Eastport (Maine)	NW.	S.	Chicago	W.	NE., SW.
New Orleans	N.	SE.	Cincinnati	SW.	SW.

The winds in the east and south of the continent show a monsoonal change from the winter direction, but there is not a complete reversal. On the east coast they blow from the south-west, on the coast of the Gulf of Mexico from the south-east. The Great Plains west of the Mississippi have humid southerly winds. On the Pacific coasts the wind shows a marked tendency to blow into the continent, from the west and north-west in British Columbia, and from the north-west in Washington and Oregon almost with the constancy of the trades. California has trade winds, blowing from the north; the local topography, however, gives San Francisco almost constant south-west and west winds. The North Pacific anticyclone controls the weather and winds of almost all this coast, but in the centre and east of the continent cyclonic activity still goes on though less vigorously than in winter.

As an indication of the monsoonal change in North America and Asia respectively the following figures, calculated by

Hann, are instructive. They express the frequency of the
various wind directions as percentages of all observations.

		N.	NE.	E.	SE.	S.	SW.	W.	NW.
NE. Asia.									
Winter	. .	17	8	5	6	6	8	18	32
Summer	. .	10	9	12	26	16	10	7	10
E. coast, N. America.									
Winter	. .	11	15	6	6	7	18	14	23
Summer	. .	8	12	6	11	13	28	9	13

The more variable winds and less complete change from
summer to winter in North America shown by these figures
are no doubt due partly to the smaller area of the continent,
but chiefly to the lack of a transverse barrier to separate
the cold dry air of the north from the moist warm air over
the Gulf of Mexico. The meeting of currents of air with such
physical differences intensifies atmospheric disturbances,
which develop into cyclones and anticyclones giving variable
winds. Perhaps the barring of the westerlies by the western
mountain system which lies athwart their course may conduce
to the same result.

In spite of the fact that the mean pressure over North
America is lower in summer than in winter, there is much
less cyclonic activity, the weather is finer, the wind much
lighter and the relative humidity of the air lower. The Pacific
coast is under anticyclonic influences and has hardly any
rain. In the interior summer has most rain owing to the
development of shallow pressure irregularities and local convection, which give much heavier precipitation than the
vigorous depressions of winter owing to the higher temperature. But the weather is brighter and less cloudy, and
Canada especially has the advantage of long daylight, including the whole 24 hours in the north.

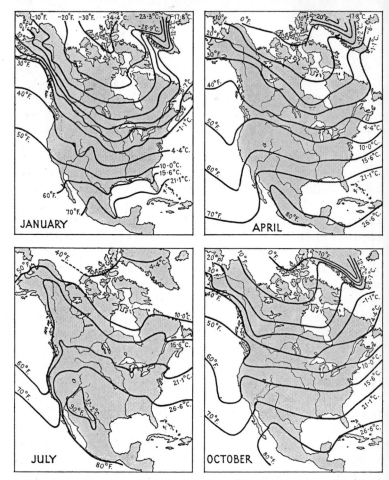

Fig. 104. Mean temperature (based on Köppen u. Geiger, II. J.).

CHAPTER XXXIII

TEMPERATURE

Winter. In January (Fig. 104) almost all Canada and the northern third of the United States have a mean temperature below 32°. The 50° isotherm skirts the northern shores of the Gulf of Mexico, and the 70° isotherm appears over the southern point of Florida. The north of Canada is the coldest part of the continent, with a mean below −30° F. The only parts of Canada which have never recorded temperatures below −30° are Newfoundland, Nova Scotia, and the western half of British Columbia; zero has been recorded even in Vancouver Island.

The isotherms swing farthest south over the Mississippi valley, and trend northward somewhat as they approach the east coast; thus the 30° isotherm passes through St. Louis, and reaches the east coast at Long Island. In the west the isotherms diverge from the parallels of latitude in a very striking way and run north-west–south-east, almost parallel with the coastline; evidently the warm waters of the ocean are as important a source of heat as direct insolation. In Vancouver Island the 40° line runs from north to south, much as in the British Isles. The cold increases rapidly inland, and the 32° isotherm is reached within 40 miles, the warm oceanic conditions being shut off from the interior by the mountain ranges. In Europe in the same latitude the 32° isotherm is 500 miles eastward from the ocean. Latitude for latitude the coast is not quite so warm as that of West Europe; at Sitka (lat. 57° N.) the mean is 30°, at Portree, Scotland (lat. 57·5° N.), 39°.

British Columbia enjoys the mild and moist climate of North-west Europe on its coasts, which have the double advantage of warm cyclonic weather from the ocean, and shelter by the mountains from Arctic and continental cold, but immediately behind the Coast Range, in the Fraser valley, the climate is that of Central Europe. Victoria (Vancouver Island) has a mean temperature in January of 39°, Vancouver 36° (abs. min. 2°), Kamloops, 250 miles from the open Pacific and half-way from the coast to the Rockies, 23° (abs. min.

—31°). The sheltered valleys are free from strong winds, and the winter cold is pleasant and exhilarating. The vigorous relief of the land gives rise to prominent weather features, including föhn winds in the valleys which, like the chinook east of the Rockies, are valuable in rapidly removing snow. The interior plateau of British Columbia between 2,000 and 5,000 feet has severe cold in winter, the January mean being about 14° with minima down to —55°, and there is occasional frost even in July. The Selkirks and the Rockies rise to over 10,000 feet for long distances and have everlasting snow.

East of the Rockies there is an extreme continental climate with very large range of temperature both annual and diurnal. At Calgary the mean temperature in January is 12°. The altitude of the Great Plains in this neighbourhood is over 3,000 feet, and there is a steady descent eastward, but in spite of this the temperature becomes lower and lower, for increasing distance from the Pacific Ocean more than neutralizes the decrease in altitude. The mean temperature is 11° at Medicine Hat (2,160 feet), 0° at Qu'Appelle (2,115 feet), —1° at Minnedosa (1,400 feet), —4° at Winnipeg (760 feet). But the warmth of the Great Plains at the eastern foot of the Rockies is the result not only of proximity to the ocean, but also of the 'chinook' winds. These are dry and warm west winds blowing on the south side of depressions crossing the continent. They are warm and damp after their passage over the Pacific and in crossing the Western ranges lose their humidity as rain, and in favourable circumstances descend to the plains of the interior with föhn heat and dryness due to compression. Their influence is greatest along the east foot of the range, where they rapidly melt and dry up the snow and make grazing possible all the winter. They are an important factor in the climate from the south of Colorado northward as far as settlement has advanced in Canada and even in the lower Mackenzie valley. The rise in temperature when the chinook sets in is sometimes exceedingly rapid, as much as 40° in 15 minutes being occasionally recorded. As a rule the temperature does not exceed 40°, but this appears very warm after the intense cold which may have prevailed during a preceding spell of anticyclonic weather. Alberta being close under the Rockies is specially favoured by chinooks, and

Calgary has recorded 58° in January. When chinooks are strong and frequent the western Prairie Provinces have a comparatively open winter, and their absence causes a severe winter with heavy losses of stock.

'The day preceding had been mild with a soft wind blowing out of the east, sure harbinger of bad weather. The morrow, however, brought a lower temperature and stronger wind. That night the wind dropped. We awoke to find the thermometer standing at −52°. The steam rose in little clouds from the stables, and the smoke from the house chimneys went up so straight and far, ere spreading out into a huge mushroom-shaped growth, that it could easily have been mistaken for a natural cloud. Little pools of mist marked the spots where the cattle stood in huddled bunches, the heat from their bodies combined with their breath hanging over them exactly as mist will gather over a pool on a chilly summer's night. . . . Our main bunch of horses were on a pasture four miles from home when the blizzard struck. In an ordinary winter they would have been able to forage for themselves and grow fat. It was ten days before a man could be spared to see how they were doing. . . . When the snow finally cleared dead horses were to be found with manes and tails eaten off by their starving companions, lying in every sheltered corner. . . . And then almost as suddenly as it had commenced, the siege was raised; the snow vanished like magic, grass coming up green and fresh as fast as it had disappeared. Horses that had seemed about to die fattened over night' (SYKES, quoted by Koeppe in *The Canadian Climate*).

In the United States, as in Canada, there is a decrease in temperature from the Great Plains to the Mississippi valley:

	Altitude. Feet.	Mean Temp. Jan.		Altitude. Feet.	Mean Temp. Jan.
Cheyenne .	6,088	26	Des Moines .	861	20
Lexington .	2,385	25	Davenport .	580	21
Omaha .	1,103	22	Chicago .	824	26

Manitoba is the coldest part of the continent in winter for its latitude, especially the north-east near Hudson Bay where Churchill has never recorded a temperature above 32° in January and has known −57°; here there are no chinook winds. Farther east near the Great Lakes temperature rises rapidly, and on the northern shores of Lake Superior the January

mean is 10°. The warmest part of Canada in winter, excluding
the west coast, is the Lake Peninsula of Ontario, which lies
farthest south, and is most subject to the warming influence
of the lakes. At Toronto the mean temperature for January
is 21°, for February 22° and the lowest record −28°; most of
the peninsula has only 3 months with a mean temperature
below 32°, a clear advantage over the St. Lawrence valley
which has 5 months; the St. Lawrence at Montreal is closed
to navigation by ice from mid-December to mid-April. Eastward from the lakes the mean temperature first falls and
then rises again near the east coast. The January mean at
Ottawa is 12°, at Halifax 23°. These stations are hardly
comparable with Winnipeg, which is farther north, but even
the bleak coast of Labrador is warmer than the interior of
Canada; inhospitable summers rather than specially cold
winters are the most unpleasant feature of the climate of
Labrador, and its coasts are heavily ice-bound against navigation except from mid-June till November.

It is interesting to examine the influence of the Great Lakes
on their neighbourhood in more detail. They cause a slight
northward bend in the isotherms in October owing to the
retention of the summer heat by the water mass, and the
bend becomes more and more pronounced till January, after
which it diminishes; in March the lakes probably cease to
act as a source of warmth. The east shores are more warmed
by the lakes than the west owing to the prevailing westerly
winds. At Milwaukee, on the west shore of Lake Michigan,
the mean January temperature is 20°, the absolute minimum
−25°; at Grand Haven on the opposite shore the mean is
25°, and the absolute minimum only −12°; at Dubuque,
160 miles west of the lake, −32° has been registered. Duluth,
at the western end of Lake Superior, has a mean temperature
in January of 10°, absolute minimum −41°; at Sault Ste.
Marie the corresponding figures are 15° and −28°. A strip
of country, 20 to 30 miles wide, along the east shore of Lake
Michigan, is known as the 'Fruit Belt', because the lake so
ameliorates its climate that peaches, grapes, and other tender
fruits are cultivated with a success which is impossible in
other districts in the same latitude not similarly favoured.
Lake Erie warms its shores in the same way; the lowest

temperature ever recorded at Toledo, on its south shore, is —16°, but Columbus, 100 miles south of the lake, has recorded —20°.

The shores of the lakes except the south of Michigan are usually frozen and the harbours closed in winter (in general during December to March), and the melting of the ice delays the coming of spring. In summer the water cools the neighbourhood, but not so much as it warms it in winter; 'land' and 'sea' breezes are frequent on the shores.

'The Grape Belt which extends along the southern shore of Lake Erie for a distance of about 60 miles, and is from 2 to 6 miles wide, has the most temperate climate in New York State except the region along the Atlantic coast. This is directly due to the tempering influence of the lake, which holds vegetation in check in the spring until danger from frost is over, gives long mild autumns with unusually late fall frosts, and winters much less severe than elsewhere. The tempering influence of the lake is noticeable for a distance of about 30 miles inland' (*Climatological Data for the United States*).

The effect of Lake Ontario is especially valuable when cold waves at very low temperatures sweep down from Canada, the difference in temperature between the north and south sides of the lake at such times amounting even to 20° (*ibid.*).

The Atlantic Provinces of Canada have a peninsular configuration, with strong maritime tendencies in spite of their situation on the leeward side of the continent. The mean winter temperature is 10° to 20° higher than in the Prairie Provinces, and the lowest readings are also much higher. Spring is late and cold, and autumn correspondingly warm. The mean temperature of July and of August is about 65°, and readings as high as 100° seem to be very rare, the summer being short and cool; in Newfoundland the warmest month, August, has a mean below 60°, and 70° is not reached in most years. It is a windy region with frequent gales.

The coldest part of North America in winter is the tract between Hudson Bay and Alaska. The north coasts are not quite so cold, since even the ice-covered seas and channels provide more warmth than the land of the continent during the Polar night, but the strong winds, often blizzards, and the high humidity make the cold more penetrating and difficult to bear. In the interior the cold is intense, especially in the valley bottoms, with monthly means far below freezing-point in October to April, but not so intense as in north-east Siberia. The Great Bear Lake is covered with ice 8 feet thick, much of which remains unmelted throughout the year. In the lower Mackenzie valley the temperature falls at times below −70°, and the mean monthly temperature is below freezing-point for 8 months out of the twelve. But the air is dry and calm, and the weather often beautifully fine and invigorating. Fort Good Hope, on the Mackenzie near the Arctic Circle, has had temperatures below zero in all except the three summer months, including the lowest official record in Canada, −79°. But Fort Vermilion, in a valley bottom in lat. 58° 27′ N., has recorded −76°, and this station has recorded 98° in summer, giving an extreme range of 174°. At Dawson City −68° has been recorded; the river Yukon freezes in September and remains frozen till late May. The Barren Lands have a January mean below −20°, and the north central area, including Victoria Island, Banks Island and the islands to the north, below −30°. The coldest area, with a mean about −35°, is probably between Boothia Peninsula and the north-west of Hudson Bay. In at any rate much of this tract the ground is permanently frozen down to a depth of, in places, about 200 feet, except for the summer thaw of the surface 4 or 5 feet. The southern boundary of the permanently frozen ground probably runs south-east from the Yukon and the Great Slave Lake to the middle of James Bay and thence east to Labrador. On the west coast of Alaska the temperature is much higher than in the interior, but still far below freezing-point, and owing to the damp and often foggy air the climate is less pleasant.

Hudson Bay has considerable influence on its neighbour-hood, though less than its area might suggest. The Bay is thickly frozen for many miles from its shores except in July, August, and September, and it has much drift ice all the year. The ice conditions in summer, especially in Hudson Strait, depend chiefly on the direction and force of the winds which drive the ice; in some years there is little ice, in others navigation is almost stopped. The mean navigable period in Hudson Strait is August and September. In winter the mean temperature is about 10° higher over the Bay than in the same latitudes in Manitoba, and the east side of the Bay with onshore winds is appreciably warmer than the west; but the January mean is only −5° in the south of James Bay, −30° in the north-west of Hudson Bay, and the shores are completely ice-bound. The weather is more stormy, damp, and cloudy than in the forests and prairies, and especially the high plains of the west, and there is no chinook to give even occasional warm spells. In summer the cold water, little above freezing-point with its abundant floating ice, chills the air, giving a mean temperature about 10° lower than in the Prairie Provinces. The July mean is the same at Moose Factory on the south end of James Bay as at Fort Good Hope on the Mackenzie, 1,000 miles farther north and almost on the Arctic Circle. The maxima are considerably lower, and the weather is less bright and dry than farther west. Fog is fairly frequent over the cold water. Owing to the short and cool summers the northern limit of tree growth bends south round the Bay, the shores of which, excluding James Bay, are for the most part tundra. Spring is late and cold, but autumn often gives some warm dry and sunny weather.

The warmest part of the continent in winter is the lower Colorado valley. At Yuma, 141 feet above the sea, the January mean is 55°, and 81° has been recorded in that month, but, as is usual in an arid climate, the nights are often cold and a reading of 22° has been observed. On the higher plateaux in this district the nights are far colder; 10° has been recorded at Fort Grant, Arizona, 4,916 feet above the sea, where the clear dry air favours very rapid radiation of heat. On the plateaux of Oregon, Washington, and the north of Nevada and Utah it is much colder than in Arizona in winter. Swan Valley, Idaho, 5,434 feet above the sea, has a mean temperature in January of 21°, with an absolute minimum of −35°. But the minimum readings are not so low as east of the Rockies, where the altitude is less; Fort Laramie, on the north Platte River in Wyoming, 4,270 feet above the sea, but situated in a valley bottom, has recorded −48°. The lowest minima in the country lying immediately to the east of the Rockies are in the bottoms of the valleys, and the absolute minima for the whole of the United States are

—65°, at Miles City in the south-east of Montana, a town in the bottom of the Yellowstone valley, 2,371 feet above the sea, —63° at Poplar River, another station in a similar situation in the same state, —66° in Yellowstone Park. The plateaux and mountain summits have lower mean temperatures, as

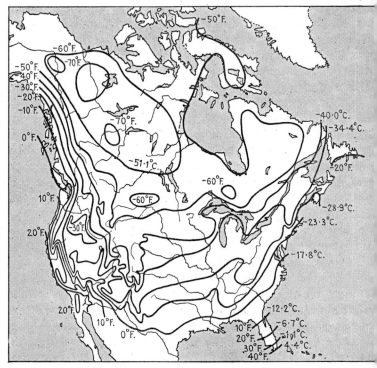

FIG. 105. Absolute minimum temperature (based on *Atlas of American Agriculture* and Koeppe).

might be expected from their elevation, but the absolute minima are not so low. Lake Moraine, Colorado, 10,265 feet above the sea, has no record below —31°, and even Pikes Peak, 14,134 feet, none below —39°. Clearly the very low readings in the valley bottoms are the result of the drainage of the coldest air to the lowest ground, giving an inversion of temperature. The Pacific littoral is notably warmer than the Atlantic, but even San Diego has recorded 25°. The extreme south of Florida is the only part of the continent (excluding Mexico) which has never recorded frost (Fig. 105).

No account of the American winter would be complete
without a reference to the 'cold waves'. The great cyclonic
activity in the continent has already been mentioned. As
they travel east the pressure systems sometimes become
elongated in a north–south direction and form a long belt of
high or low pressure, which causes northerly currents of air
to sweep over great expanses of country from north to south

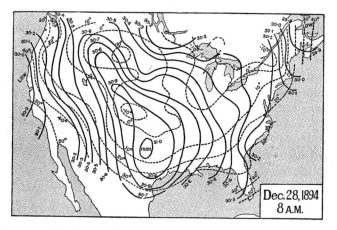

Fig. 106. Pressure and temperature conditions during a cold wave
in the Mississippi valley and the eastern states. Full lines are isobars,
broken lines isotherms, °F.

behind the cold front (Fig. 106). They often originate in the
north-west of Canada where the clear skies of an anticyclone
may be permitting rapid radiation, and producing great cold,
and as they advance southward they bring Canadian cold,
modified somewhat by the southward journey, even to the
coasts of the Gulf of Mexico. They are an important factor
in causing the variable weather for which the States are noted.
The rapidity of the weather changes is due to the rapid movement of the cyclones. The warm inflow from the south in
front of a depression is of almost as pronounced a character
as the cold wave which suddenly takes its place when the
trough of the depression has passed. Cold waves are coldest
in the north of the United States. In the mid-course of the
Mississippi the extremes are not so great, but the changes are

especially noteworthy since the temperature often drops suddenly from well above, to well below, freezing-point, and such a change entails the maximum of inconvenience and discomfort. St. Louis has recorded 74° and −22° in January, that is to say, 42° above, and 54° below, freezing-point. In December 1831 the Mississippi was frozen over for 130 miles below the mouth of the Ohio; the ice at New Orleans was thick enough for skating.

Nearer the Gulf, especially in Texas, cold waves are called Northers. Since the average temperature is fairly high in these parts the cold is severely felt. Sometimes there is sleet or snow, but generally the weather is clear, and the Norther blows as a strong dry north wind for one or more days, with a temperature considerably below freezing-point. At San Antonio the mean temperature in January is 53°, and 83° has been recorded; but during a Norther the thermometer has dropped to 6°. At Galveston on the coast −8° has been recorded.

The Blizzards of the northern States and Canada are cold waves of a special type, in which there is a howling gale of wind, and the air is full of dry powdery snow. The wayfarer easily loses his bearings, and it is impossible to remain alive for many hours without shelter. The Blizzard is closely akin to the Buran of Siberia.

Cold waves often reach Florida, and may even bring frost almost to the extreme south of that state. Key West, an island off the south coast, alone has never recorded frost, the thermometer not having been known to fall below 41°. Cold waves sometimes appear in a severe form in all the Atlantic States. On the Pacific coasts they are much less important, but they have been felt as far south as the Mexican frontier; they never bring such low temperatures as in the centre and east of the continent. They are keenly felt on the high plateaux of Arizona and New Mexico, and prevent the cultivation of the sub-tropical fruits which are usual crops in California.

To end this account of the winter temperature a comparison of the west and east coasts of North America, with one another, and with the west and east coasts of Eurasia, is shown in the following table:

West Coast.	Lat. °N.	Mean Jan. Temp.	East Coast.	Lat. °N.	Mean Jan. Temp.
North America.					
Sitka .	57·0	32	Nain .	56·5	−7
Victoria	48·5	39	St. John's (NF.)	47·5	23
Eureka	41·0	47	New York .	41·0	31
San Diego .	32·5	54	Savanna	32·5	50
Eurasia.					
Portree	57·5	39	Aian .	56·0	−5
Brest .	48·5	43	East Siberia	48·5	0
Oporto	41·0	47	Vladivostok	43·0	7
Mogador	32·5	57	Shanghai .	31·0	38

The west coast of America is very much warmer than the east in all latitudes, its advantage being greatest in the north. Sitka, Alaska, is never icebound, and is 39° warmer than Nain on the Labrador coast, from which icebergs are to be seen even at midsummer, and continuous icepack during much of the year. The mean temperatures in similar latitudes in Eurasia show that on the west coast the Old World is the warmer; the difference is small in the latitude of California, but it is considerable in the north, Portree being 7° warmer than Sitka. The difference is greater on the east coasts, greatest in the latitude of New York, which is 24° warmer than Vladivostok. This is the result of the more constant monsoonal conditions in East Asia where the north-west winds from the cold interior of the continent hardly ever cease to blow in winter; but in the east of America south winds are not infrequent as cyclones approach from the west. Labrador is north of the usual cyclone tracks, and in those latitudes the temperature difference between America and Asia is small, America being the colder.

Summer. The fall in temperature from south to north is much less rapid in summer than in winter, for in summer the decrease in the sun's altitude with increasing latitude is compensated in part by the greater length of the day. The mean temperature in June and July is similar over wide areas. In July the isotherms bend sharply poleward over the warm land. The 50° line has retreated almost to the north coast of the continent; over a large area the temperature exceeds 90°.

The isotherms, which it must be remembered denote 'sea-level' temperatures, run considerably farther north in the west of North America than in the east, which shows that the plateaux in the west are unduly warm for their altitude; the air being less dense offers less obstruction to insolation, so that the arid and semi-arid uplands are heated strongly during the long cloudless summer days. The following table, the temperatures in which are not reduced to sea-level, shows that Beowawe, Nevada, is even warmer than Springfield, 4,000 feet lower; the temperature at Austin also is remarkably high for its altitude:

	Alt. Feet.	Locality.	Mean Temp. July.	Abs. Max.
Beowawe .	4,695	Humboldt R., Nevada .	77	105
Austin . .	6,594	Plateau, Nevada . .	69	101
Springfield .	609	Mississippi Valley .	76	107
St. Louis .	568	,, ,, . .	79	107

In the lowlands of Arizona, the Colorado and Mohave Deserts, temperatures comparable with those of the Sahara are produced by the blazing summer sun shining through the dry air. The highest record for the continent, 134°, occurred on 10 July 1913, in Death Valley, California, where the mean temperature for July is 102°. On the plateau the temperatures are somewhat lower:

	Altitude. Feet.	Mean Temperature. July.	Absolute Maximum.
Mohawk Summit (Gila R.) .	538	98	126
Tucson	2,390	87	112
Fort Grant . . .	4,916	78	106

But the dryness of the air helps to make the intense heat supportable and, moreover, the hot days are followed by cool nights on the higher plateaux; at Fort Grant the thermometer has been known to fall to 48° in July, at Tucson to 55°, but not below 79° at Mohawk Summit. Thus there is a great range of temperature, both annual and diurnal; the latter is greatest in the warmest months.

The course of the summer isotherms on and near the west coast of the United States is very striking, and shows an extraordinarily rapid increase in temperature from the coast towards the interior (Fig. 107). The plateau, as has been seen, is unduly hot for its latitude and altitude, while the coast is abnormally cool owing to the presence of the cold California current, which not only chills the air directly, but also causes much fog, which screens off the sun's warmth. These sea fogs are essentially a summer phenomenon, and their total dura-tion covers about 50 per cent. of the summer hours. Sea-ward they form a belt along the coast with a width of about 50 miles and a thickness of 1,500 feet. But they are dissolved before they can pene-trate far inland. The fog-belt on the Coast Ranges which rise steeply from the Pacific is the home of the redwood tree, the leaves of which are adapted to condense copious moisture from the fog. Beyond the

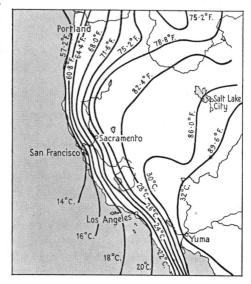

Fig. 107. Mean temperature in July.
(Brooks.)

Coast Ranges is the Great Valley of California, a flat-bottomed depression 400 miles long and 50 miles wide, drained by the River Sacramento in the north, and the San Joaquin in the south. The Great Valley is walled on the east by the lofty Sierra Nevada, which rises to over 14,000 feet. The cool foggy weather of the coast in summer is shut out by the Coast Ranges; San Francisco has a very low mean temperature, 57°, in July, far lower than the coast of Europe in the same latitude; but Bakersfield in the south of the Great Valley has 89°, and Red Bluff in the north 82°. The difference between coast and interior is as great as between Scotland and the north of Africa, though the distance in the case of California is only about 75 miles. The strong sea breeze finds its way into the Great Valley by the opening through which the drainage of the valley reaches the sea at the Golden Gate, and it spreads to north and south, up the Sacramento and San Joaquin. Its influence on the temperature is clearly traceable; Stockton, which is situated opposite the opening to the sea, has a July mean of 73°, and the temperature increases up the valley both northward and southward to over 80° at Bakersfield and Red Bluff. As we ascend the Sierra Nevada there is an increase in temperature at first in spite of the greater altitude, since the sea influence is being left behind; as the slope becomes steeper the reduction due to altitude asserts itself more strongly, but an ascent to 7,000 feet is necessary to reach as low a temperature as at San Francisco.

At San Francisco late September is the warmest part of the year. The long retardation of the maximum is explained by the fact that at midsummer the interior of California is very hot, and a strong sea breeze sets in through the Golden Gate, and brings the low temperatures of the California current to San Francisco. But in the beginning of autumn the interior is cooling, and the sea breeze becomes weaker and finally ceases, so that although the sun has already retired to the Equator September is the warmest month.

The summit of Mount Tamalpais, which overlooks San Francisco from the other side of the Golden Gate, is very much warmer than that town in summer, for although its altitude is 2,375 feet, its mean July temperature is 70° (Fig. 108). Its advantage is due to the fact that it rises into bright sunshine, and looks down from above on to the top of the fog layer which so often shrouds the coast; its altitude, too, removes it from the cool sea-water. In winter, however, when fog is less frequent and temperature depends less on the direct rays of the sun, Mount Tamalpais is cooler than San Francisco. The mean annual range of temperature is 25° at the former station, only 10° at the latter.

In winter the Great Valley is cooler than the coast, but the difference is not nearly so great as in summer; frost is frequent in the interior, and at Fresno the thermometer has fallen to 20°.

California represents the Mediterranean climatic region in North America. The Mediterranean of the Old World is recalled both by the rainfall régime, to be described later (p. 341), and the temperature. The contrast between the cool Atlantic coast and the hot interior and east of the Mediterranean region is repeated in an exaggerated form, for the coast of California is much cooler, damper, and foggier than the coast of Portugal, and the Great Valley is even hotter and more sunny than the south of Italy and Greece, the

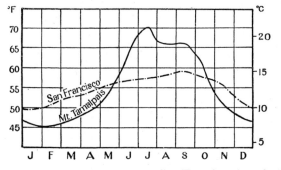

Fig. 108. Mean temperature at San Francisco (207 feet) and Mount Tamalpais (2,375 feet).

summers being remarkably dry and cloudless. This is partly explained by the fact that California is farther south than the corresponding region in the Old World, partly by the difference in the topography, the Great Valley being continental, Greece and Italy peninsular. The closest parallel to the cool foggy Californian coast is found in Morocco, where, however, the temperature is much higher. Gibraltar is about 16° warmer in July than San Francisco which is in the same latitude. Like the Mediterranean region, south California sometimes experiences hot winds, called Santa Ana, which blow from the deserts in the east, often with great force. They are most frequent in winter, and are exceedingly dry, hot, and dusty.

'On the coast they are hot and are skin-drying, lip-cracking, unpleasant visitants. In places they pierce window-panes with little round holes as if drilled by the coarse gravel they carry like a dose of small shot. If they come in the spring after the first blooms form, both the bloom and the young fruit drop off the trees after a short time' (*Climatological Data of the United States*).

These winds are of the föhn type, being heated by compression in their descent from the mountains, like the Sirocco of north Sicily. The northern part of the Great Valley experiences similar hot winds, which blow down from the plateau on the east of the Cascade Range. Their dry heat is very destructive to vegetation if they come in late spring; they are sometimes known as 'Northers', but their characteristics are very different from those of the cold Northers of Texas.

'Apricots, cherries, almonds, walnuts, peaches, pears, plums, grapes, figs, and olives are grown most successfully (in California), and citrus fruits of all kinds flourish in the foothills. This is the only section of the United States in which raisin making is carried on' (*ibid.*).

In British Columbia there is a similar contrast between the cool coast and the warm interior in summer. Vancouver Island has a July mean of about 60°, the temperature being very similar to that of the British Isles in summer as in winter; at Kamloops the July mean is 70° and probably these sheltered valleys enjoy the warmest summers and the finest weather in Canada, but the increase in temperature towards the interior is much less rapid than in California. The warmest part of the Plains of Canada is the east of Alberta. Farther east, in spite of decreasing altitude, the temperature becomes lower; Winnipeg is cooler than Medicine Hat in summer as in winter. Most stations in the Prairie Provinces of west central Canada have recorded temperatures well above 100° (Medicine Hat 108°, and even Fort Vermilion, lat. 58° 27' N., 98°). But it can be cold as well as hot in summer in this region, for all of it except the southern strip has recorded frost even in July, though the frost is never severe in July and August. In the middle and north of the Prairie Provinces snow has been known to interrupt the wheat harvest. However, the average frost-free period is about 90 days, ranging from 60 days in the north to 110 days in the south. At Fort Vermilion the average frost-free period is from June 16 to August 13. The Great Lakes cool their neighbourhood appreciably; at Dubuque the July mean is 74° (absolute maximum 106°), at Milwaukee 70° (absolute maximum 100°).

The coast of Labrador and Newfoundland is cool and foggy in summer. The 50° isotherm for July dips south almost to Newfoundland, nearly all the Labrador coast and the north of Quebec having a mean below 50°, and in an average year the temperature never reaches 80°. Except July a month rarely passes without frost, and though the latitude of south Labrador is that of Liverpool, the summers are as cool as in the delta of the Mackenzie River. The inclement weather is due to the cold Labrador current which chills the inblowing winds, and causes much fog. The interior enjoys less inhospitable conditions and in parts bears coniferous forest, not very luxuriant, but a pleasing contrast to the coast. St. John's, Newfoundland, has fog on 41 days a year, most in April (6 days) and May (4 days) and least in October (2 days). Fog is much more frequent on the Banks, south and west of which there is less, but it continues to be an important element as far as the neighbourhood of Portland (Maine) with 30 days a year.

The north coasts of the continent have similar summers to those of Labrador, the temperature being kept low, in spite of weeks of continuous daylight, by the numerous lakes and marshes, and the drifting ice which usually fills the adjoining channels except in August. Away from the coast the Mackenzie and Yukon basins in the latitude of the midnight sun have warm, if short, summers. Dawson City, which has had a winter minimum of −68°, once recorded 95° in July, giving an extreme range of 163°; but a reading of 29° has been known in July. The Yukon is much warmer in summer than the neighbourhood of Hudson Bay; Fort Yukon has even recorded 100°.

The Canadian Arctic islands can hardly claim to have a real summer, for the mean temperature of the warmest month is less than 50° in the south, and probably little above 32° in the north. Frost and snow are not unknown even in July, but on the other hand in spells of fine calm weather in June and July the sun shines throughout the 24 hours and the south-facing slopes become remarkably warm. The sea-ice only begins to break up in early July in most years, and is frozen solid again in September.

The isotherms loop northward between the Great Lakes and the Gulf of St. Lawrence. The south of the Lake Peninsula of Ontario has a July mean of about 70°; the snow is melted in March, and spring comes on apace with rapidly rising temperature; June, July, August, and September have very warm and sunny weather with high day temperatures. Montreal and Ottawa have a mean July temperature of 69°, a higher figure than the coast of the Atlantic or the shores of the Lakes, or even the Prairie Provinces. The summers of the Hudson Bay region are described on p. 319.

In the middle and east of the United States temperature is very uniform in summer; the isotherms are far apart, in striking contrast to those of the west coastal region. The south-west of the States is warmest, the neighbourhood of the lakes and the coast of Maine coolest. In the Mississippi valley the temperature is kept down by the cloudy sky and damp air; the Great Plains on the east of the Rockies enjoy clearer skies, but the altitude prevents a very high mean temperature, the warm days being followed by cool nights. East of the Mississippi sea influence is stronger and hence the temperature is lower. The following table shows the summer and winter temperatures at typical stations:

	Altitude. Feet.	Mean Temp. Jan.	July.	Absolute Extremes. Min.	Max.
Key West . .	14	70·0	84·0	41	100
Galveston . .	69	53·6	82·9	8	98
San Antonio .	701	52·7	83·2	4	107
Vicksburg . .	247	48·2	81·3	−1	101
Denver . .	5,272	29·9	72·2	−29	105
Omaha . .	1,103	21·5	77·0	−32	106
Chicago . .	824	25·6	74·0	−23	103
New York . .	140	30·6	73·5	−6	100
Halifax . .	88	23·0	64·8	−21	99
Montreal . .	187	13·0	69·5	−27	96
Winnipeg . .	760	−3·9	66·4	−46	103
Medicine Hat .	2,144	11·3	67·9	−51	108
Vancouver . .	136	35·6	63·3	2	92
Fort Vermilion .	950	−14·3	60·0	−76	98
Dawson . .	1,052	−23·1	59·3	−68	95

The temperature is much lower than in the arid western States, but the high humidity, especially on the shores of the

Gulf, makes the climate oppressive for white labourers. This is one reason for the employment of negroes in the southern States, with far-reaching social consequences.

Almost all agricultural Canada is handicapped by liability to severe late frosts in spring and early frosts in autumn which may cause widespread damage to crops. Frost has occurred in every month of the year nearly everywhere, except on the coast and in the sheltered valleys of British Columbia, and near the coasts of the Maritime Provinces and Newfoundland, which are frost-free in June, July, and August, and in the extreme south of Alberta where frost has never been recorded in July. In the northern part of the agricultural lands of the prairies frost may be severe in July, for Fort Vermilion has recorded 20° in that month. But in still higher latitudes there is less frost in summer owing to the very long days, for the thermometer has never been known to fall in July below 28° at Dawson (lat. 64° N.), Fort Good Hope (66° 25′ N.), or even at Fort Conger (81° 44′ N.). At Winnipeg, which is favoured by the proximity of the lake, the absolute minimum in July is 36°.

The cold waves of winter have a summer parallel in the hot waves of the south and east of the United States, which are spells of hot weather with very moist air, brought by the south and south-east winds which blow when an anticyclone is situated off the east coast, and a low-pressure system lies over the Mississippi valley. The moist heat is very enervating though the thermometer may not rise above 100°, and it causes many cases of heat stroke and prostration. The greater heat of the western plateau is much easier to bear since the air is dry and exhilarating.

The table on p. 332 shows the July temperatures at typical stations on the west and east coasts of North America and Eurasia, the winter conditions at which have been already considered (p. 323). The slow change of temperature from north to south on the west coasts as compared with the east is noticeable. The south part of the west coast of America is remarkably cool owing to the California current (compare Eureka and New York), but the east coast has remarkably low temperatures in the north, caused by the Labrador current. America is cooler than Eurasia everywhere on the west coast; the east coasts are very similar in the south, but Labrador is much cooler than east Siberia.

West Coast.	Lat. °N.	Mean July Temp.	East Coast.	Lat. °N.	Mean July Temp.
North America.					
Sitka	57·0	55	Nain	56·5	46
Victoria	48·5	60	St. John's (NF.)	47·5	59
Eureka	41·0	55	New York	41·0	74
San Diego	32·5	67	Savanna	32·5	80
Eurasia.					
Portree	57·5	56	Aian	56·0	54
Brest	48·5	64	East Siberia	48·5	63
Oporto	41·0	67	Vladivostok	43·0	65
Mogador	32·5	68	Shanghai	31·0	80

Almost everywhere in North America autumn is warmer than spring. Texas and the interior of British Columbia are exceptional in having April slightly warmer than October. That the coasts should have warmer autumns is not surprising; but it is noteworthy that even the plains in the far interior, such as Dakota, have the same characteristic, and differ in this respect from the steppes of Asia. The explanation lies in the easy access offered by North America to oceanic influences.

	April.	October.	MEAN TEMPERATURE Difference October–April.
Victoria	48	50	2
Kamloops	50	48	−2
Medicine Hat	45	46	1
Kingston	42	48	6
St. John's (NF.)	35	45	10

Spring and autumn are only short transition periods, especially in the interior and east of Canada, for as soon as the winter snows have melted the temperature rises very rapidly with the lengthening days and clear skies to the full heat of summer, and autumn changes to winter almost as rapidly. But there is often time for a spell of delightful weather, the 'Indian Summer', in autumn. The air is calm and the cloudless skies give beautifully sunny warm and peaceful days followed by crisp frosty starlit nights, and the bright colours of the autumn foliage ranging from yellow to deep purple make a memorable picture. The Indian Summer is a feature especially in the Maritime Provinces of Canada and in New England.

The range of temperature from the warmest to the coldest month is greatest in the north-west of Canada, where it exceeds 80°, least on the coasts, especially on the west coast. The effect of the Western Mountains is seen clearly in the rapid decrease in the range from the interior towards the Pacific. On the coast of British Columbia the range is only 20°, and the Californian coast has the remarkably low range of less than 10°, a lower figure than is found even in the most equable parts of the west coasts of Europe.

Tornadoes. All the United States east of the Rockies is liable in summer to very severe storms, called Tornadoes. These rapidly revolving whirls, which have a diameter in most cases of about 400 yards, travel in a more or less straight line along their path of destruction, at a speed of 20 to 40 miles an hour, and many die out after about 20 miles. The winds near the core of a vigorous tornado may attain speeds far above 100 miles an hour, possibly the highest wind velocities on the earth. They are secondary disturbances in the south or south-east sector of extensive low-pressure systems, and many may develop on the same day in a suitable meteorological environment, and claim even hundreds of lives. They are most frequent and violent in the Plains where the open passage facilitates the meeting of cool dry currents from the north and hot moist air from the Gulf, and especially vigorous in the valleys of the Upper Mississippi and Missouri where, in the centre of the continent, the opposing winds have the greatest differences of heat and humidity (Fig. 109). They are most frequent in the warmest months especially in spring and early summer, and they occur almost entirely in the warmest part of the day. The following description is given in the *Climatology of the United States* by an eye-witness of a tornado which passed over Sherman, Texas, in May 1896.

'When the cloud passed in front of me it seemed to be going at the speed of a galloping horse. The speed was not so great but that almost any one running to the east or to the west could have got out of the way. The cloud swelled out above the ground, but the top of it was higher than the sides. It seemed to be churning up all that it touched and throwing out the fragments at the top. At the same time as it moved along the mass had a rotary motion. It whirled round and round in a direction from right over to left. Only the outlines of the mass could be dis-

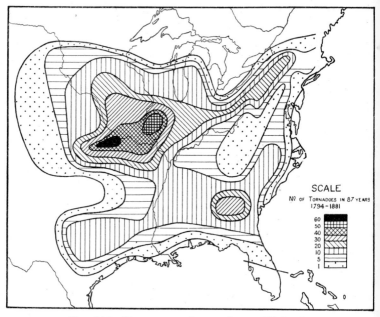

SCALE

Nọ of Tornadoes in 87 years
1794-1881

60
50
40
30
20
10
5
1

0

FIG. 109. Frequency of tornadoes. (Finley.)

tinguished. It was impossible to see into it. Houses and other things went up as the cloud reached them, disappearing in the revolving interior. At the top and around the edges I could see things whirling and then falling as they got beyond the edges. The revolving velocity was so great that it set the adjacent air in motion, and the lighter things, such as leaves and twigs and bits of pine and particles of mud, circled far outside of the cloud and fell at considerable distances from the path of the cyclone.'

The hurricanes which sometimes work havoc on the coasts of the Gulf are referred to in the section on the West Indies (p. 396).

CHAPTER XXXIV

RAINFALL

WE shall first consider the yearly amount of rainfall, and afterwards the seasonal distribution (Figs. 110 and 111). The rainiest part of the continent is the Pacific littoral, where the westerlies, blowing from the warm ocean, meet the mountains on the coast, and the resulting ascent, together with the usual cyclonic activity of the westerlies, produces very copious condensation. The heaviest rainfall is in the neighbourhood of the international frontier, where it exceeds 100 inches per annum in many places. The highest record for the United States, 133 inches, is at Glenora, 575 feet above the sea, on the west face of the Coast Range in north Oregon. The rainfall is even greater in the west of Vancouver Island (Henderson Lake on the west coast has 260 inches), and on parts of the coast of British Columbia. South of Cape Mendocino it diminishes rapidly from 50 inches to 22 inches at San Francisco, and 10 inches at San Diego. It is to be noted that the east slopes of the Coast Ranges as well as the west receive a considerable rainfall, since they are the windward slopes for south-east winds in front of depressions approaching the coast. The close relation between rainfall and relief is evident also in the great longitudinal depression, known in its various parts as the Strait of Georgia, Puget Sound, the Willamette Valley, and the Great Valley of California. The depression has from 30 to 50 inches in British Columbia, 30 to 40 inches in Washington and Oregon, 15 to 20 inches in the Sacramento Valley, less than 10 inches, and in places as little as 5 inches, in the valley of the San Joaquin. The rainfall is least in many parts not on the floor of the valley, but on the lower slopes of the eastern side.

In the Cascade Range of British Columbia and the northern States, and the Sierra Nevada, the rainfall increases again, but only up to about 4,000 feet, above which it decreases slowly ('inversion of rainfall'). The decrease is continued on the lee slopes; unlike the case on the east slopes of the Coast Ranges, south-east winds blowing into depressions here give but little rain. The intermont plateaux of the west of the continent are very dry, since the double mountain barrier on the west deprives the westerlies of their vapour, and the Rocky Mountains on the east help, though in a much less degree, to intensify the aridity. As in the west of the

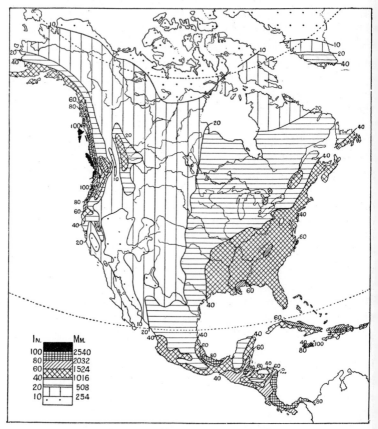

Fig. 110. Mean annual rainfall.

continent generally the rainfall of these plateaux is heaviest in the north; the interior of Washington and Oregon and the west of Idaho have 10 to 20 inches, but Nevada and the Colorado basin less than 10 inches, since the westerlies are less strong and the enclosing mountains higher. The driest tract is the lower Colorado basin with many annual means of 3 inches, 2 inches, and even 1 inch. As in most deserts the rainfall is very variable from year to year. Thus Yuma, Arizona, had less than 1 inch in 1899, but over 11 inches in 1905; the average is 3 inches, falling on 13 days. Fort Apache, Arizona, had 12 inches in 1903, 33 inches in 1905. Pinal Ranch, Arizona, 5,000 feet above the sea, had 12 inches in 1903, 58 inches in 1905. This arid region has very dry air and remarkably clear skies, the sunshine record of more than 3,250 hours per annum being the highest for the continent. The ranges which rise on the plateau have a somewhat heavier rainfall, the Wahsatch Range over 15 inches. The interior of British Columbia has less than 10 inches a year in the most sheltered valleys (Clinton only 6 inches), but the amount is less variable from year to year than in the Colorado basin; moreover, since the air is cooler and less dry, there is less evaporation so that more of the rainfall is available for agriculture, which is helped, too, by the good irrigation facilities.

The rainfall increases again on the Rocky Mountains, but surprisingly little considering their altitude. A small part of Kootenay, B.C., has over 50 inches, but in the United States most of the Rocky Mountains have not much more than 25 inches, and many parts even less. The heaviest precipitation seems to be on the top of the mountains, not on the lower slopes as in the Sierra Nevada. Pike's Peak, 14,111 feet, has 29 inches. The western face of the Rockies is the rainier in most parts, owing to the prevailing westerly winds.

East of the Rockies the rainfall is less in the steppe lands of the Great Plains, but considerably more than on the arid plateaux; the effective rainfall is least in the Prairie Provinces in south Saskatchewan, a dry tract with rather more than 10 inches; in the northern forest belt there is probably more than 15 inches, and less than 10 inches in the Barren Lands where the vapour content of the cold air is low. All Canada east of the Rockies has under 100 days with precipitation, except the St. Lawrence basin which has between 110 and 150 days. In the United States the strip of country between the foot of the Rockies and 100° W. long. has a mean rainfall between 12 and 20 inches. It is very variable from year to year, and this is one of those semi-arid regions where the rainfall is just enough for agriculture in good years, but quite inadequate in bad years, and a series of dry years is disastrous.

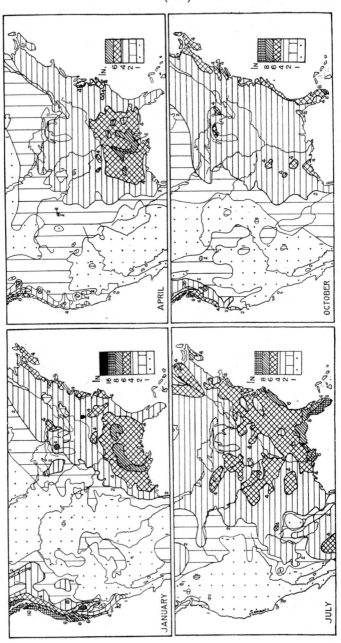

Fig. 111. Mean monthly rainfall. (Harrington and Herbertson: *Atlas of Meteorology.*)

Not only do the crops fail, but the dry surface soil is blown away by the high winds, and the infertile subsoil left bare, gigantic black clouds of dust three miles or more thick being carried right across to the Atlantic seaboard. All the Middle West from Canada to Texas may be stricken at once.

From the 100th Meridian the rainfall increases steadily towards the east and south. An irregularity is caused by the Appalachians, the southern end of which being lofty, and within range of the moisture-bearing winds from both the Gulf and the Atlantic, has more than 70 inches, the highest total in the United States excluding the Pacific coast. The coast of the Gulf of Mexico has over 60 inches between New Orleans and Mobile; the heavy rainfall here is largely caused by the hurricanes of the West Indies region in late summer. The Great Lakes give an increase of precipitation to more than 30 inches in their neighbourhood, and there is a further increase to over 50 inches in much of the Atlantic Provinces of Canada (about 45 inches in the sheltered parts as at Annapolis). The increase is chiefly in the winter when the vigorous cyclonic activity brings warm maritime and cold continental air into conflict. The precipitation is much more reliable as well as more abundant than in the far interior. But strong damp winds, often of gale force in winter, much fog from the sea, and rather cloudy skies are drawbacks.

Snow. In most of the east of America as well as in the west there is considerable precipitation in the winter months; on part of the east coast it even exceeds that of summer, a peculiarity which will be referred to again later. The winter temperature is so low that a large part of the precipitation north of lat. 37° N. is in the form of snow; America is the snowiest of the continents. On the Pacific coast and coast ranges it is too warm for much snow to fall, but on all the other ranges of the western mountains in both Canada and the United States (except the extreme south) there is a heavy snowfall of at least 16 feet per annum, and in many parts much more. Over large areas in the Sierra Nevada and the Cascades the mean exceeds 40 feet a year. On the plateaux and in the valleys there is much less, but the total rises again in the Selkirks, with over 400 inches, and the Rockies, with over 20 feet in many parts in and north of Colorado;

the melting of the masses of snow provides abundant water for irrigating the lower lands in summer. In the south of Saskatchewan and in North and South Dakota in the heart of the continent there is a mean annual snowfall of 2 to 4 feet; during November to March snow falls on about seven days a month. The amount increases rapidly towards the east, and probably exceeds 4 feet everywhere east of Winnipeg; on the east shores of the Lakes the snow is especially heavy, as much as 17 feet in some places. The neighbourhood of the Gulf of St. Lawrence also has much snow, over 8 feet in most parts. East Canada is the snowiest region of America outside the mountains, and the heavy winter snowfall is one of the most striking features of the climate; at Montreal it snows on an average on 18 days in January and rains on only 4 days. Most of New York State has 60 inches of snow a year, Pennsylvania 40 inches. The region south of a line joining the mouth of Chesapeake Bay to the south end of the Rockies has less than 10 inches, and on the shores of the Gulf of Mexico the snow is negligible.

Cloudiness. The mean for the year is highest, over $\frac{7}{10}$, on the coast of British Columbia and Washington, but there is a large seasonal range from $\frac{8}{10}$ in winter to $\frac{5}{10}$ in summer. It decreases along the coast of California from $\frac{6}{10}$ to $\frac{3}{10}$; the summer figure is raised here by the frequent fogs. The plateaux and valleys of the Western Mountains have much clearer skies, with a cloudiness of only $\frac{4}{10}$ in British Columbia, $\frac{3}{10}$ in Nevada and Arizona. The middle and south-east of the continent has about $\frac{5}{10}$ generally, the St. Lawrence basin and the Maritime Provinces of Canada $\frac{6}{10}$, and there is not much difference between summer and winter; but in the Prairies winter is cloudier than summer, e.g. November $\frac{6}{10}$, July $\frac{4}{10}$ at Winnipeg, though the precipitation is heavier in summer. Spells with drab overcast skies are a depressing feature of the winter climate in the monotonous Prairies.

The seasonal distribution of rainfall. The main types of rainfall distribution are mapped in Fig. 112. The abundant rainfall records in the United States enable the bounding lines to be drawn with confidence, so that the best use can be made of the more scanty records from Canada. The characteristics of the types are as follows.

1. The Pacific type (Olympia, Fig. 113) covers the coastal strip as far as and including the Cascade Range. There is a pronounced winter maximum, December being the rainiest month, July and August the driest. The same type extends north to Alaska, but north of Vancouver Island the maximum

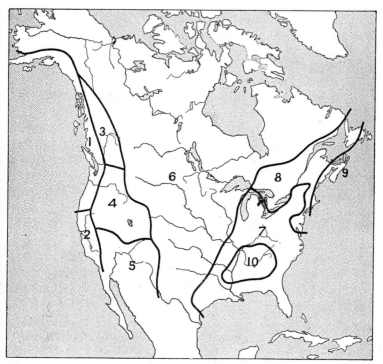

FIG. 112. Rainfall régimes.

comes rather earlier, at Port Simpson in November (Fig. 114), at Sitka in October. The régime recalls the coasts of North-west Europe, but the much drier summers are characteristic; they are connected with the great extension of the North Pacific anticyclone at that season. The rain is cyclonic, and in most of the region orographic also, and it is very heavy.

2. The California type (San Francisco and San Diego, Fig. 115), like the Pacific, belongs essentially to the coast, but extends over the great valley of California and the Sierra Nevada. The rain falls in winter, as farther north, but the

rainless summer of two to four months is distinctive. The prevailing summer winds at San Francisco are south-west and west, and might be expected to be rainy; but they are mostly merely sea breezes, and having crossed the cold current bring no rain. This type corresponds to that of the Mediterranean lands in the Old World, but the autumn and spring maxima of rainfall which characterize a large part of that area are not found in California, where the rainfall increases steadily to its December maximum, and then decreases steadily to the rainless summer. The rainfall ranges from moderate to scanty.

3. The interior of British Columbia (Kamloops, Fig. 116) shows the transition from the Pacific coast with a strong winter maximum to the Plains with a summer maximum. The rain is evenly distributed over the year, summer having a little more than the other seasons, spring a little less; the winter and summer half-years have nearly equal amounts (but in the southern valleys summer has appreciably more than winter). The windward upper slopes of the ranges probably have a pronounced maximum in winter, which explains their remarkable depth of snow.

4. (Boisé and Salt Lake City, Fig. 117.) South of the international frontier the Pacific coast influence is stronger, and considerably more rain falls in the winter than in the summer half-year. December and January are in most parts the rainiest months, and there is a secondary maximum, clearly marked everywhere, in spring and early summer (compare 3), which is the rainiest part of the year in the plains to the east. Late summer is dry. This 'Snake River' type extends as far east as the western foot of the Rockies.

5. The Arizona type (Gila Bend and Flagstaff, Fig. 118) includes the driest tracts of the continent. The rainfall curve shows two influences at work, the cyclonic activity of the Pacific, which gives a maximum in winter, and the intense local heating in late summer, which causes convectional overturnings and showers of rain in July and August, especially on the mountains. June is almost rainless.

6. This type prevails with great uniformity over an enormous area, from the extreme south of the United States to the Barren Lands of north Canada, and it may be named the

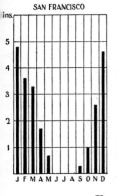

FIG. 115.

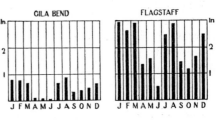

FIG. 113.

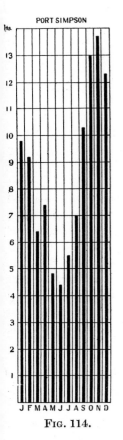

FIG. 114.

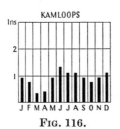

FIG. 116.

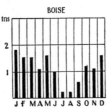

FIG. 117.

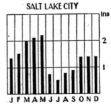

FIG. 118.

Plains type (Omaha, Bismarck, and Winnipeg, Fig. 119). The rainfall shows a strong periodicity. The early summer months are the rainiest, with a pronounced maximum in June. In the central part of the area, including Alberta, Saskatchewan and most of Manitoba, and in the United States the plains west of the line Duluth–El Paso and most of the adjacent Rockies, more than half the rain comes in the months May to August (in the south of Alberta 70 per cent.). North and South Dakota have about 80 per cent. of their rain in the summer half-year. This concentration of the rain in the agricultural months helps to compensate for the small total amount. Winter is a dry season, but no month is rainless, though December and January have less than half an inch each, all of it in the form of snow, in the central parts of the region. The heavy rainfall of the early summer is instability rain, often with thunder. The prairies have four thunderstorms a month in June, July, and August. The damp south-east of the United States has far more thunderstorms, thunder being heard on the average on about 70 days a year.

The neighbourhood of Lake Superior is included in this region, but the lake modifies the rainfall régime somewhat. The maximum is in June as elsewhere, but the fall in the curve towards autumn is checked.

Towards the north of the continent there is a somewhat similar modification; the summer maximum is delayed till July, and autumn is rainier than spring (Fort Chipewyan, Fig. 120). A similar modification appears to be general round Hudson Bay and east of it including Labrador. Its cause is doubtless the proximity of the sea, and the fact that the ground is frozen hard and snow-covered in winter, so that the spring rise in temperature is delayed. In autumn on the other hand the extensive water surfaces are still warm and providing vapour. We cannot draw the boundary of this modified type in view of the scantiness of the records from north Canada.

7. (Galveston and Raleigh, Fig. 121.) This Gulf type is distinguished by its late summer maximum, the rainfall increasing very noticeably in August and September; winter is much rainier than in the Plains, and there is considerable

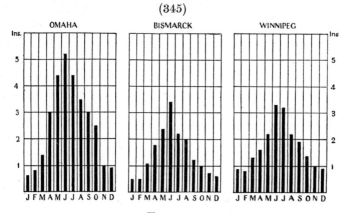

Fig. 119.

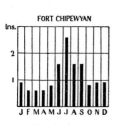

Fig. 120.

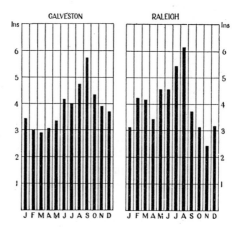

Fig. 121.

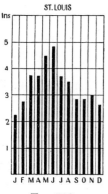

Fig. 122.

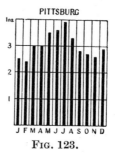

Fig. 123.

rain in all seasons. There are several cyclone tracks, much frequented all the year, in or near this region, notably on the Gulf of Mexico, off the Atlantic coast, and in the Mississippi valley, and owing to the proximity of the sea the disturbances give heavy rain. The late summer maximum is in part due to the extremely heavy downpours associated with hurricanes. These storms originate east of the West Indies and often travel into the Gulf, whence they recurve towards the north-east (p. 396), causing terrible havoc on any land they touch.

The true Gulf type is found on the coast of the South Atlantic States as well as near the Gulf of Mexico, but it does not extend very far from the coast. In eastern Missouri, part of Illinois, Indiana, Michigan, and Ohio, there is an approxi-mation to the Plains type in that the maximum is in early summer (St. Louis, Fig. 122), but the abundant rain in winter shows that this region must be classed with the Gulf rather than with the Plains. Still farther towards the north-east, in Pennsylvania and western New York, the influence of the Great Lakes, and perhaps of the Atlantic Ocean, is seen in the retardation of the maximum which occurs here in late summer, so that the régime again approaches that of the shores of the Gulf (Pittsburg, Fig. 123); but there is less difference between the rainiest and driest months, and this feature shows the transition to the St. Lawrence type.

Types 8 and 9 present the most anomalous feature in the meteorology of North America.

8. The St. Lawrence type (Toronto, Montreal, and New York, Fig. 124). The chief feature is the remarkable uni-formity of the rainfall throughout the year. At most stations there is a slight maximum in late summer, and a slight minimum in spring, and the summer half-year has more rain than the winter half.

9. The Nova Scotia type (Parry Sound, St. John's, Halifax, Fig. 125). On the eastern shore of Lake Huron there is more rain in the winter half-year, and the monthly maximum is in January. The same régime is found in a large area along the east coast of the continent and on the islands from New-foundland to Long Island.

Here, then, is the very striking peculiarity of a pronounced winter maximum of rainfall on the east coast of a continent

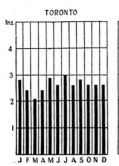
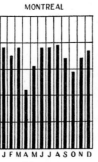
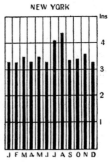

FIG. 124.

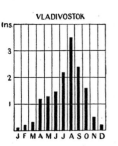

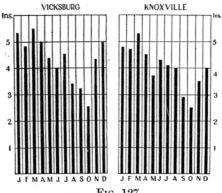

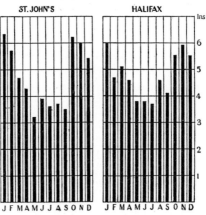

FIG. 125.

FIG. 126.

FIG. 127.

in the temperate zone. Vladivostok (Fig. 126), situated in the same latitude on the east coast of Asia, shows the régime which might be considered more normal, with a maximum in summer and a minimum in winter. The abundant winter precipitation of the St. Lawrence basin is no doubt due primarily to the presence of the Great Lakes, the Gulf of St. Lawrence which extends far into the land, and the warm Gulf Stream. The humidity and warmth over these bodies of water cause depressions coming from the west to show a pronounced tendency to make for the Lakes, and pass over them and the Gulf of St. Lawrence to the sea, and many other depressions follow the warm water off the east coast of the United States. In other words the most frequented cyclone tracks converge in this neighbourhood, and there is a probability that a depression which appears anywhere in the continent will leave it via the St. Lawrence. As cyclonic activity is specially vigorous in winter the precipitation is heavy at that season, in spite of the low temperature and the resulting low vapour-capacity of the air.

It is interesting to notice how the St. Lawrence type of rainfall régime spreads north and south near the coast, especially southward, where it can be recognized as far as Washington. But a few miles inland continental influences assert themselves, and summer convection effects, seen in afternoon thunderstorms, override the winter cyclonic control.

10. The Southern Appalachian type is anomalous like 9 in having more rain in the winter than in the summer half-year, but while 9 has a wet autumn and a dry spring the Southern Appalachian region has least rain in autumn, and the early spring months are in some places the rainiest of the whole year; the rainfall curve sinks in May and rises again to a secondary maximum in summer (Vicksburg and Knoxville, Fig. 127). On the whole this type has affinities with the Gulf type, from which it differs chiefly in having no pronounced summer maximum.

STATISTICS

MEAN TEMPERATURE (°F.)

CANADA

Station.	Alt. Feet.	Jan.	Feb.	Mar.	Apr.	May.	June.	July.	Aug.	Sept.	Oct.	Nov.	Dec.	Year.	Range.
Fort Good Hope	214	−31·6	−26·1	−12·3	14·5	35·1	56·3	61·2	53·0	38·7	16·6	−15·2	−25·0	13·8	92·8
Dawson City	1,200	−23·7	−11·3	3·8	29·1	46·4	56·7	59·3	54·3	42·4	25·1	0·7	−13·1	22·5	82·4
Sitka	62	31·7	34·1	36·5	41·3	46·6	51·3	54·8	55·5	51·7	45·8	38·2	35·4	43·6	23·8
Port Simpson (B.C.)	26	34·0	34·8	37·6	41·6	48·3	52·8	56·0	56·7	52·2	47·1	39·7	36·9	44·8	22·7
Victoria (B.C.)	85	38·9	40·3	43·4	47·8	52·9	57·0	60·2	59·8	56·0	50·3	44·5	41·1	49·3	21·3
Kamloops	1,193	22·9	26·3	37·8	49·8	57·7	63·7	69·5	68·0	58·1	47·5	35·3	28·1	47·1	46·6
Prince George (B.C.)	1,867	12·6	18·4	28·8	40·2	48·4	55·6	59·3	58·4	49·6	40·9	29·6	16·1	38·2	46·7
Ft. Vermilion (B.C.)	950	−14·3	−5·6	7·8	30·2	47·0	54·9	60·0	56·8	45·6	32·0	10·3	−4·1	26·7	74·3
Calgary	3,389	12·4	15·4	25·3	40·2	49·1	56·3	61·1	59·4	50·8	41·8	27·6	19·4	38·2	48·7
Winnipeg	760	−3·9	0·1	15·0	37·7	52·0	62·3	66·4	63·8	53·7	40·7	21·3	5·8	34·6	70·3
Churchill	55	−20·2	−15·6	−3·0	22·4	32·5	42·8	55·5	52·6	42·3	27·3	7·9	−9·0	19·6	75·7
Port Arthur	644	6·3	8·2	19·9	35·6	47·0	57·0	62·8	59·8	53·0	42·0	28·0	14·3	36·2	56·5
Toronto	350	22·2	21·1	29·6	42·1	53·8	63·8	69·1	67·2	60·3	48·6	37·0	27·1	45·2	46·9
Ottawa	294	12·0	13·5	25·7	42·7	55·8	65·1	69·7	66·7	58·9	46·6	32·3	16·9	43·0	57·7
Montreal	187	13·0	14·7	25·4	41·1	55·1	64·7	69·3	67·0	58·7	46·7	32·7	19·1	42·3	56·3
Quebec	296	9·7	11·5	22·3	36·4	50·9	61·3	66·7	63·6	55·6	43·5	29·7	15·6	38·5	57·0
Halifax	88	23·0	23·0	30·4	39·4	49·3	57·8	64·8	64·5	58·3	48·7	38·8	28·3	43·8	41·8
St. John's (Newfoundland)	125	23·4	22·0	27·6	35·0	43·2	51·4	59·1	59·1	53·8	45·3	37·2	29·2	40·5	37·1
Nain	13	−7·1	−3·1	5·2	18·9	30·2	39·9	46·2	46·9	40·6	31·3	19·8	2·8	22·6	54·0
Hebron	49	−5·7	−5·1	5·8	18·3	31·5	40·0	47·1	48·1	40·9	31·2	19·8	4·2	23·0	53·8

UNITED STATES OF AMERICA

Station.	Alt. Feet.	Jan.	Feb.	Mar.	Apr.	May.	June.	July.	Aug.	Sept.	Oct.	Nov.	Dec.	Year.	Range.
Albany	97	23·4	24·4	33·3	46·7	59·2	68·4	72·3	70·5	62·5	50·2	39·1	28·0	48·2	48·9
Albuquerque	5,200	35·2	40·3	48·0	55·4	63·7	73·0	76·0	74·2	67·7	56·2	44·0	35·2	55·7	40·8

MEAN TEMPERATURE (°F.), *continued*

UNITED STATES OF AMERICA (*continued*)

Station.	Alt. Feet.	Jan.	Feb.	Mar.	Apr.	May.	June.	July.	Aug.	Sept.	Oct.	Nov.	Dec.	Year.	Range.
Austin	6,594	27·6	30·6	35·6	44·2	50·7	60·2	69·2	68·1	58·4	47·7	38·4	30·0	46·8	41·6
Bismarck	1,674	9·1	9·2	23·9	43·1	54·0	64·4	69·9	67·7	58·1	44·6	28·1	16·0	40·7	60·8
Boisé City	2,770	29·3	33·8	42·2	50·1	57·6	66·0	72·8	71·8	61·9	50·3	39·6	32·2	50·6	43·5
Boston	124	27·9	27·8	35·7	46·0	57·1	66·3	72·0	69·9	63·4	53·3	41·9	31·9	48·8	44·1
Charleston	48	49·8	51·2	57·5	63·9	72·1	78·1	80·6	80·0	76·2	67·0	57·8	51·0	65·4	30·8
Chicago	824	25·6	27·0	36·6	47·4	58·4	68·1	74·0	72·9	66·3	54·8	41·5	30·3	50·2	48·6
Cleveland	571	27·1	27·9	34·7	46·7	58·3	67·7	71·9	69·6	63·4	52·1	40·4	31·3	49·3	44·8
Denver	5,272	29·9	31·6	38·9	47·4	56·7	67·2	72·2	70·9	62·4	50·5	39·2	31·6	49·9	42·3
Duluth	1,133	10·4	13·3	24·0	38·4	48·0	57·7	65·7	64·6	56·6	45·2	29·4	16·8	39·1	55·3
Eureka	64	46·9	46·8	48·0	49·5	52·1	54·6	55·3	55·8	54·9	53·1	51·0	48·0	51·3	9·0
Galveston	69	53·6	55·8	62·2	68·5	75·0	80·8	82·9	82·7	79·6	72·2	63·1	56·4	69·4	29·3
Harrisburg	361	28·7	29·9	37·8	50·7	61·7	70·3	74·5	72·1	64·9	54·0	41·7	32·8	51·6	45·8
Helena	4,110	20·4	22·6	31·9	43·7	51·8	60·0	67·8	66·7	55·7	44·8	32·5	24·7	43·6	47·4
Indianapolis	822	28·4	30·4	40·1	52·4	63·3	72·3	76·1	73·9	66·9	55·1	41·4	32·5	52·7	47·7
Miami	5	67·0	67·6	71·1	73·6	77·8	80·2	81·7	82·0	81·0	77·8	72·8	68·4	75·4	15·0
Montgomery	240	47·8	51·0	58·2	65·2	73·4	79·9	82·1	80·8	76·3	65·7	55·9	49·2	65·5	34·3
Nashville	573	38·8	40·9	49·5	58·9	68·4	76·0	79·0	77·6	71·9	60·5	49·0	41·1	59·3	40·2
New Orleans	51	53·9	56·8	63·1	68·7	74·6	80·0	81·5	81·3	77·6	68·8	61·1	54·8	68·4	27·6
New York	coast	30·6	30·5	38·0	48·5	59·4	68·5	73·5	72·1	66·4	55·8	44·1	34·3	51·8	42·9
Olympia	,,	38·7	40·3	44·3	48·9	54·6	59·2	63·0	62·7	56·9	50·8	44·4	41·1	50·4	24·3
Omaha	1,103	21·5	24·6	36·8	51·2	62·5	72·0	77·0	74·7	66·2	54·0	38·6	27·1	50·5	55·5
Oswego	335	23·7	24·1	30·6	42·5	53·6	63·1	69·1	67·8	61·3	49·8	38·6	28·4	46·0	45·4
Pike's Peak	14,111	2·4	3·7	7·9	12·9	22·6	32·8	40·0	38·6	32·2	21·6	11·2	6·2	19·3	37·6
Pine Bluff (Ark.)	215	42·5	45·0	54·5	63·6	72·0	79·1	82·4	81·4	75·7	63·3	52·8	45·3	63·1	39·9
Pittsburg	842	30·7	31·8	39·5	51·0	62·6	71·1	74·6	72·5	66·1	54·9	42·9	34·7	52·7	43·9
Portland (Maine)	99	23·4	23·3	32·2	43·6	54·4	63·7	69·8	67·8	61·0	50·7	39·0	27·8	45·4	47·4
Raleigh	390	41·7	42·5	50·6	58·9	68·5	75·3	78·3	77·2	71·5	60·8	50·7	42·6	59·9	36·6

UNITED STATES OF AMERICA (continued)

Station.	Alt. Feet.	Jan.	Feb.	Mar.	Apr.	May.	June.	July.	Aug.	Sept.	Oct.	Nov.	Dec.	Year.	Range.
Sacramento . .	71	45·6	50·2	54·2	58·0	62·9	68·9	72·5	72·1	69·1	62·2	53·4	46·3	59·6	26·9
Salem . .	120	40·7	43·1	45·8	50·6	56·2	61·2	66·4	66·3	60·7	53·6	47·0	42·2	52·8	25·7
Salt Lake City	4,366	29·1	33·1	41·4	50·0	58·2	68·5	76·6	75·3	64·9	52·3	40·5	31·7	51·8	47·5
San Antonio	701	52·7	54·7	63·0	69·4	75·2	81·0	83·2	83·3	78·6	70·3	60·8	54·3	68·9	30·6
San Diego	93	54·0	54·9	56·5	58·3	60·5	63·5	66·8	68·4	66·9	63·2	59·1	55·6	60·6	14·4
San Francisco	207	49·4	51·4	52·8	54·3	55·5	57·2	57·3	57·8	59·9	58·9	55·5	50·6	55·0	10·5
St. Louis .	568	31·6	33·7	44·2	55·8	66·2	75·0	79·2	77·3	70·1	58·3	45·4	35·6	56·0	47·6
St. Paul .	848	12·1	15·2	29·0	45·6	58·6	67·4	72·3	69·4	60·6	48·1	32·1	19·8	44·1	60·2
Vicksburg .	247	48·2	51·3	58·7	65·6	72·8	79·3	81·3	80·9	76·2	66·5	56·6	49·8	64·8	33·1
Washington .	75	33·8	34·7	42·9	53·6	64·1	72·3	74·3	74·3	68·2	56·9	45·5	36·4	54·9	42·7
Yuma . .	141	54·7	59·2	64·5	70·1	76·8	84·7	90·9	90·1	83·9	72·4	61·0	55·7	72·1	36·2

RAINFALL (inches)

CANADA

Station.	Alt. Feet.	Jan.	Feb.	Mar.	Apr.	May.	June.	July.	Aug.	Sept.	Oct.	Nov.	Dec.	Year.
Fort Good Hope .	214	0·5	0·5	0·6	0·5	0·7	1·0	1·4	1·6	1·1	1·0	0·7	0·5	10·2
Dawson City .	1,200	0·8	0·8	0·5	0·7	0·9	1·3	1·6	1·6	1·7	1·3	1·3	1·1	15·1
Sitka . .	10	7·6	6·5	5·6	5·5	4·1	3·4	4·2	7·1	10·1	12·2	9·5	9·0	84·8
Victoria (B.C.) .	85	4·5	3·2	2·5	1·6	1·2	0·9	0·4	0·6	1·8	2·5	5·7	5·8	30·9
Kamloops .	1,193	1·0	0·7	0·3	0·4	0·9	1·2	1·1	1·1	0·8	0·6	1·0	0·9	10·0
Prince George (B.C.)	1,867	1·8	1·0	1·5	0·9	1·1	1·5	1·2	1·9	1·7	1·9	1·6	1·7	17·9
Fort Vermilion (B.C.)	950	0·6	0·3	0·5	0·7	1·0	1·9	2·1	2·1	1·4	0·7	0·5	0·4	12·3
Calgary . .	3,389	0·5	0·5	0·7	0·7	2·3	2·9	2·6	2·5	1·3	0·6	0·7	0·5	15·8
Qu'Appelle .	2,115	0·8	0·8	1·0	1·1	2·3	3·5	2·8	2·0	1·6	1·1	0·9	0·7	18·6
Winnipeg .	760	0·9	0·7	1·2	1·4	2·0	3·1	3·1	2·2	2·2	1·4	1·1	0·9	20·2
Port Arthur .	644	0·7	0·6	0·9	1·5	2·0	2·7	3·6	2·9	3·1	2·2	1·3	0·9	22·5

RAINFALL (inches), *continued*

CANADA (*continued*)

Station.	Alt. Feet.	Jan.	Feb.	Mar.	Apr.	May.	June.	July.	Aug.	Sept.	Oct.	Nov.	Dec.	Year.
Toronto	379	2·8	2·4	2·4	2·3	2·8	2·7	2·8	2·8	2·7	2·6	2·6	2·5	31·3
Ottawa	294	3·0	2·6	2·6	1·9	2·7	3·5	4·0	2·1	2·6	2·3	2·5	2·7	32·5
Quebec	296	3·7	3·1	3·2	2·4	3·2	3·9	4·1	3·9	4·0	3·5	3·6	3·4	42·1
Halifax	88	5·6	4·5	5·0	4·5	4·2	3·7	3·9	4·5	3·6	5·2	5·4	5·4	55·5
St. John's (Newfoundl'd)	125	5·4	5·1	4·5	4·2	3·6	3·5	3·7	3·6	3·8	5·4	6·1	4·9	53·8
Ramah	16	0·8	1·0	2·5	4·3	1·1	2·4	3·5	1·7	2·0	4·1	5·4	4·2	33·0

UNITED STATES OF AMERICA

Station.	Alt. Feet.	Jan.	Feb.	Mar.	Apr.	May.	June.	July.	Aug.	Sept.	Oct.	Nov.	Dec.	Year.
Albany	97	2·4	2·6	2·6	2·5	2·9	3·4	3·3	3·6	3·1	2·7	2·8	2·6	34·5
Albuquerque	5,200	0·4	0·2	0·2	0·5	0·4	0·8	1·2	1·3	0·9	0·7	0·5	0·4	7·5
Austin	6,594	1·2	1·3	1·5	1·5	1·6	0·6	0·4	0·6	0·5	0·6	0·7	1·2	11·7
Bismarck	1,674	0·5	0·5	1·0	1·6	2·4	3·3	2·2	1·9	1·3	1·0	0·7	0·6	17·0
Boisé City	2,770	1·7	1·6	1·3	1·2	1·4	0·9	0·2	0·2	0·5	1·2	1·3	1·5	13·1
Boston	124	3·5	3·7	3·5	3·4	3·1	2·9	3·4	3·5	3·2	3·1	3·4	3·4	40·1
Charleston	48	3·1	3·3	3·4	2·9	3·4	4·8	7·1	6·6	5·0	3·6	2·9	2·9	48·4
Chicago	824	2·7	2·1	2·6	2·9	3·6	3·3	3·4	3·0	3·1	2·6	2·4	2·1	33·0
Cleveland	571	2·5	2·7	2·7	2·5	3·1	3·1	3·4	2·7	3·4	2·8	2·7	2·4	33·8
Denver	5,272	0·4	0·5	1·0	2·1	2·4	1·3	1·8	1·4	1·0	1·0	0·6	0·7	14·3
Duluth	1,133	1·0	1·0	1·6	2·1	3·4	4·2	3·8	3·2	3·4	2·5	1·5	1·2	28·8
Eureka	64	7·0	7·0	5·2	3·4	1·8	0·7	0·1	0·2	1·0	2·3	5·3	6·2	39·8
Galveston	69	3·3	2·8	2·7	3·2	3·6	4·3	3·7	4·7	5·7	4·6	3·7	3·8	46·1
Harrisburg	361	2·7	2·8	3·2	2·4	3·7	3·4	3·9	3·9	2·9	3·0	2·3	2·8	37·0
Helena	4,110	0·9	0·6	0·8	1·1	2·1	2·3	1·1	0·7	1·2	0·9	0·7	0·8	13·4
Indianapolis	822	2·9	2·9	3·9	3·7	3·8	3·7	3·3	3·2	3·4	2·8	3·4	3·0	39·9
Miami	5	2·5	2·0	2·1	3·1	6·1	7·0	5·4	6·1	8·5	8·3	3·0	1·7	55·7
Montgomery	240	5·1	5·9	5·9	4·4	3·8	3·8	4·8	4·1	3·0	2·4	3·3	4·8	51·2
Nashville	573	4·7	4·2	5·1	4·4	3·8	4·2	4·1	3·5	3·5	2·4	3·5	3·9	47·4

UNITED STATES OF AMERICA (continued)

Station.	Alt. Feet.	Jan.	Feb.	Mar.	Apr.	May.	June.	July.	Aug.	Sept.	Oct.	Nov.	Dec.	Year.
New Orleans	51	4·5	4·1	4·5	4·7	4·2	5·5	6·6	5·7	4·6	3·5	3·7	4·7	56·5
New York	coast	3·3	3·3	3·4	3·3	3·5	3·5	4·1	4·3	3·4	3·4	3·3	3·3	42·1
Olympia	,,	7·9	6·8	5·2	3·8	2·6	1·8	0·7	0·7	2·8	4·4	8·9	9·7	55·3
Omaha	1,103	0·7	0·9	1·3	2·8	4·1	4·7	4·0	0·7	3·0	2·3	1·1	0·9	28·9
Oswego	335	2·9	2·9	2·6	2·4	3·0	3·3	2·9	3·2	2·8	3·2	3·4	3·4	35·2
Pike's Peak	14,111	1·6	1·5	2·0	3·5	3·8	1·6	4·2	2·6	1·7	1·4	1·9	2·6	29·6
Pine Bluff (Ark.)	215	5·9	3·9	5·6	4·6	5·2	4·0	3·9	3·8	3·7	2·0	4·8	4·9	51·2
Pittsburg	842	3·0	2·8	3·0	3·0	3·2	3·9	4·0	2·7	2·6	2·5	2·3	2·8	36·2
Portland (Maine)	99	3·9	3·6	3·7	2·9	3·0	3·0	3·0	3·0	2·8	3·5	3·3	3·7	39·3
Raleigh	390	3·6	4·3	3·8	3·5	3·7	4·5	5·3	5·3	3·7	2·8	2·3	3·5	46·3
Sacramento	71	3·8	2·8	2·8	1·5	0·7	0·1	0	0	0·3	0·8	1·9	3·8	18·5
Salem	120	5·8	5·3	4·7	2·8	2·2	1·3	0·4	0·4	1·6	3·1	5·6	6·2	39·6
Salt Lake City	4,366	1·4	1·5	2·1	2·1	2·0	0·8	0·5	0·8	0·9	1·5	1·4	1·4	16·4
San Antonio	701	1·4	1·8	1·8	3·3	3·1	2·5	2·1	2·4	3·1	2·2	1·9	1·6	27·2
San Diego	93	1·8	1·9	1·5	0·6	0·3	0·1	0·1	0·1	0·1	0·4	0·9	1·8	9·6
San Francisco	207	4·8	3·6	3·1	1·6	0·7	0·1	0	0	0·3	0·9	2·4	4·5	22·3
St. Louis	568	2·3	2·6	3·5	3·8	4·5	4·6	3·6	3·5	3·2	2·8	2·9	2·5	39·7
St. Paul	848	0·9	0·9	1·4	2·3	3·4	4·1	3·4	3·3	3·2	2·0	1·4	1·0	27·4
Vicksburg	247	5·3	5·2	5·5	5·3	4·3	4·0	4·4	3·4	2·9	2·7	3·8	5·2	51·9
Washington	75	3·2	3·0	3·5	3·3	3·6	3·9	4·4	4·0	3·1	3·1	2·5	3·1	40·5
Yuma	141	0·5	0·4	0·3	0·1	0	0	0·2	0·6	0·3	0·2	0·3	0·4	3·3

A a

(354)

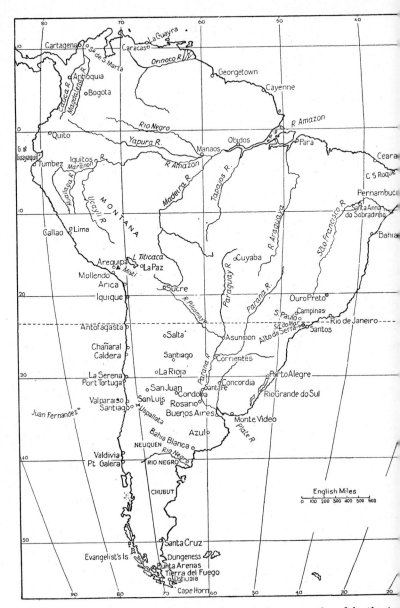

Fig. 128. Key map, showing the position of places mentioned in the te

PART VI

SOUTH AMERICA, ETC.

CHAPTER XXXV

GENERAL FEATURES

SOUTH AMERICA is the only one of the three southern continents which projects far into temperate latitudes. Unlike the
land masses of the northern hemisphere it tapers poleward,
with a resulting absence of that continental variety of temperate climate, with great extremes of temperature, which is
characteristic of the northern hemisphere. There is nowhere
in South America any very great range of temperature from
summer to winter; even in the north-west of the Argentine
Republic, where it is greatest, it is less than 30°. Farther
south the diminishing breadth of the continent more than
neutralizes the increase in range which the higher latitude
tends to produce. The continent is widest in the neighbourhood of the Equator, and the typical equatorial climate prevails over vast areas. But the lofty ranges and plateaux of
the Andes extend from Panama to Cape Horn, and their
highest parts have a perpetual arctic climate even on the
Equator; while South America has the widest expanse of
true equatorial climate of all the continents, it also may claim
to have the greatest area in equatorial latitudes with a temperate or even an arctic climate. The Andes not only make
their own climate by their height, but also form a most important meteorological barrier, and thus affect the climate of
the lands on either side.

Temperature (Fig. 129). The inter-tropical parts of South
America are considerably cooler, due allowance being made
for elevation, than the corresponding parts of Africa and
Australia, owing to the greater cloudiness, heavier rainfall,
and denser forests of the former. In January the hottest area
is the south of Brazil and the north of the Argentine Republic,
in July, Venezuela and Guiana. Practically all the continent
as far south as the tropic of Capricorn, except the west coast

region, has a mean monthly sea-level temperature of over 70° in every month. The south of the continent is much warmer

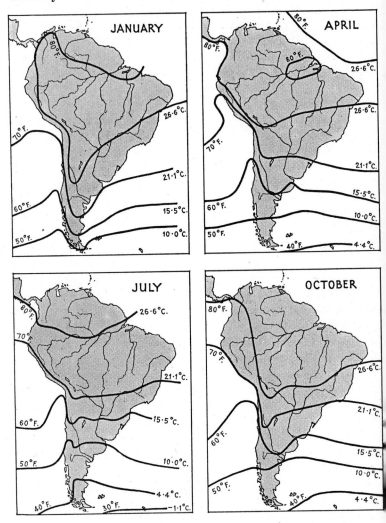

FIG. 129. Mean temperature (based on Knoch).

in winter and cooler in summer than the same latitudes in North America and Asia. In the southern winter the 32° isotherm remains south of Cape Horn; but in China it curves equatorward as far as the 35th parallel in January. The narrowness of the continent, and the vastness of the surrounding oceans, preclude any extreme continental winter in South America. And the same causes produce remarkably cool summers, for in January the 50° isotherm crosses Tierra del Fuego in lat. 55°, but in the northern continents this isotherm lies in general beyond the Arctic circle. Off the west coast of South America from Cape Horn to the Equator the isotherms show a very pronounced northward bend especially in summer, owing to the cold waters of the Humboldt current.

Oceanic Conditions. The Antarctic current, moving from west to east, meets the coast of Chile in about 40° S. lat., and spreads to north and south. The north-flowing branch is the Humboldt current, which is carried as far as the Equator by the south-east trades. Owing to its direction it is a cool current, but close inshore there is still colder water, which wells up from the depths of the ocean to take the place of the surface layers which the trades waft towards the north-west. The main features of the climate of the coast are to be attributed largely to this cold water; there is much fog and cloud, but hardly any rain, and the temperature is remarkably low. The other branch of the Antarctic current flows south off southern Chile and shows no great abnormality of temperature; the prevailing winds are onshore, and hence there is no upwelling cold water along this coast. The west coast of Colombia, between the Equator and the isthmus of Panama, is beyond the reach of the Humboldt current, and is washed by the warm waters of the equatorial counter-current.

On the east coast of the continent there is warm water nearly everywhere. The south equatorial current of the Atlantic meets the Brazil coast at Cape S. Roque, which, projecting like a wedge, divides this great stream into two branches, one of which flows past the Amazon mouth, the Guianas, and Venezuela, into the Caribbean Sea, while the other goes southward as the Brazil current and reaches the Plate estuary. Beyond this, cool water derived from the Antarctic flows north from Cape Horn as the Falkland current.

A direct climatic effect of the oceanic conditions is seen in the temperatures of the west and east coasts of South America. Between the Gulf of Guayaquil and Callao the west coast is cooler than the east all the year. The greatest difference is in winter, amounting to about 12° in July, and it is only about 4° in January, for a warm current from the north (el Niño) replaces the cool Humboldt current off north Peru from January to April. Between Callao and lat. 25° S. the west coast is about 10° cooler than the east in every month of the

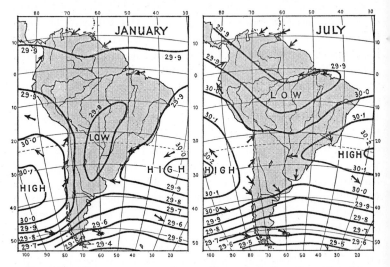

FIG. 130. Mean pressure and prevailing winds (based on Knoch).

year, but south of lat. 25° the summer months alone are appreciably cooler, with a deficit of about 10°; in winter the west coast is even warmer than the east in some latitudes, the oceanic onshore winds being warmer than the winds blowing off the land on the east side of the continent.

Pressure (Fig. 130). The equatorial low-pressure system swings north and south with the sun in South America as in Africa. In April the lowest pressures are over the Equator, and as the sun enters the northern hemisphere the low-pressure trough follows, till in July it covers the continent from the Equator to Panama, and runs far north over Central America to join the low pressures over North America. By November it has returned to the Equator, and in January it is at its farthest south, over southern Brazil. Over the oceans the doldrums migrate less, and on the Pacific coast and the adjoining waters they remain north of the Equator even in the southern summer, since the cold water off the coast south of the Equator is unfavourable to low atmospheric pressures. Over the Atlantic Ocean they migrate only a few degrees, being just north of the Equator in August and just south of it in February.

The subtropical high pressures are centred in July about lat. 30° S. in the Pacific, and lat. 27° S. in the Atlantic, and a band of high pressure crosses the continent. In January the high-pressure belt is broken over the heated continent, and there are detached anticyclones over the oceans; the pressure at their centres is somewhat less than in July, but the gradients are steeper. The Pacific system covers much of the coast of central Chile, giving it fine dry weather. Poleward of the anticyclonic belt pressure diminishes rapidly and uniformly towards the low pressures, which form a belt right round the globe about lat. 60° S.

Prevailing Winds. The north coast of Colombia, and the coasts of Venezuela and British and Dutch Guianas, have north-east trade winds all the year, strongest and steadiest in January, weakest and often interrupted in summer, when the doldrums belt is close to the coast; the latter is the chief rainy season. French Guiana also has predominant north and north-east winds, but the south-east trades make themselves felt from June to November everywhere from Cayenne to Cape S. Roque. The Amazon basin has easterly winds blowing up-stream, very steady and fairly strong in the dry season, but liable to be interrupted by sudden storms from all quarters, often followed by rain, in the rainy season. The equatorial belt has a double pressure wave, as the low pressures make their way north and south with the sun; the rainfall tends to be heaviest about the time of each passage of the sun, and the trades make their influence felt during the intervening months, blowing from the north-east in January, and from the south-east in July. There are but few precise observations to establish this, but probably it is correct as a general statement for parts of equatorial America.

The east coast of Brazil from Cape S. Roque to the tropic has easterly winds in all seasons, south-east in July, east and north-east in January, when there is a monsoonal inflow to the heated interior. The doldrums migrate only from British Guiana to the mouth of the Amazon, and the coast even of British Guiana sometimes has weak south-east winds in July.

The coast between the tropic and the Plate estuary is on the west of the South Atlantic anticyclone all the year, and has north-east winds, warm, moist, and rainy. This is in strong contrast with the regular monsoonal change on the east coast of Asia in the same latitudes, where the land mass is large enough to produce very high pressures and outblowing winds in winter.

On the west coast of South America the winds blow parallel to the coastline and the Andes, except in the south. The coast of Colombia has south-westerlies and variables all the year, and there is heavy rainfall in every month. In general the lofty barrier of the Andes cuts off the surface air circulation of the Pacific from that of the Atlantic and the interior of the continent. In Colombia the barrier is not very important since the ranges trend from north-east to south-west, parallel to the direction of the trade winds and the south-westerlies. But south of the Equator the mountains probably form a complete barrier. The south-east trade winds of the Pacific Ocean are associated with the anticyclone of that ocean and have not crossed the continent from the Atlantic. The aridity of the west coast can hardly be attributed to the prevailing winds having been robbed of their moisture in crossing the Andes. But mention must be made of the extremely violent winds which sometimes sweep through the high passes of the Andes; they seem to be in large part only intensified valley breezes, but possibly they do indicate a tendency of the lower atmosphere to cross the mountain barrier. From the Equator to lat. 30° S. in July, 42° S. in January, southerly —generally south-west owing to the strong sea-breeze effect —winds prevail. On the coastal strip of central Chile between lats. 30 and 42 the climate is 'Mediterranean', with south-west winds in summer and variable westerlies in winter.

South of lat. 42° S. the Andes are still a continuous range, but the altitude is much less and the stormy westerlies which prevail to Cape Horn and far beyond all the year are able to cross them; probably the great thickness of the air stratum involved in the westerlies helps them to surmount the barrier.

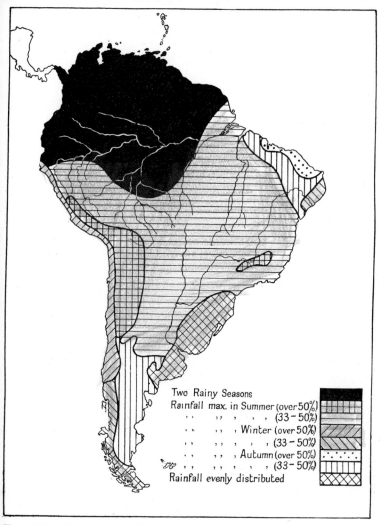

Fig. 131. The seasonal distribution of the rainfall of South America
(Voss).

Their ascent gives south Chile its excessive rainfall and they
descend in the rain shadow of Patagonia where the annual
rainfall is less than 10 inches. The winds of the westerlies
are very strong, and variable in direction, but the resultant
air movement is from west to east. The low-pressure belt

is the scene of a procession of numerous depressions with
very steep barometric gradients. The wind swirls into them

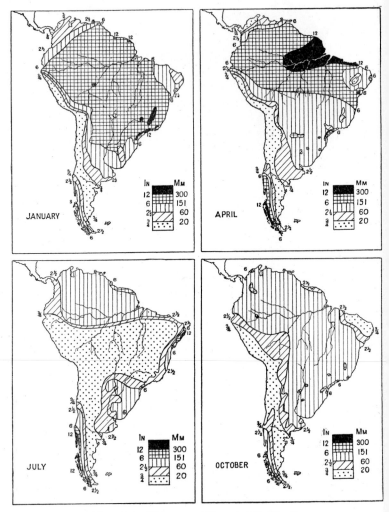

Fig. 132. Mean monthly rainfall (Voss).

with great violence and this region of the Roaring Forties is
probably the wildest on the Earth over the year as a whole.
Since most of the depressions pass south of Cape Horn, the
coast of southern Chile is usually under the influence of winds

from a northerly direction, and the climate is, therefore, mild and very damp. The rainfall, heavy in any case in this stormy area, is especially heavy owing to the mountains. The

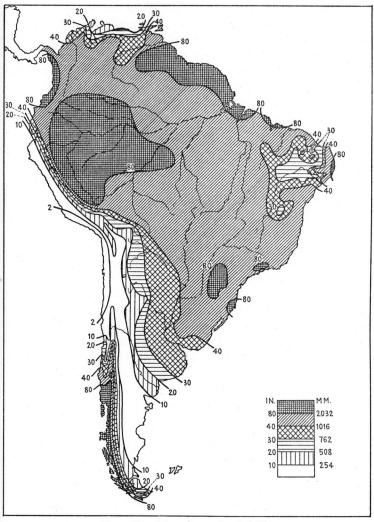

FIG. 133. Mean annual rainfall.

climate and weather sequence is much as in the north-west of Europe, which occupies a corresponding meteorological position. A mild northerly wind heralds the approaching depression, the sky is overcast with driving clouds and there is heavy rain. As the depression passes on towards the east the wind veers to the north-west and west, and often blows furiously.

The Roaring Forties extend farther north in winter than in summer, and reach central Chile. The region round Santiago has, therefore, mild rainy winters and fine rainless summers, that is to say the 'Mediterranean' climate type.

Rainfall. By far the greater part of the continent as far south as lat. 35° S. receives its rain in summer (Figs. 131 and 132). The double rainfall maximum associated with the overhead sun in the equatorial zone occurs in the equatorial Andes, but elsewhere in equatorial South America there is rather one long rainy season, in some districts with two maxima of specially heavy rain. The rainfall of the whole west coast from Ecuador to central Chile is anomalous in season and notably scanty in amount, for what little rain occasionally falls is in the coolest months. South of lat. 35° S. there is in most parts much rain in all seasons, but most in autumn and winter.

The Andes of Colombia and Ecuador have heavy rainfall from the onshore winds. South of this, as far as about 30° S. lat., the east slopes of the Cordillera are very wet, but the west are dry; and in south Chile the western slopes have excessive rain, the eastern slopes little. The subtropical high-pressure belt crosses the Andes about 30° S. latitude, and here it is very dry on both sides of the range. The eastern slopes face the prevailing winds north of the high-pressure belt, the western slopes south of it.

CHAPTER XXXVI

THE WEST COAST, SOUTH OF THE EQUATOR

THIS region comprises the long strip between the shore and the upper slopes of the western Cordillera of the Andes. Along the west coast of South America a coastal range rises steeply from the ocean, but its elevation is never much more than 5,000 feet, so that it is insignificant by comparison with the giant ranges inland (Fig. 134), though it is high and continuous enough in places to shut out the true maritime climate from the longitudinal valley between it and the Andes. The coast range is drowned in the south, and forms the islands of south Chile.

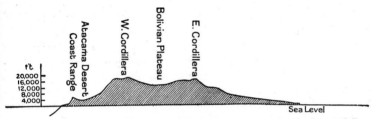

FIG. 134. Section across the west of South America in lat. 20° S.

From the Gulf of Guayaquil almost as far as Valparaiso, it is an arid land, dominated by the trade winds all the year. The Andes entirely shut out the winds of the Atlantic Ocean and the interior of the continent. The land is warmer than the sea, and there is a constant tendency, especially by day, for the south-east trade of the Pacific to be attracted, so that the prevailing winds on the coast itself are south, parallel to the mountain ranges. There is no rain, since the trades are, by their nature, dry winds, and when they reach the warmer land from the cool water which washes the coast their humidity is still further reduced. The coast range sometimes receives a very little rain when the breeze from the sea is more than usually moist, but in the valley east of the coast range the chance of rain is always small. The only streams of water are those derived from the snows and rains of the lofty Cordillera, and these form strips of verdure across the arid sand at distant intervals.

The northern frontier of Peru forms a true physical, not less than a political, division, for it marks the sudden change from excessive to scanty rainfall; the north-east of the Gulf of Guayaquil has 40 inches of rain in the year, but Tumbez on the south coast only about 10 inches, and southward for more than 2,000 miles there is less than 10 inches. At Lima the mean rainfall is 2 inches, and nearly all of it is received in the months June to September; heavy showers are rare, the usual rain being a fine drizzle or a wet mist called garua, which suffices to call into life a bright show of vegetation after the arid months. The air is often very damp though the amount of rainfall is that of a desert. A thick pall of cloud may lie for weeks over the arid grey coast, and sometimes rests on the surface of the earth forming the misty fogs, garuas, just mentioned. Darwin describes them in these words:

'A dull heavy bank of clouds constantly hung over the land, so that during the first sixteen days I had only one view of the Cordillera behind Lima. It is almost become a proverb that rain never falls in the lower part of Peru. Yet this can hardly be considered correct; for during almost every day of our visit there was a thick drizzling mist, which was sufficient to make the streets muddy and one's clothes damp; this the people are pleased to call Peruvian dew.'

Winter is the cloudiest and dampest season along all this coast—an interesting anomaly for a tropical region, which finds its probable explanation in the fact that the land is then relatively coolest, and the warmer air carried inland in the sea breeze is chilled to dew-point over it. The fog, cloud, and precipitation are heaviest on the coast, the interior being sheltered by the coast range. From the sea the coast may often be seen to be enshrouded in cloud, while through the gaps in the hills a glimpse is caught of the landscape beyond bathed in bright sunshine. The fog is usually not more than 1,000 feet deep. The sea breeze (virazon) and land breeze (terral) are regular and prominent features.

The cool and arid conditions of this coast are liable to interruption at uncertain intervals by spells of warm weather with very heavy downpours of rain, when the normal cool Humboldt current is replaced along-shore by a warm current from the north, a change which has remarkable effects on the bird and fish life of the region; in March 1925 Trujillo had about 16 inches of rain, a striking contrast to its mean annual total of about 1 inch (Murphy, R. C., in *Geogr. Rev.* 1926).

On the east of the longitudinal valley, that is to say, on the west slope of the Andes, above 7,000 feet near Arequipa, the rainfall increases. But here summer is the rainy season, and the rain falls in heavy showers, which are derived from the clouds blown over from the Andean plateau; Arequipa has an annual mean of about 4 inches. The mountain streams fed by this rain provide facilities for irrigation at the foot of the mountains, which enables cotton to be grown. The summer rain belt descends lower and lower towards the Equator, and finally merges with the coastal equatorial rains about Guayaquil. Thus there are in Peru and northern Chile three rainfall regions parallel to the coast—a very arid central strip, on the seaward side of it a region with drizzle-rain, mostly in winter, and on the other side the upper slopes of the Cordillera, with summer rain.

Temperature is remarkably low and uniform on the west coast. At Callao, 12° S. lat., the annual mean is 67°, at Mollendo, 350 miles farther south, 65°; while Bahia, on the east coast of America in the same latitude as Callao has 77°. The highest temperatures recorded rarely exceed 80°. Towards the interior there is only a very slight fall in temperature in spite of the increasing altitude as far as the steep slope of the Cordillera; Lima, though 520 feet above its port Callao, is less than half a degree cooler. The annual range of temperature is only 8° at Callao, 13° at Lima. February is the warmest month in most places, but March at Callao.

The aridity of Peru is intensified south of the bend in the coast at Arica, and Chile may be truly described as rainless even on the coast, for the rare and uncertain showers are quite valueless for vegetation. The prevailing wind blows from the south-west; rarely is any other direction experienced at Iquique, where out of 1,000 observations (8 a.m., 2 p.m., and 9 p.m.) 420 are calm, 475 south-west, and only 105 from all other points. At Juan Fernandez, an island some hundreds of miles out in the open ocean, the predominant directions are south-east and south. The cool Humboldt current is equally prominent here as off Peru, with similar results. The damp sea air at Iquique, where the mean monthly relative humidity varies from 74 to 77 per cent., is very destructive to furniture, and causes all bare iron to rust. But the mist-drizzle of Callao is not a feature of the climate. At Iquique during five years no rain at all fell in the first four, and a heavy shower gave 0·6 inches in July of the fifth year; thus the mean annual rainfall of the period was 0·1 inch, and winter is the 'rainy season'. On another occasion a single shower gave 2·5 inches. The climate may be best described as rainless, but liable to a heavy shower at long intervals. On the average there is only one rainy day a year, and it has been well said that on this coast a week of rain is much rarer than an earthquake. Other stations with annual means of less than 1 inch are Mollendo, Antofagasta, and Caldera. South of this the rainfall increases steadily; Chañaral Island has 3·4 inches, La Serena 4·3 inches, Port Tortuga 6·7 inches, and on one occasion 5·5 inches fell here within 16 hours. Valparaiso is beyond the arid tract, and is in a well-watered land with 20 inches. The fogs to which the arid coast is subject occur especially with winds from north and east. The sky is cloudy for the latitude in winter; it is cloudier in August at Iquique than in the British Isles. The cloud layer rests on the mountains about 2,000 feet above the sea, and supports a belt of vegetation which is almost entirely dependent on it for moisture. In summer the Chile coast is sunny, the mean cloud covering being only three-tenths in February. As in Peru the temperature is remarkably low, and the range small. On an average day in summer the thermometer does not rise above 75° even at Arica, nor fall below 55° in winter. The uniformity of temperature of the Peru coast is continued in Chile; at Callao the annual mean is 67°, at Arica 65°, at Iquique 64°, and at Antofagasta 63°. Southward the temperature is somewhat lower, but even at Valparaiso it is 58°.

Behind the coast range the aridity is at a maximum. In the nitrate fields of the Atacama desert, shut off from the sea mists, the air is very dry, and even the slightest shower is exceedingly rare. A few streams bring water from the Andes, and occasionally a great flood descends on the desert when the rain in the mountains is very heavy; but at most times this is an unbroken desert of brown earth, and the air is hazy with dust and heat. Not a plant, even of the humblest form, is to be seen. It is warmer than on the coast in spite of an altitude of 2,000 to 3,000 feet, and in summer the temperature may rise to 85° or 90°; but on winter nights radiation cools the ground rapidly and a thick fog often settles on the desert, with a temperature below freezing-point.

The upper western slope of the Cordillera, overlooking the longitudinal valley, has the characteristics of the corresponding region in Peru, and there is a considerable rainfall in summer—evidently an extension of the summer rains of the Puna.

South of lat. 30° the climate is entirely different, the land is no longer arid, and beyond lat. 40° is the zone of the westerlies, one of the rainiest regions on the earth. The westerlies extend their influence farther north in winter, and the coast of central Chile between lat. 30° and 37° has a 'Mediterranean' climate, with rain in winter but dry trade-wind conditions in summer. The winter rain is associated with depressions, in which the 'Northers' sometimes blow with terrific force, but nevertheless the mean barometric pressure is higher in winter than in summer. The comparatively cloudy, rainy, and equable coastal strip is to be distinguished from the warm and drier central valley. At Valparaiso on the coast the mean monthly temperature ranges from 64° in January to 52° in July, and the thermometer rarely rises above 85° or falls below 38°. The corresponding climatic region of Europe is represented by Lisbon, which, however, though 400 miles nearer the Pole, has considerably warmer summers and cooler winters. Valparaiso has 20 inches of rain a year, 89 per cent. falling in the four months May to August. This is one of the least cloudy and foggy parts of the west coast between the Equator and Cape Horn. In the Central Valley, sheltered by the coast range, summer is warmer, but winter considerably cooler, than on the coast; Santiago, 1,700 feet above the sea, has recorded extremes of 96° and 25°. Santiago has far cooler summers than the eastern part of the Mediterranean region of Europe; the annual rainfall is

B b

14 inches, and suffices with the available irrigation for such fruits as peaches, grapes, and oranges. Snow is not unknown, but it is rare. The climatic conditions of central Chile are in all respects delightful for Europeans.

South of lat. 37° the summer months are rainier and at Valdivia no month has less than 2 inches, but the summers have much less rain than the winters; the whole region is densely forested. Valdivia receives 106 inches of rain a year and the west slopes of the Andes between lats. 40° and 45° more than 100 inches, one station recording more than 200 inches; the southern Andes have smaller but still very large totals. Evangelist's Island has 117 inches and has recorded a spell of 72 days with rain every day. The rainfall exceeds 80 inches all the way to Cape Horn.

The prevailing winds are shown by the records from Punta Galera. Being controlled by the depressions of the westerlies they are much more variable in direction, as well as stronger, than on the rainless coast of north Chile represented in the table by Iquique:

Wind frequency (mean for the year, of observations at 8 a.m., 2 p.m., 9 p.m.), expressed in thousandths (Mossman):

	N.	NE.	E.	SE.	S.	SW.	W.	NW.	Calm.
Iquique . .	9	16	3	15	27	475	5	30	420
Punta Galera .	283	23	27	34	279	80	56	128	90
Evangelist's Is. .	81	14	32	43	95	167	214	289	65

The most frequent directions at Punta Galera are north, south, north-west, and south-west; winds from any easterly point are comparatively rare. Evidently the west winds are deflected by the Andes near sea-level, and appear as along-shore winds, though the main air current of the westerlies crosses the mountain barrier. At Evangelist's Island the prevailing winds are north-west and west; they seem to be less deflected, owing to their greater strength and the less lofty barrier. Here the average speed of the wind is 35 miles an hour—about three times as great as in the south of England—and a speed of 151 miles an hour from north-west has been recorded; there is little difference in wind velocity between summer and winter. The Strait of Magellan shares these wild conditions, the violent squalls being known as williwaws. Winter is mild in this stormy region, but summer is remarkably cool, the January mean at Evangelist's Island being only 47°. The range of temperature is small, for the absolute extremes recorded are 59° and 24°; the former figure is significant of the cool summers. Owing partly to the cool summers, partly to the excessive precipitation, the snow-line on the southern Andes is as low as 2,600 feet, and glaciers reach the sea at the heads of the fiords south of lat. 46°. Records are scanty from the mountains but the precipitation is certainly much heavier than on the coast. Winter is the rainiest season on most of this coast, but summer in the extreme south.

After crossing the Andes the westerlies blow over Patagonia as dry winds, and at the eastern base of the mountains föhn effects are often developed. The scanty rainfall of Patagonia is no doubt partly due to the cool Falklands current since winds from the east, blowing in to depressions, are cool, and can give little rain. It has often been pointed out how the heavy rain of the western slopes of the Andes has caused the rivers on that side to work eastward and capture the headwaters of the feebler east-flowing streams. The rapid decrease in the rainfall is well seen from the following records:

MEAN ANNUAL RAINFALL

Evangelist's Island (off west coast) . .	117 inches.
Punta Arenas (Strait of Magellan) . .	15 ,,
Dungeness (east end of Strait of Magellan) .	10 ,,

In most of Patagonia autumn, not winter, is the rainiest season. This is perhaps due to the fact that in winter the cold land area has a tendency to higher pressures than in autumn so that the depressions of the westerlies find more obstacle to their advance.

CHAPTER XXXVII

THE ANDES PLATEAU

THE plateau extends from the Equator to the tropic of Capricorn, through Ecuador, Peru, and Bolivia, at an elevation averaging 9,000 feet in Ecuador, and over 12,000 feet in Bolivia. The ranges of the Andes form fairly continuous walls on both sides, with peaks more than 20,000 feet high. The region may be regarded as being above the lower atmosphere of the west coast and the Amazon valley, and belonging to the middle atmosphere.

Quito is representative of the lower Puna of Ecuador, a bleak region with some cultivation, but no forests and hardly any trees. Potatoes and barley are the chief crops, and even these are not possible a few hundred feet above the town. There is perpetual snow above 15,000 feet, the snow-line being rather lower on the eastern than on the western Cordillera, since the eastern side has the heavier precipitation. Quito with a mean annual temperature 20° lower than the west coast is not so cold by comparison as might have been expected from its altitude. But this is due more to the abnormal cold of the Ecuador coast than to any remarkable warmth at Quito.

Perhaps the most striking feature is the remarkable uniformity of the temperature and weather, from day to day and from season to season, a reminder that Quito is on the Equator in spite of the absence of equatorial heat (Fig. 135). The mean temperature throughout the year is much the same as in the south of England in May, and Quito has been said to enjoy a perpetual spring. The annual range is less than 1°, and the extremes are moderate, for the air temperature is rarely above 75° by day or below 35° at night. The rarefied air favours radiation, and ground frost is frequent.

Though Quito is on the Equator the rainfall régime is rather that of the south hemisphere, for there is comparatively little rain in June, July, and August, and the months September to May are the rainy season. The total rainfall, 44 inches, is only about half as much as that of the Amazon valley, owing partly to the low temperature, and still more to the rain shadow

effect, which is prominent in the great longitudinal valleys of
the Andes.

It is generally agreed that if Quito has a perpetual spring
it has the unpleasant, rather than the pleasant, features of
that season, with violent changes from hot sun to chill wind
and snow. The complex sequence of the daily weather is in
great contrast to the uniformity of the climate from month
to month. The night and early morning are cold and raw,
but the powerful sunshine raises the temperature rapidly, and

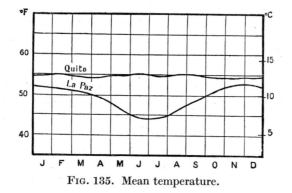

FIG. 135. Mean temperature.

by noon it feels hot in the sun, though in the shade it is still
cool. About midday clouds gather and there is often a violent
thunderstorm in the afternoon with heavy rain, hail, and
frequently snow. These clouds and storms are essentially convectional, and they die away after the heat of the day which
caused them. Hann has computed striking figures of the
daily periodicity of cloudiness, which show that during the
rains only two afternoons a month are clear, and in the whole
year it is clear at noon on only forty-five days, but at sunrise
clear skies are more than three times as frequent. The early
mornings are fine, and the air at these great altitudes is remarkably clear; but in the afternoons the clouds hang low
over the gloomy landscape, so that the mountains are almost
invariably hidden, and hail, snow, and rain chill the air.

Bolivia, being at a distance from the Equator, has a considerable seasonal change. Owing to the generally clearer
skies the temperature is somewhat higher than in Ecuador
if allowance is made for the greater altitude. At La Paz,

lat. 16·5° S., the mean temperature of the warmest month, November, is 53°, of the coolest, June, 44° (Fig. 135). The weather is warmest just before the heaviest rains set in. The rainy season is summer, when the overhead sun causes convectional rainfall. The rains begin in November and last till March or April. May, June, and July are almost rainless. La Paz has 23 inches, but the annual rainfall is probably less than 10 inches over the middle of the plateau which is over-shadowed by the ranges of the Andes, and lies where the arid belt crosses the Cordillera obliquely from Patagonia to the west coast. The daily cycle of weather during the rains is the same as has just been described for Quito. The morning is clear, but as the heat increases masses of cloud are seen rising on the eastern Cordillera, and pouring through the gaps from the moist montaña beyond the mountains, till they over-spread the sky, and usually give a violent thunderstorm. The loudness of the thunder is always commented on by visitors; perhaps the electrical phenomena are especially intense, or perhaps the peals are merely intensified by the echoes from the mountain walls. During the rains the rivers swell, and Lake Titicaca rises to 5 feet above its winter level. But the air is very dry in the dry season; the plateau is a region of continental drainage. Sir Martin Conway observed during his mountaineering expeditions that there was remarkably little water derived from the melting of the ice of the glaciers, and very few avalanches fell; he attributes these facts to the rapid evaporation of the snow and ice. The snow-line is very high, few of the summits in Bolivia reaching it.

The diurnal range of temperature is everywhere large on this high plateau, especially at places which, like La Paz, lie in hollows. Owing to the clear dry air radiation is rapid, and frost is recorded at La Paz in every month of the year; probably during the dry season it freezes every clear night, and Lake Titicaca is frozen round its shores. But the sun's rays are powerful, and in the dry season it is about 25° warmer at midday than before sunrise, and the contrast between sun-shine and shade is very noticeable. Conway gives a vivid picture of the weather:

'Early in the morning and late in the evening, when the sun is below the horizon, the cold is liable to be intense even in September and one suffers from almost frozen feet. In the winter, when the winds blow and the frosts are yet more severe, the dry cold is so trying that even the natives cover up their faces in thick woollen masks, and wrap shawls about their heads and ponchos over their bodies. But as soon as the sun is a little way above the horizon, its direct rays scorch the traveller with their great heat, so that he soon begins to pray for the night, as the lesser evil of the two. . . . By day the burning sunshine so envelops all the brown, dry, dusty ground that everything in view seems to vanish in brightness; and the eye, unprotected by dark glass, cannot gaze steadily in any direction. . . . When the sun is hottest little cyclones raise dust whirlwinds which dance along, often by scores at a time.'

The air pressure on the Puna is only about 20 inches of mercury, and visitors suffer much discomfort from mountain sickness. Even natives who have to travel from the coast to the Puna are not immune. The 'soroche' as the complaint is called locally causes breathlessness and palpitation, loss of appetite, and sometimes nose-bleeding. Lung troubles are very common at these high altitudes.

Above 13,000 feet are the bare uncultivable paramos up to about 18,000 feet, where perpetual snow begins. As in Ecuador the snow-line is lower on the side of the damp Amazon valley than on the west.

On the Andes ranges and plateau the wind blows very strong, and often sweeps through the passes with such excessive violence especially by day that all traffic is held up. The temperature may be below freezing-point and the sky quite clear all the time.

CHAPTER XXXVIII

SOUTH AMERICA, NORTH OF THE EQUATOR

COLOMBIA, Venezuela, and the Guianas make up most of this region, which lies between the Equator and 12° N. lat.; in spite of the low latitude the climate is far from uniform. The north-east trades blow on the coast all the year; they are strong and steady in January, when the equatorial low pressures are over southern Brazil, but in July when they have moved north, almost to the north coast, the trades are interrupted by calms and variables, especially inland, where west and north-west winds blow. There is a sharp contrast everywhere between the dry and the rainy seasons, but the seasons do not synchronize in all places. Generally speaking the dry season is the northern winter, when the trades sweep the whole region (except the west coast of Colombia, which will be described later). They contain abundant moisture, picked up as they cross a warm sea, but as they are reaching warmer regions they do not precipitate it except on the windward side of the mountains, such as the north slopes of the Sierra Nevada de Sta. Marta. From the llanos there are no long series of records, but experience indicates an almost rainless period from the end of November till the middle of March, with very clear skies and dry air. April brings a great change. With heavy clouds and much thunder and lightning, the rains begin, and they last for 8 months during which the low-pressure trough is over the region. The rain is heaviest in June, July, and August, each with about 8 inches. Here, and in other parts of Spanish America, the rainy season is called 'invierno', winter, and the dry season, 'verano', summer—the popular language appreciating the meteorological rather than the astronomical aspect.

The Andes of Colombia is the only part of the continent which has the 'normal' equatorial rainfall régime with maxima at the equinoxes. At Antioquia the heaviest rain is in the months April to June and August to November, July being somewhat drier; December to March is a dry period. Bogotá, 8,730 feet above the sea, on the Andes, has a well-marked equatorial régime, rain all the year, with maxima in

March to May and October to December, July being the driest
month. The great valleys of the Magdalena and Cauca have
abundant rain almost everywhere, owing to their opening
towards the prevailing north-east winds; but the upper part
of the Magdalena valley, south of lat. 5° N., has less rain and
poorer vegetation. The daily cycle of the moisture in the
atmosphere is a prominent feature in these valleys. In the
night and early morning the bottoms are often hidden in a
lake of white mist. The mist dissolves when the sun rises,
and before midday clouds collect round the mountain tops,
whither the valley breezes have transferred the vapour. At
night the clouds disappear and the valleys fill with cold mist
again. Snow falls on the ranges above 14,000 feet, but is rare
below.

The west coast of Colombia has few records, but it is certainly a very rainy district, and probably rainy in every
month, with a slight intermission in the rains from December
to April. This is a natural result of the facts that the doldrums
belt remains north of the Equator here all the year and that
there is a warm current along the coast.

The Guianas have excessive rainfall, most stations recording
more than 80 inches, and Cayenne 118 inches. But on the
other hand, the coastal strip of Venezuela about 10 miles
wide, between Margarita Island and the Sierra Nevada de Sta.
Marta, has the remarkably low rainfall of less than 20 inches,
in parts only 10 inches a year, and less than 20 rainy days,
despite the mountain range that rises steeply from the shore.
The semi-arid sun-baked cactus-strewn slopes and the bare
and brilliant purple rocks of the sides of the gorges above La
Guayra proclaim the dry climate; the mean annual rainfall at
La Guayra is only 10 inches. It is difficult to explain why
the trades are so rainless; one suggestion is that the sea surface
is somewhat cooler off this coast. Along the north coast of
South America the régime as well as the amount of the rainfall
is remarkably different from place to place. The arid Venezuelan coast has most rain in September–December, but the
very rainy Guianas in November–August, with May, June,
and July the rainiest months; but British Guiana has two
maxima, in May–June and December, the former being associated with the doldrums which then cover the region and

the latter perhaps due to the strong and steady north-east winds drawn over the coast towards the southern half of the continent.

Temperature is remarkably uniform in all this region, the annual range being less than 5°, at Georgetown only 3°. Near sea-level it is very hot, but there are large areas in the mountains where the heat is moderate. Carácas, 3,000 feet above the sea, is naturally chosen as the capital of Venezuela, instead of its port La Guayra, where the heat is stifling, especially in late summer. But, as in all equatorial countries, no excessively high temperatures occur, 90° not being often exceeded; on the other hand the thermometer does not often fall below 70°.

In the Andes the usual classification by altitude is: tierra caliente, from sea-level to 3,000 feet, with a mean annual temperature from 83° to 75°, and luxuriant tropical vegetation, banana, sugar, and cacao plantations, and coco-nut groves; tierra templada, from 3,000 to 6,000 feet, temperature 75° to 65°, suitable for maize and especially coffee, of which valuable crops are produced; tierra fria, 6,000 to 10,000 feet, temperature 65° to 54°, where wheat, potatoes, and temperate fruits grow, but pasture predominates; paramos from 10,000 to 13,000 feet, too cold for trees and cultivation, temperature 54° to 43°; above 14,000 feet there is perpetual snow. Bogotá, 8,700 feet above the sea, is in the tierra fria, with a mean annual temperature of 58° and an annual range less than 2°.

The Guianas especially, owing to the combination of a constantly high temperature day and night (e.g. Georgetown, absolute maximum 92°, absolute minimum 68°, mean annual range of temperature 2·9°) with a very heavy rainfall and very moist air and soil, are unhealthy, and a free exposure to the trade winds, and good drainage, are essential to a European's comfort. Perhaps it is its fatal climate which has won for French Guiana its chief fame as a convict settlement. Mangrove swamps fringe the coasts and creeks.

CHAPTER XXXIX

BRAZIL, URUGUAY, AND PARAGUAY

The Amazon basin. The trade winds find ready access into the Amazon basin up the wide opening between the highlands of Guiana and east Brazil, as well as over the llanos of Venezuela, and through the Argentine. Forced to ascend in the equatorial low pressures, especially when they reach the wall of the Andes, which bars the way in the west, they give a very heavy rainfall—far heavier than that of the Congo basin, the corresponding region in Africa, for the relief of Africa tends to shut out the trades from the interior. In consequence of the heavy rainfall the Amazon is the mightiest river on the Earth, and this fact reacts on the rainfall; for there is a vast water surface, especially in flood time, from which vapour is poured into the atmosphere to be condensed again as rain. Moreover, nearly the whole region is a dense equatorial forest, and the transpiration from the trees must add greatly to the humidity of the air. It is remarkable that the rainfall records from the lower and middle Amazon show no sign of the double maximum in the year which might be expected near the Equator.

There are not many good series of meteorological observations available. The few records are from the Amazon itself, and there are hardly any from the Amazon above the confluence of the Rio Negro; they show a south hemisphere régime, the latitude being about 3° S. The annual rainfall is more than 80 inches in much of the basin; this is the widest expanse in the world with such a heavy fall. Pará has 90 inches; the rains last from January to June inclusive, the rainiest months being February, March, April, and May, each with 12 inches or more; the rest of the year has dry fine weather, and September, October, and November have only about half an inch of rain each. Even in the rainy season the mornings are often clear, but clouds appear before noon, to culminate in a copious downpour frequently with thunder; 'before the rain' and 'after the rain' are ordinary expressions of time. But sometimes it rains almost continuously for 24 hours or more, and a day without rain is rare. The dry season

has afternoon thunderstorms, which occur on the average
every other day, and seem to form in the damp air of the
sea breeze (for the Rio Pará is almost a sea). There are 243
rainy days and 170 days with thunder in the year.

In the middle of the basin the rainfall is less, but the dry
season is shorter and less pronounced than at Pará, lasting
at Manáos from June to October; July, August, and Sep-

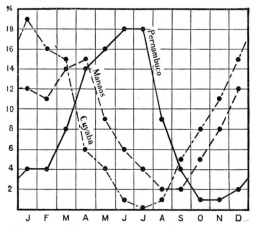

Fig. 136. Mean monthly rainfall in Brazil, expressed in percentages
of the annual total. Manáos represents the Amazon region; Cuyabá
the south of Brazil, with pronounced summer rain; Pernambuco the
east coast, with winter rain.

tember have about 2 inches of rain each. The annual rainfall
is 70 inches, and thunder is heard on only 30 days.

The less rainfall of the middle Amazon is reflected in the
much less luxuriant vegetation. Instead of the unbroken rain-
forest of the lower and upper parts of the basin there is much
savanna, forming good pasture on the flat land near the river,
but dry and almost useless bush, deep in dust in the dry season,
on some of the higher ground, as south of Santarem.

In the upper basin east of the Andes the rainfall increases
again; Iquitos has probably over 100 inches, and there is no
dry season, even the driest month, August, having nearly
5 inches. It must be noted, however, that there are very few
records, and no long series of observations from the Amazon
basin above the Rio Negro. The fading out of the dry season

up-river is perhaps due to the weakening of the trades, for in the basin generally the east winds blow fresh, and even very strongly at times, in the dry season, but weaken and give way to variables during the rains.

An interesting phenomenon on the lower Amazon is the bright lightning which may sometimes be seen overhead without any thunder being audible.

At Obidos the Amazon is lowest in November, highest in June. The Madeira is highest in April and May, and lowest in September. In the Rio Negro basin the rains begin in February, and the river is highest in June. There is a rise of 40 feet during the rains in the middle Amazon.

Temperature is not excessive, but is uniformly high. At Pará the hottest month has a mean of 80° (La Guayra, 10·5° N., has a mean of 83° in its hottest month), and the maximum temperature on the hottest days does not usually exceed 90°, the highest record being 94°, so that the heat is considerably less than in Venezuela and in the north of the Argentine. But the nights are sultry, and at Pará the thermometer has never been known to fall below 64°; the air is damp during the rains, and the atmosphere is that of a hot-house; the conditions are those typical of most equatorial lands. The mean relative humidity at Pará is 93 per cent. in the rains, 85 per cent. in the dry season. The coolest months on the Amazon are during the rains, but the annual range of temperature is only about 3°. A more important relationship between temperature and season is that in the dry season the nights are cooler and the days hotter than during the rains when the excessive cloud and moisture check radiation. The highest reading recorded at Manáos is 99°, at Obidos 102°.

On the middle Amazon there is sometimes a cool spell of 5 or 6 days in May or June brought by a south wind; it is called 'friagem'. The temperature may fall about 8°, and the natives shiver and are liable to catch colds owing to even this slight drop from the normal.

In the Montaña of Peru, Ecuador, and Colombia in the west of the Amazon basin, in spite of the distance from the Atlantic, the rainfall is excessive, since the mountains force the east winds upwards. Near the Equator there is very heavy rain

throughout the year, as at Iquitos, but with increasing latitude a winter dry season becomes prominent. The air is
always moist, and the vegetation is very luxuriant; dense rain-
forest, with rubber, vanilla, and cacao, flourishes up to about
4,000 feet. Above 12,000 feet there is nearly always thick
fog. The eastern Cordillera is the main climatic divide in
this part of the continent, the plateau conforming rather to
the west coast than to the Amazon basin.

South and east Brazil, Uruguay, and Paraguay. These lands
are well outside the equatorial belt and have the tropical
climate of the southern hemisphere with sharply divided wet
and dry seasons. Summer is the rainy season; the weather
is considerably hotter than in the selvas of the Amazon,
partly owing to the more open vegetation; but the dry season is
much cooler, and waves of 'polar' air sometimes bring cold
which is severe for the latitude. At Cuyabá, lat. 15° 30′ S.,
November the warmest month has a mean temperature of 82°,
and June the coolest month 75°; the absolute minimum is
43°. The Chaco Mission Station on the tropic on the River
Paraguay has means of 84° and 64° in January and June,
and absolute extremes of 110° and 28°. Asuncion has means
of 80° and 63° in January and June, and an absolute maximum of 109°. The winter cold increases rather rapidly south
of the tropic. On the high plateau of São Paulo hoar frost
is frequent in winter and snow is not unknown; the best
coffee of Brazil grows here, but the sites of the plantations
must be chosen with care, for the plant cannot stand much
frost; but by avoiding the valley bottoms (which have the
keenest frosts) and also the highest parts of the plateau very
suitable conditions are obtained, the best between 600 and
2,500 feet above the sea.

South of lat. 30° S. frost may occur even on the coast, as
at Porto Alegre, and at Monte Video the temperature has
fallen to 20°.

Even in the south of Minas Geraes the cold may be severe
for the latitude in the dry season. At Ouro Preto there is
sometimes snow, and water occasionally freezes; sugar-cane
plantations may suffer great damage.

The rains are associated with the southward migration of
the low-pressure system of the continent, and the replacing

of the steady dry trades by variables and calms, but few satisfactory records of pressure are available. At Cuyabá (Fig. 136) the rains last from October to April; June, July, and August are almost rainless, and vegetation lies dried up and dormant, to wake to new life in the beginning of October. The rains fill the rivers, which overflow and form vast lakes and marshes. The seasons are similar in Minas Geraes. During the dry season the sky is almost cloudless, but the atmosphere is often hazy with dust and the smoke of bush fires. The fresh dry air is a great contrast to the steamy heat and clouded skies of the rains.

As far south as the Plate River the rainy season is summer, except in certain regions. The coast of Brazil, from the mouth of the Amazon to Bahia, is exceptional both in the amount and in the season of its rain (Fig. 131). From the Amazon to Cape S. Roque there is more rain in the summer half-year than in the winter half-year, but the rainiest season is autumn; Ceara has 62 per cent. of its rain in the months March to May. Conditions are still more abnormal beyond Cape S. Roque, for here June is the rainiest month; 43 per cent. of the yearly rainfall is received in winter, 39 per cent. in autumn, and October, November, and December are dry (Pernambuco, Fig. 136). No satisfactory explanation has yet been suggested for this curious variation. The same region has a remarkably low rainfall (Fig. 133). The amount diminishes southward from the Equator, as is usual where there are no mountains to cause a local increase, but the decrease is much more rapid in the east of Brazil, on and near the coast, than in the interior. The driest region is the middle course of the São Francisco, and the district to the north of the great bend in that river, a region of caatinga or dry thornwood, with a yearly rainfall of less than 20 inches, and in places less than 10 inches, and a long winter of six almost rainless months; the rainiest period is autumn and summer, and most of the rain is of the thunderstorm type. The explanation of this aridity accepted by some authorities is the existence of mountain ranges around, which tap the rain-bearing winds from the east and south-east. The coastal slopes have more than 40 inches, and some parts more than 80 inches, which may perhaps account for the deficiency in the interior. The rainfall in the caatinga region is uncertain as well as scanty. A native writer, quoted by Voss, says:

'As soon as the rains begin, the country, which until then had been desert, clothes itself with a luxuriant vegetation, and the coffee and sugar plantations, which seemed almost ruined, recover with a speed unknown in other lands; in a short time the cattle are strong and fat again, thanks to the abundant fodder now at their disposal. But, unfortunately, the rains often fail for one or two years, and famine with all its terrors spreads over the hapless land. Cattle die by hundreds, all business is suspended, and long caravans of refugees make their way to the coast, strewing the route with the corpses of those who succumb to hunger and thirst.'

Sievers mentions that over 25,000 such refugees died in 1878 in the town of Ceara. The most serious droughts occur in the interior of the states of Ceara, Piauhy, and Pernambuco. At the town of Ceara the annual rainfall has varied in the last 66 years from 96 per cent. above, to 66 per cent. below, the mean. On the coast south of Pernambuco the winter maximum of rainfall dies out, and at Bahia the rainfall is nearly equal in all months, January, however, being the rainiest. Towards Cape Frio the normal summer maximum is well established.

The extreme south-east of Brazil, Santa Catharina, and Rio Grande do Sul, and all Uruguay and the southern coast of the Plate estuary have their rainfall well distributed over the whole year. In most parts summer is the rainiest season, but some places, as Porto Alegre, have their maximum in the winter months. At Monte Video the rainfall is very uniform, the winter half-year getting rather more than the summer. On the opposite shore at Buenos Aires the summer half has more than the winter, but the difference is again small. This region corresponds to south China in geographical position, but in China there is a summer monsoonal rainfall maximum, and a dry though not rainless winter. South America is too narrow in these latitudes to develop a great high-pressure system over it in winter, with resulting offshore winds and drought, and it is open to invasion by the disturbances from higher latitudes.

On the coast between Santa Catharina and C. Frio the régime is normal, with most rain in summer. The rainfall in

many parts is greater than even on the Amazon, wherever
mountains rise in the path of the trades. Thus, owing to the influence of the Serra do Mar, Santos receives 82 inches, and even
in winter has considerable precipitation. The rainfall increases
rapidly up the steep slope of the Serra do Mar, to a maximum
of 142 inches at Alto da Serra, 2,600 feet above the sea near
the top of the range, where even the driest month, July, has
over 6 inches. On the railway from Santos to São Paulo
16 inches has fallen within 24 hours; 'the rain is so continuous
and heavy that the railway company, which was laying a
new line in the Serra in the years 1897–9, state in their report
that on 382 out of 975 work days, work had to be suspended
on account of rain.' (Voss.) The lee slopes have much less
rain, São Paulo only 56 inches a year, with less than 2 inches
in July. Rio de Janeiro has the comparatively small total of
43 inches, but the air is always moist owing to the strong onshore winds; the damp heat in the rainy season, October to
April, is enervating and unhealthy, but the rest of the year
is by no means uncomfortable, thanks to the lower temperature, drier air, and low rainfall. The temperature has never
been known to exceed 99° or to fall below 50°; at Hong Kong,
off the coast of China, in almost the same latitude, freezing
temperatures sometimes occur.

CHAPTER XL

THE ARGENTINE REPUBLIC

THE Republic extends from lat. 22° S. to 55° S., over 2,000 miles, and includes varied climates. Patagonia (Fig. 137) is the coldest part of the country owing to its altitude, more than 2,000 feet except near the coast, and its high latitude; the mean temperature in January is from 75° in the north to 55° in the south, and in July from 45° to 35°; very low temperatures are precluded even in the far south by the narrowness of the land mass. Owing to the shadow of the Andes the rainfall is very low, about 20 inches a year round Bahia Blanca, and less than 10 inches in most of the rest of the country except in the extreme south where it rises to 20 inches again, and on the eastern slopes of the Andes, which have probably about 80 inches. The coast round Santa Cruz is very arid, with about 5 inches. In most parts winter is the rainiest season, but the rain is well distributed over the year.

The rest of Argentina is distinguished by its much higher temperature, the monthly means being from 75° to 80° in January, and from 45° to 65° in July. The subdivisions shown on the map (Fig. 137), Eastern, Central, Western, and Andean, are based mainly on the amount of rain. The Eastern has good rainfall, everywhere more than 40 inches and in the hills of Misiones as much as 80 inches. Summer and autumn are the rainiest seasons, but winter also has a considerable rainfall. This division has the finest cattle ranches in the Republic.

The Central division is distinguished from the Eastern by its longer dry season, which includes the five winter months; the mean annual rainfall is about 30 to 40 inches. Most of the wheat lands of Argentina are in the middle and south. The slopes of the Andes in the north-west are rainy and well forested.

The Western division is semi-arid, and in some districts almost a desert, with a mean rainfall of 20 to 10 inches and in parts considerably less than 10 inches (San Juan 4 inches, Mendoza 8 inches); the rain is very variable from year to year. There is hardly any in winter, and not enough for agriculture in the three summer months, so that even the vine needs irrigation. The Salinas Grandes, great salt-pans, are only sometimes filled with water. The climate is the most 'conti-

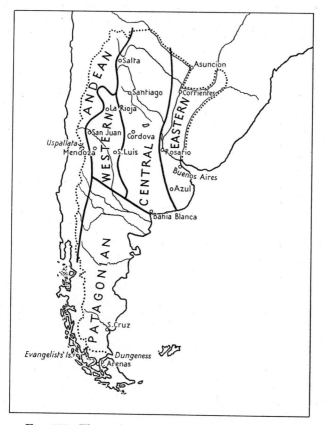

FIG. 137. The main climatic divisions of Argentina.

nental' in South America; the summer days are very hot and dry, with clear skies and powerful sunshine, and the winters are cool by contrast.

The Andean subdivision consists of mountains over 5,000 feet. The northern part is almost rainless and for a mountain region is remarkably dry and bare; it is part of the belt of low rainfall that crosses the continent from north Chile to

Patagonia. Only the highest summits bear a cap of perpetual snow, for owing to the scanty precipitation and the strong insolation the snow-line is as high as 21,000 feet near the tropic, this being the highest snow-line on the globe. South of lat. 35° S. the precipitation increases rapidly.

The following table illustrates the conditions, and the rest of the chapter gives additional details:

Station.	Alt. Feet.	Mean annual Range.	Mean daily Range. Summer.	Winter.	Absolute Maximum.	Absolute Minimum.
Eastern.		°F.	°F.	°F.	°F.	°F.
Buenos Aires	72	23	23	14	103	23
Corrientes .	180	20	23	16	109	33
Central.						
Santiago .	660	25	28	21	115	27
Cordoba .	1,437	23	21	22	111	16
Western.						
San Juan .	2,139	31	39	25	114	22

The range of temperature is greater in the two western divisions than near the sea, and the highest temperatures are considerably higher, and the lowest somewhat lower. Even the extreme north of the Republic has recorded slight frost in winter, and in the centre and south frosts may be severe enough to damage crops. The highest temperature on record which may be considered reliable is 116° at Chilcas (in the Province of Salta), the lowest —27° in the south of Chubut (in the Patagonian climate province), and here, and everywhere south, frost may occur even in the warmest month.

The northern divisions differ widely in respect of rainfall. In the first place there is, in general, a very rapid diminution from east to west in the mean annual amount, from more than 30 inches in most of the Eastern to less than 8 inches in much of the Western province: that is to say, the difference between a well-watered land near the coast, and a dry tract in the interior, where the streams wither away in the arid sands. Though the rain falls mostly in summer nearly every where, yet the excess in that season is not very marked in the east; indeed, at Buenos Aires, autumn is rainier than summer. The following statistics show the rapid decrease in the proportion of winter rain towards the west. At Buenos Aires 56 per cent. is received in the six months October to March,

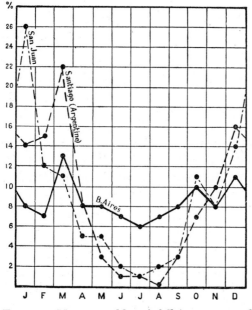

Fig. 138. Mean monthly rainfall (percentage of the annual total).

at Cordoba 83 per cent., at San Juan 83 per cent., and at Salta 90 per cent., the periodicity being at a maximum here (Fig. 138).

SEASONAL PERCENTAGE OF RAINFALL

	Spring.	Summer.	Autumn.	Winter.
Buenos Aires . . .	26	26	29	19
Rosario	30	30	28	12
Santiago . . .	20	45	32	3
Cordoba . . .	26	47	23	4
San Juan . . .	17	55	21	7

The rainfall is very uncertain everywhere, some years

having much more than the mean, others much less. How serious the deficit may be is seen from the following figures:

RAINFALL (inches)

	Mean Annual.	Most ever recorded in a year.	Least ever recorded in a year.
Buenos Aires . . .	37	80	21
Cordoba . . .	28	40	18
San Juan . . .	4	7	0·2

The distress caused by drought is most serious in the arid west, but the Central province also has suffered very much. Sometimes the drought lasts two or three years; San Juan has had a spell of 671 days without measurable rain, Cordoba 103 days. A dry summer is the more calamitous owing to the fierce, almost continuous, sunshine.

The decrease in the humidity of the air, and in the cloudiness, towards the west is shown by the next table:

	Mean Rel. Humidity.		Sunshine per annum.	Mean Cloudiness.	
	Driest month.	Dampest month.		Clearest month.	Cloudiest month.
	%	%	hours.	tenths.	tenths.
Buenos Aires	69 (Jan.)	87 (June)	2,396	4 (Jan.)	6 (June)
Cordoba .	56 (Sept.)	73 (Mar.)	2,728	5 (Aug.)	6 (June)
San Juan .	44 (Nov.)	60 (June)	—	3 (Dec.)	3 (June)

Fig. 139 shows the sharp contrast between the rainfall curves on the two sides of the Andes in these latitudes.

A striking weather phenomenon in the northern provinces and over the Plate estuary is the Pampero. In the Argentine the weather is controlled by the passage of cyclones and anticyclones, moving usually towards the east; the indraught from the north in front of a depression is warm and rainy, but as the depression passes on there is often a violent line-squall of 'polar' air (Pampero) behind it from a southerly or westerly quarter, which brings a sudden drop in temperature. The squall often lasts only a few minutes, but its violence, together with the striking roll of cloud which accompanies it—usually giving rain, and sometimes thunder—and the turmoil of dust blown up from the pampas, make it very noteworthy, and shipmasters have reason to fear it. Pamperos are most frequent in summer. They may be compared with the Southerly Bursters of Australia, which appear to be of precisely the same type. The north-west of the Argentine sometimes experiences hot sultry breezes from the north-west known as zondas; they seem to be föhn winds from the Andes.

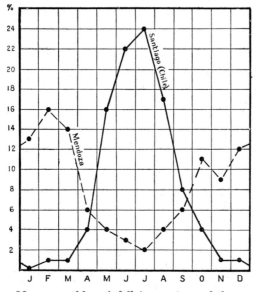

Fig. 139. Mean monthly rainfall (percentage of the annual total); Santiago (Chile) has a very pronounced winter maximum, Mendoza (Argentine) a marked summer maximum.

Some main features of the climate of the Patagonian region have been pointed out already. The summers are cool, the decrease in temperature from north to south being more rapid in that season than in winter, when Patagonia is mild for the latitude. The temperature is highest near the sea coast in winter. The heaviest rainfall is in the mountains, especially in the province of Neuquen, the Switzerland of the Argentine; the amount decreases very rapidly towards the east, the interior of Rio Negro and Chubut having less than 8 inches. Most of Patagonia is in the rain shadow of the Andes, since the region is in the belt of the stormy westerlies, but the wind sweeps with great violence over the open plains.

CHAPTER XLI

MEXICO, CENTRAL AMERICA, AND THE WEST INDIES

THE Caribbean Sea and the Gulf of Mexico are filled with the very warm waters of the north equatorial current of the Atlantic, which become still warmer during their circuit of the basin so that the surface temperature exceeds 80° all the year. The West Indies and the shores of the mainland enjoy a uniformly warm and humid climate, with heavy to very heavy rainfall and yet abundant but not overpowerful sunshine, which produces the rich green vegetation from strand to mountain top that makes of these lands a tropical paradise.

Speaking generally, the region lies between the subtropical high pressures of the Atlantic and the equatorial low pressures all the year, with the result that the prevailing winds in every month are the trades, blowing from almost due east. There is little to add to this statement in the case of the West Indies, which are right in the main current of the trade winds, for their area is too small to produce any important local modification except the daily land and sea breeze on the coasts; nearly all the important harbours are on the sheltered west side of the islands. On the Pacific coast of Central America north-east winds ('Papagayos') predominate only in winter, and strong monsoonal south-west winds ('Temporales') blow in summer, but Panama has north-east winds all the year, steadiest and strongest in winter. The winds are more complex in the neighbourhood of Mexico, where the influence of the North American continent is felt, for the winter offshore winds of Texas continue their course down the east coast of Mexico as far as Yucatan. They are cool winds, and when a 'norther' blows out from Texas the cold is sometimes felt even in Central America and the Gulf of Tehuantepec. The Isthmus of Tehuantepec has almost constant strong north winds in winter, which give heavy rain on the north side but are dry when they reach the Pacific. Such 'nortes' may quickly send the temperature down 10° or 15° for a couple of days, a severe visitation in such latitudes, and they may blow with gale force on exposed coasts and sometimes give very heavy rain. Cool winds from the north, a continuation of the cold waves of the United States, occur in January in Jamaica, Cuba, and the Bahamas, but not in Haiti and the islands to the east. The thermometer falls to freezing-point occasionally on the northern part of the Gulf coast of Mexico, and in Central America frost must be expected in winter down to 4,000 feet above sea-level. In summer on the east coast of Mexico east and south-east winds blow strong towards the hot land. On the west coast of Mexico the prevailing wind is north-west, blowing down the Gulf of California, all the year, but more onshore in summer.

Rainfall is abundant nearly everywhere, but yet the sunshine records are high all the year, as high as in the sunniest Mediterranean lands. Summer is the rainy season; but, since most of the islands are mountainous, the trade winds are cooled below the dew-point in crossing them even in winter, and the windward slopes receive a good rainfall all the year. In summer the cooling of the trades by ascent over the mountains is assisted by convection, and the resulting rain is far heavier both on windward and leeward sides. Position on windward or leeward is a most important factor in determining the rainfall and humidity, as the lee coasts are fairly dry in winter. For example, in Jamaica the mean annual rainfall at Kingston on the south coast, under the lee of the mountains, is 29 inches, at Port Antonio on the windward north-east coast 137 inches, at Blue Mountain Peak, 7,400 feet above the sea, 175 inches, and at Moore Town, 1,660 feet above the sea on the north-east slope, 225 inches. At Port Antonio the least rainy month of the year, March, has nearly 5 inches of rain, and at Blue Mountain Peak, 8 inches, so that there is no dry season; but Kingston has only about 1 inch in each of December, January, February, March, and April, and here these months form a pronounced dry season. At most stations in Jamaica and the neighbouring islands there are two maxima in the rainfall curve, the first in May and June, and the second, rather more pronounced, in October and November; in July there is a break in the rains, this being one of the driest months. The second maximum is partly due to the heavy rainfall which accompanies hurricanes and the lesser storms of autumn, which may give more than 20 inches of rain in 24 hours; violent floods may sweep down from the mountains, tear up the country, and carry away roads and bridges. In the more southern islands of the Windward group the first rainfall maximum is delayed till July or August, and there is no appreciable drop before the next maximum, the rainy season continuing from June to December under the influence of the equatorial low pressures. Exceptionally dry islands are Curaçao (mean annual rainfall 23 inches) and the other islands off the Venezuelan coast as far as Margarita, whose arid slopes tell their tale in the absence of rainfall records; they share the low rainfall of the mainland (p. 377) with annual means of probably 20 inches or less, and are liable to serious droughts.

The rain of summer tends to fall in heavy thunderstorms in the hottest hours of the day; but in winter the rain is lighter, often a drizzle, and lasts longer, and not such a large proportion falls in the afternoon. At times there are excessively rainy spells; 135 inches of rain fell in the east end of Jamaica in the 8 days, 4–11 November 1909; during the same period another station recorded 96 inches in 4 days.

The islands enjoy a remarkably uniform temperature and rather high humidity, thanks to the warm surrounding seas and the low latitude. In the Greater Antilles the mean monthly temperature at sea-level ranges from about 70° in January to 82° in August; at Kingston, Jamaica, the mean minimum of the year is 62°, the mean maximum 95°, and the absolute extremes are 57° and 98°. The more southerly islands such as Barbados are equally warm in summer and much warmer in winter with a mean January temperature of about 77°, giving a mean annual range of only 4°, and mean annual extremes of about 66° and 90°. The thermometer very rarely rises above 100°, or falls below 60°, at sea-level. The winters are coolest in the islands nearest the North American continent. Tropical and subtropical products including bananas, sugar, citrous fruits, and at high elevations coffee, flourish, and in the southern islands cacao. The islands are an excellent health resort in winter, but are too hot and damp in summer.

In Mexico the climates of the west coast, the interior plateau, and the east coast must be distinguished, and also the altitude zones: tierra caliente from sea-level to 2,000 feet, tierra templada up to 6,000 feet, and tierra fria over 6,000 feet (see p. 378). Most of the plateau of Mexico is above 6,000 feet, and is therefore in the upper tierra templada or lower tierra fria zones. The east, being a windward coast, has moist air and, especially in the south, a heavy rainfall, and is clothed with luxuriant tropical forest. The west coast presents a great contrast, for the northern part of it, as well as the adjoining plateau, is largely arid desert, a continuation of the deserts of Arizona, the constant north-west winds giving little rain. This desert region is, in summer, the hottest part of the whole area under consideration. The north and south sides of the isthmus of Tehuantepec also illustrate the difference in rainfall between windward and leeward coasts, the windward slopes on the north having over 80 inches, the leeward south coast less than 40 inches of rain. All the plateau enclosed by its mountain rim suffers from a deficiency of rain, the yearly total being under 10 inches in parts. The mean temperature here is, of course, much lower than on the coasts, but the heat is often greater on summer days; the winter nights are far colder on the plateau, and frost is not unknown at Mexico City, 7,500 feet above the sea. The mean annual range of temperature is nearly the same at Mexico City as at Vera Cruz on the coast.

Central America has a hot, moist, and unhealthy climate; its long seaboard gives it almost insular conditions. From the annual rainfall map, constructed for the most part from inadequate data, it appears that most of the east coast has more than 80 inches of rain a year, the interior basins and most of the Pacific coast between 60 and 80 inches. Greytown on the Atlantic coast of Nicaragua has 259 inches, one of the highest annual means recorded; the driest month here has over 6 inches, and the rainiest, November, 37 inches. In Costa Rica and Panama the rainfall exceeds 130 inches on the windward Atlantic coast, but is only 70 inches on the Pacific. The dry season lasts from December to April, but on the Atlantic slope these months are only dry by comparison with the rest of the year, which has excessive rain and very humid air. On the Pacific coast there is a true dry season, with less than 3 inches of rain in the period January to March; the rainiest months are October and November, and May and June, but there is little difference from May to November; in most of Central America there are two distinct maxima in the rainfall curve, about May and October. Temperature is high and uniform in the Canal Zone, rarely falling below 70° or rising above 90°; the annual mean is about 80° and the annual range about 2°. The Zone had an extremely bad reputation in former times, which the high mortality suffered during the early

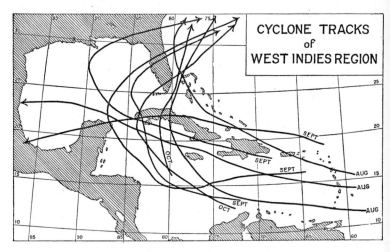

FIG. 140. Some typical tracks of hurricanes.

attempts to dig a canal seemed to justify. But rigorous application of sanitary, especially anti-malaria, measures by the American engineers of the present canal worked a wonderful improvement, and now it is notably healthy for a region so near the Equator.

Hurricanes. The climate of the West Indies is a particularly pleasant one for the tropics, but it suffers from one great disadvantage, a liability to hurricanes. These violent tropical cyclones generally originate east of the islands, occasionally as far east as the Cape Verde Islands, and sometimes work destruction on one island after another in their westward journey. Some typical tracks are shown in Fig. 140. Not only the West Indies, but also the east side of Central America as far south as the Mosquito Coast and the Gulf coasts of the United States, are within their reach; Costa Rica, Panama, the north coast of South America, and Trinidad are outside the hurricane region. An instance is the hurricane which devastated Galveston on 8 September 1900.

'The loss of life in the city alone was 3,000, and throughout the whole of Texas it probably exceeded twice that total. Scarcely a house was left standing in the hitherto thriving city, the grain elevators were all overturned, the waterworks a complete wreck, and ships of all sorts were driven on shore. The land is low near Galveston; the water piled up by the storm swept completely over it, and torrential rain added to the distress. Eight ocean-going steamships of considerable tonnage were borne far inland. The *Kendal Castle* was over eight miles inland when the gale took off' (Pilot Chart).

But most hurricanes recurve towards the north-east, well to the east of the meridian of Galveston. In the 36 years 1876–1911, there were 143 hurricanes in the West Indies region, distributed as follows:

Jan.	. . 0	Apr.	. . 0	July	. . 5	Oct. .	. 44
Feb.	. . 0	May	. . 1	Aug.	. . 35	Nov.	. 3
Mar.	. . 0	June	. . 8	Sept.	. . 45	Dec.	. 2

Jamaica had 14 hurricanes with winds exceeding 60 miles an hour in last century.

STATISTICS

MEAN TEMPERATURE (°F.)

SOUTH AMERICA

The West Coast, south of the Equator

Station.	All. Feet.	Jan.	Feb.	Mar.	Apr.	May.	June.	July.	Aug.	Sept.	Oct.	Nov.	Dec.	Year.	Range.
Callao	coast	68·9	70·2	70·9	69·8	66·9	65·5	63·0	62·4	62·4	64·2	65·1	68·5	66·6	8·5
Lima	518	71·1	73·4	72·9	70·0	66·0	62·1	60·6	60·3	61·3	61·9	65·8	69·8	66·2	12·8
Iquique	30	69·4	69·4	67·6	64·8	62·6	61·2	60·4	60·3	61·2	63·0	65·3	67·5	64·4	9·1
Santiago	1,703	67·3	66·0	61·9	56·1	50·5	46·0	46·0	48·2	52·2	56·1	61·0	65·7	56·5	21·3
Valparaiso	135	63·7	63·1	61·3	58·1	55·6	52·3	52·3	53·1	54·1	56·7	60·1	62·4	57·7	11·4
Valdivia	141	61·9	60·4	57·9	53·1	49·6	45·5	45·7	46·4	48·0	52·0	55·0	59·0	52·9	16·4
Evangelist's Island	174	47·2	46·6	46·3	44·8	41·3	39·8	37·4	38·6	40·1	41·6	43·0	45·3	42·7	9·8

The Andes Plateau

Station.	All. Feet.	Jan.	Feb.	Mar.	Apr.	May.	June.	July.	Aug.	Sept.	Oct.	Nov.	Dec.	Year.	Range.
Quito	9,350	54·5	55·0	54·5	54·5	54·7	55·0	54·9	54·9	55·0	54·7	54·3	54·7	54·7	0·7
La Paz	12,100	51·6	51·3	50·7	49·1	46·9	44·1	44·6	45·9	48·4	50·4	52·7	52·2	48·9	8·6
Misti	19,200	21·4	21·0	19·8	18·0	15·6	14·0	13·5	14·5	16·3	18·7	20·3	21·0	17·8	7·9
Sucre	9,190	54·7	54·7	56·5	55·0	52·5	50·0	49·5	52·7	55·6	55·9	58·1	57·2	54·3	8·6

South America, north of the Equator

Station.	All. Feet.	Jan.	Feb.	Mar.	Apr.	May.	June.	July.	Aug.	Sept.	Oct.	Nov.	Dec.	Year.	Range.
Bogotá	8,730	57·6	57·9	58·6	58·6	58·5	58·1	57·2	57·0	57·0	57·9	58·3	58·1	57·9	1·6
La Guayra	coast	78·4	78·4	79·3	80·2	81·1	81·7	81·1	82·6	82·9	82·6	81·5	78·8	80·8	4·5
Caracas	3,020	64·4	64·9	65·8	68·2	69·4	68·7	68·0	68·4	68·5	68·4	67·3	65·3	67·3	5·0
Ciudad Bolivar	125	78·8	79·9	81·0	82·2	82·4	80·1	79·7	80·8	81·7	81·7	81·0	78·8	80·6	3·6
Georgetown	10	79·3	79·3	79·9	80·6	80·6	80·2	80·6	81·3	82·2	82·0	81·5	79·9	80·6	2·9

SOUTH AMERICA (continued)

Brazil, Uruguay, and Paraguay

Station.	Alt. Feet.	Jan.	Feb.	Mar.	Apr.	May.	June.	July.	Aug.	Sept.	Oct.	Nov.	Dec.	Year.	Range.
Pará	33	77·7	77·0	77·5	77·7	78·4	78·3	78·1	78·3	78·6	79·0	79·7	79·0	78·3	2·7
Manáos	148	80·6	80·4	80·4	80·4	80·4	80·8	81·1	82·0	82·4	82·9	82·6	81·0	81·3	2·5
Quixeramobim	679	82·8	81·9	80·6	80·6	79·7	79·7	79·5	80·4	82·0	82·8	83·1	83·3	81·3	3·8
Pernambuco	98	82·0	82·0	82·2	81·7	79·9	78·3	77·0	77·4	79·0	80·6	81·3	82·0	80·2	5·2
Rio de Janeiro	197	77·7	78·1	77·0	74·3	71·2	68·9	68·0	68·9	69·6	70·7	73·2	76·3	72·9	10·1
Cuyabá	738	81·0	81·0	80·8	80·2	77·5	75·4	75·9	78·3	82·0	81·7	82·0	81·3	79·7	6·6
São Paulo	2,690	68·9	69·1	68·0	64·6	60·4	58·6	57·9	59·0	61·5	63·0	65·5	68·0	63·7	11·2
Asuncion	300	80·4	79·9	77·9	72·1	66·6	62·6	64·0	66·0	69·6	72·5	76·1	79·9	72·3	7·8

The Argentine Republic

Station.	Alt. Feet.	Jan.	Feb.	Mar.	Apr.	May.	June.	July.	Aug.	Sept.	Oct.	Nov.	Dec.	Year.	Range.
Rosario	95	76·6	75·2	71·2	64·9	58·3	52·0	51·8	53·6	58·6	63·5	68·9	73·9	64·0	24·8
Buenos Aires	72	73·6	72·5	68·7	61·3	55·0	49·6	48·9	51·1	55·0	59·9	65·8	70·9	61·0	24·7
Bahia Blanca	49	73·8	71·8	66·9	59·5	52·7	47·1	46·6	48·9	54·0	58·8	65·5	71·1	59·7	27·2
Santiago	659	83·3	81·0	76·6	69·8	64·0	57·9	57·9	60·3	68·5	73·4	78·1	81·3	71·1	25·4
Cordoba	1,437	73·8	72·5	68·5	62·1	55·8	49·6	50·4	53·4	58·6	63·3	68·4	72·3	62·4	24·2
San Juan	2,140	78·4	75·9	71·1	61·9	54·1	47·1	48·2	50·4	59·0	64·8	70·7	76·3	63·1	31·3
Uspallata	9,335	53·4	52·2	50·9	45·9	38·3	34·3	35·8	37·8	38·5	41·9	48·2	52·7	44·1	19·1
Santa Cruz	85	58·8	57·6	54·5	47·8	41·2	35·4	35·1	38·3	43·5	48·7	53·1	56·3	47·5	23·7
Ushuaia	112	49·6	49·1	46·8	40·5	36·7	33·3	33·6	35·2	39·2	43·0	44·4	49·1	41·7	16·3

Mexico, Central America, and the West Indies

Station.	Alt. Feet.	Jan.	Feb.	Mar.	Apr.	May.	June.	July.	Aug.	Sept.	Oct.	Nov.	Dec.	Year.	Range.
Vera Cruz	49	70·0	71·2	74·1	77·9	80·6	81·3	80·6	81·1	80·1	78·4	74·7	71·2	76·6	11·3
Mazatlan	250	68·5	68·5	70·0	72·1	76·5	81·3	82·8	82·9	82·6	80·1	75·2	70·2	75·9	14·4
Mexico City	7,474	55·0	57·0	60·6	63·9	64·9	63·9	62·1	62·1	61·0	59·0	56·5	54·0	59·9	10·9
Belize	coast	74·8	76·8	79·2	79·9	81·9	82·4	82·6	82·6	81·9	79·3	76·1	73·6	79·3	9·0
Guatemala	4,855	61·3	62·8	65·7	66·2	68·0	66·2	65·8	66·0	65·7	64·8	62·8	61·3	64·8	6·7

MEAN TEMPERATURE (°F.), continued

SOUTH AMERICA (continued)

Mexico, Central America, and the West Indies (continued)

Station.	Alt. Feet.	Jan.	Feb.	Mar.	Apr.	May.	June.	July.	Aug.	Sept.	Oct.	Nov.	Dec.	Year.	Range.
San José (Costa Rica)	3,724	66·0	66·7	67·8	68·7	68·9	68·2	67·6	67·5	67·6	67·3	66·9	65·8	67·5	3·1
Colon	164	80·0	80·0	80·5	80·9	80·8	80·3	80·3	80·2	80·4	79·9	79·3	80·0	80·2	1·6
Havana	62	71·4	71·8	73·8	76·3	78·6	80·4	81·7	81·7	80·8	79·0	75·0	72·7	77·0	10·3
Kingston	49	75·7	75·7	76·5	78·3	79·9	81·1	81·7	81·0	80·6	79·3	78·6	76·8	78·8	6·0
Bridgetown (Barbados)	56	77·5	77·0	77·4	79·0	80·2	80·4	80·1	80·8	81·1	80·2	79·5	78·4	79·3	4·1
Port of Spain (Trinidad)	coast	75·2	75·4	76·3	77·8	79·1	78·1	77·9	77·8	78·3	78·2	77·5	76·3	77·3	3·9

MEAN RAINFALL (inches)

SOUTH AMERICA

The West Coast, south of the Equator

Station.	Alt. Feet.	Jan.	Feb.	Mar.	Apr.	May.	June.	July.	Aug.	Sept.	Oct.	Nov.	Dec.	Year.
Lima	522	0·03	0	0	0·03	0·03	0·2	0·3	0·5	0·5	0·1	0·03	0·03	1·8
Arequipa	7,740	0·6	3·2	0·5	0	0	0	0	0	0	0	0·1	0	4·4
Iquique	30	0	0	0	0	0	0	0·02	0	0·03	0	0	0	0·05
La Serena	33	0	0	0·1	0	1·3	1·2	1·1	0·4	0·1	0·1	0	0	4·3
Valparaiso	135	0	0	0·9	0·1	2·7	6·0	5·3	3·4	0·4	0·5	0·3	0	19·6
Santiago	1,703	0	0·1	0·2	0·6	2·3	3·2	3·4	2·4	1·2	0·6	0·2	0·2	14·4
Valdivia	49	2·6	2·9	5·5	9·3	15·7	17·2	16·3	13·7	8·4	5·5	5·0	4·4	106·3
Evangelist's Island	174	12·8	8·9	12·3	11·6	8·8	8·5	8·9	8·6	7·7	9·0	10·3	9·6	117·0

SOUTH AMERICA (continued)

The Andes Plateau

Station.	Alt. Feet.	Jan.	Feb.	Mar.	Apr.	May.	June.	July.	Aug.	Sept.	Oct.	Nov.	Dec.	Year.
Quito	9,350	4·2	4·3	5·2	7·4	5·0	1·5	0·9	1·5	3·0	3·7	3·8	3·8	44·1
La Paz	12,100	4·4	4·4	2·9	1·4	0·5	0·3	0·4	0·6	1·1	1·7	1·9	3·6	23·1
Sucre	9,190	6·5	4·8	3·6	2·0	0·2	0·2	0·2	0·2	0·9	1·3	2·7	4·6	27·2

South America, north of the Equator

Station.	Alt. Feet.	Jan.	Feb.	Mar.	Apr.	May.	June.	July.	Aug.	Sept.	Oct.	Nov.	Dec.	Year.
Bogotá	8,730	*2·3*	2·4	4·1	5·7	4·5	2·4	*2·0*	2·2	2·4	*6·4*	4·6	2·6	41·6
Cartagena	coast	*0*	*0*	0·1	0·1	4·3	5·3	*3·2*	5·3	5·3	*8·8*	4·6	0·6	37·6
La Guayra	coast	*0·5*	*0·2*	*0·8*	0·2	0·6	0·9	*1·0*	1·1	1·2	*1·6*	1·6	1·5	11·1
Carácas	3,419	*0·9*	*0·4*	0·6	1·6	2·8	4·1	*4·3*	4·3	4·1	3·8	3·3	1·8	31·7
Ciudad Bolivar	125	*0·5*	*0·2*	0·2	0·9	2·6	5·6	*6·2*	6·3	3·1	3·4	3·4	1·9	34·6
Georgetown	10	7·9	4·6	7·2	6·0	11·1	11·7	*9·9*	6·5	*3·1*	2·9	6·7	11·1	88·7
Cayenne	20	**14·1**	*12·1*	15·2	15·5	20·0	14·8	*6·5*	2·6	*1·1*	1·3	4·6	10·6	118·4
Port of Spain (Trinidad)	coast	2·7	*1·5*	1·8	1·8	3·6	7·9	*8·9*	9·6	7·4	6·7	7·0	4·7	63·7

Brazil, Uruguay, and Paraguay

Station.	Alt. Feet.	Jan.	Feb.	Mar.	Apr.	May.	June.	July.	Aug.	Sept.	Oct.	Nov.	Dec.	Year.
Pará	33	7·6	13·3	17·0	17·8	11·8	9·1	2·3	2·8	0·6	*0·5*	0·6	2·6	89·6
Santarem	20	6·2	12·0	10·6	10·9	10·3	6·2	3·0	1·9	1·5	*1·1*	1·5	5·0	69·6
Manãos	150	9·2	9·8	9·6	8·5	7·0	3·6	2·2	*1·4*	2·0	4·1	5·5	7·7	69·7
Iquitos	328	10·2	*9·8*	12·2	6·5	10·0	7·4	6·6	*4·6*	8·7	7·2	8·4	11·5	103·1
Ceara	66	3·3	6·9	11·8	13·5	9·6	4·7	2·1	1·1	0·7	*0·5*	0·6	1·5	56·3
Quixeramobim	679	3·1	3·9	5·7	4·8	3·7	1·5	0·8	0·4	0·1	*0·1*	0·2	1·1	25·1
Pernambuco	10	2·0	3·5	6·3	8·6	10·8	11·2	10·3	6·3	2·7	*1·0*	1·1	1·1	65·1
Sta. Anna do Sobradinho	1,053	3·0	1·6	5·8	0·4	0·2	*0*	*0*	0	0·5	1·5	0·4	0·9	14·6
Cuyabá	738	9·8	8·3	8·3	4·0	2·1	0·3	*0·2*	1·1	2·0	4·5	5·9	8·1	54·6
Ouro Preto	3,750	16·6	15·0	10·8	4·1	1·8	0·9	*0·9*	1·6	3·3	5·0	9·3	10·2	79·5
Rio de Janeiro	216	5·0	4·5	5·3	4·2	3·2	2·2	*1·7*	1·8	2·6	3·3	4·1	5·5	43·3
Santos	10	10·6	8·5	11·9	6·7	6·2	2·4	4·5	4·6	5·5	6·2	7·7	7·1	82·1

D d

MEAN RAINFALL (inches), *continued*

SOUTH AMERICA (*continued*)

Brazil, Uruguay, and Paraguay (*continued*)

Station.	Alt. Feet.	Jan.	Feb.	Mar.	Apr.	May.	June.	July.	Aug.	Sept.	Oct.	Nov.	Dec.	Year.
São Paulo	2,690	9.1	7.6	5.7	2.7	2.7	2.2	1.3	2.0	3.3	4.2	5.2	7.3	53.1
Ribeirão Preto	1,824	11.0	7.9	6.1	3.1	1.4	2.0	0.6	1.2	2.2	4.4	6.8	8.5	55.4
Rio Grande	56	3.5	5.7	3.5	3.2	3.2	4.5	5.2	3.6	4.8	3.3	3.4	2.9	46.5
Monte Video	26	3.2	2.4	3.5	3.4	3.9	3.3	3.3	2.7	3.1	3.7	3.0	3.1	38.5
Asuncion	300	5.5	5.1	4.3	5.2	4.6	2.7	2.2	1.5	3.1	5.5	5.9	6.2	51.8

The Argentine Republic

Station.	Alt. Feet.	Jan.	Feb.	Mar.	Apr.	May.	June.	July.	Aug.	Sept.	Oct.	Nov.	Dec.	Year.
Corrientes	256	5.2	4.9	5.4	5.7	3.9	2.2	1.9	1.5	2.8	4.7	4.8	5.4	48.1
Concordia	80	4.3	2.4	4.9	3.6	3.0	2.6	2.9	3.2	3.7	3.4	3.1	4.8	41.9
Santa Fé	66	3.3	3.5	5.1	3.3	1.8	0.9	1.0	0.9	1.9	3.4	3.4	4.6	33.0
Rosario	95	3.0	3.0	3.4	4.4	1.7	1.2	1.4	1.4	2.2	3.7	4.3	3.9	33.5
Buenos Aires	72	3.1	2.7	4.4	3.5	2.9	2.5	2.2	2.5	3.0	3.5	3.1	3.9	37.2
Azul	453	3.0	2.4	4.5	2.2	1.9	1.6	1.9	2.2	1.9	3.2	3.1	3.1	31.1
Bahia Blanca	49	1.7	2.1	2.7	2.1	1.2	1.1	1.0	1.1	1.5	2.2	3.2	1.9	20.8
Santiago	659	2.8	3.2	4.6	1.6	0.6	0.2	0.2	0.1	0.6	1.5	2.1	3.3	20.8
Cordoba	1,437	4.2	4.2	3.5	1.8	1.0	0.3	0.3	0.5	0.9	2.4	4.0	4.6	27.7
San Luis	2,490	3.3	3.0	2.4	1.0	0.6	0.2	0.3	0.4	0.6	2.3	3.5	3.6	21.2
Salta	3,940	6.8	5.8	4.0	1.2	0.4	0.1	0	0.2	0.4	1.3	2.2	5.5	28.4
La Rioja	1,230	3.1	1.9	1.5	0.4	0.1	0.1	0.2	0.1	0.1	0.8	1.3	1.9	11.3
San Juan	2,140	0.7	0.5	0.4	0.1	0.1	0	0	0.1	0.1	0.2	0.2	0.4	3.7
Uspallata	9,335	0.8	1.2	0.2	0	0.6	0.6	0.7	1.6	0.2	1.3	0.8	0.2	7.0
Santa Cruz	85	0.6	0.4	0.3	0.6	0.5	0.5	0.7	0.4	0.2	0.4	0.5	0.8	5.9
Punta Arenas (Chile)	56	1.4	1.2	1.7	1.6	1.6	1.2	1.3	1.2	1.1	0.8	1.1	1.4	15.3
Ushuaia	112	1.8	2.5	2.3	1.5	1.3	2.3	1.4	0.9	1.5	1.7	2.0	2.3	21.5

SOUTH AMERICA (continued)

Mexico, Central America, and the West Indies

Station.	Alt. Feet.	Jan.	Feb.	Mar.	Apr.	May.	June.	July.	Aug.	Sept.	Oct.	Nov.	Dec.	Year.
Vera Cruz	49	1·0	0·6	0·5	0·6	1·8	11·4	13·0	10·7	12·0	5·7	3·1	1·0	60·2
Chichuahua	4,690	0·2	0·4	0·3	0·2	0·2	1·7	3·6	3·7	3·3	0·9	0·5	0·4	15·2
Mexico City	7,474	0·2	0·2	0·5	0·7	1·9	3·9	4·5	4·6	3·9	1·6	0·5	0·2	22·8
Belize	coast	5·1	2·6	1·6	1·5	4·1	9·1	9·6	8·5	9·4	11·0	10·2	6·3	79·0
Guatemala	4,855	0·3	0·2	0·5	1·3	5·6	11·5	8·0	8·0	9·2	6·7	0·9	0·2	52·4
San José	3,724	0·6	0·2	0·8	1·8	9·0	9·5	8·3	9·5	12·0	11·8	5·7	1·6	70·8
Panama	coast	0·7	0	0·7	1·9	6·9	6·5	6·5	5·7	7·3	8·2	8·0	4·0	56·4
Balboa (Canal Zone, Pacific)	100	0·9	0·9	0·6	2·8	7·8	8·2	7·2	7·8	7·9	10·1	10·1	4·2	68·6
Culebra (Canal Zone, Interior)	350	1·6	0·7	0·6	3·6	11·1	8·8	9·3	10·3	10·7	11·5	12·3	7·2	87·7
Colon (Canal Zone, Atlantic)	coast	3·7	1·6	1·6	4·3	12·4	13·3	16·0	14·7	12·5	15·1	20·7	11·4	127·3
Havana	62	3·0	1·5	1·7	1·7	5·1	5·6	4·3	4·3	5·0	7·0	3·2	2·4	45·0
Kingston	60	0·7	0·5	0·8	1·3	3·1	3·6	1·2	2·7	4·0	6·3	3·5	1·1	28·9
Port Antonio (Jamaica)	10	8·6	6·5	4·7	7·0	15·4	16·9	10·6	11·1	10·8	14·9	17·2	13·0	137·3
Fort de France (Martinique)	13	4·7	4·3	2·9	3·9	4·7	7·4	9·4	10·3	9·3	9·8	7·9	5·9	80·5

(404)

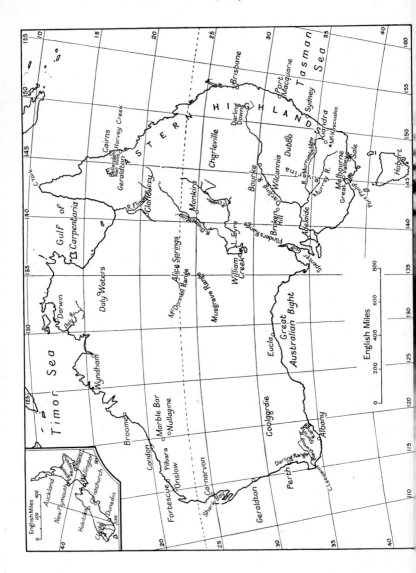

PART VII
AUSTRALIA AND NEW ZEALAND

CHAPTER XLII
GENERAL FEATURES

THE possibilities of the future development of Australia, which is the most arid of the continents, depend largely on the vital question of rainfall, so in describing the general features of position and relief chief stress is laid on the circumstances to which the scantiness of the rainfall may be attributed.

Australia lies in one of the driest belts of the earth, the calms of the subtropical high pressures, and the trade winds which blow from them towards the Equator; excluding Tasmania it lies between latitudes 11° S. and 39° S., the tropic of Capricorn crossing it near the middle. There is a close resemblance to North Africa, where the same latitudes of the north hemisphere include the Sahara. In South Africa also the parallels which bound Australia enclose the arid section which includes the Kalahari and the coastal desert of South-west Africa. About 35 per cent. of the area of Australia has less than 10 inches of rain a year, only 7 per cent. more than 40 inches.

The interior of a continent naturally tends to have a poor rainfall owing to distance from the sea, the ultimate source of moisture. In this respect Australia has the advantages of being the smallest of the continents and of being insular. But, on the other hand, the land mass is compact, the only great indentation in the coastline being the Gulf of Carpentaria, and the advantages conferred on Europe by her long coastline are conspicuously absent in Australia. There are no great lakes as in North America, only a few shallow salt-pans, usually dry when water is most needed in time of drought, and no great rivers provide rain in the interior by evaporation from their surface. The continent is placed with its greatest length from east to west, as if to ensure that the maximum possible area should be subject to the most arid conditions.

Except in the east the relief is not favourable to heavy rainfall. The western half of the continent is a plateau between 600 and 1,500 feet above the sea, on which rise various small isolated highlands, such as the MacDonnell and Musgrave Ranges, which exceed 3,000 feet. The south-western rim of the plateau also rises a little above the general level in the Darling, Blackwood, and Stirling Ranges. All these heights, especially those in the south-west, cause a local increase in rainfall. The lowest tract is the region between the Gulf of Carpentaria and Spencer Gulf, most of which is below 500 feet, while the Lake Eyre district is actually below the level of the sea, Lake Eyre itself being 39 feet below. Much of Victoria and New South Wales in the basins of the Darling and Murray must be included in the lowlands, being less than 500 feet above the sea. The eastern Highlands are the only extensive uplands in Australia. They start in the Cape York Peninsula, and for the most part do not greatly exceed 2,000 feet in height in Queensland, though small areas including the Atherton Plateau are much higher, and the Bellenden Ker Hills reach 5,000 feet, and are the rainiest part of the continent. In New South Wales the general altitude is greater, exceeding 3,000 feet, and the Australian Alps in the south-east of the state attain 7,320 feet in Mount Kosciusko, the highest point in Australia, and the only part which bears snow all the year. There are considerable areas in eastern Victoria above 3,000 feet. The heavier rainfall and lower temperature are an attraction for settlers except in the south-east and especially in Tasmania where it is too cold and wet.

A coastal plain, only slightly above sea-level, surrounds the continent. It is very narrow, 20 miles or less, in parts, but in some places it widens to 100 miles.

The influence of the relief on the climate is evident. The lowest region, the Lake Eyre depression, is the most arid, and has less than 5 inches of rain a year. The eastern Highlands are the most rainy; in Queensland the south-east trades, normally dry winds, give very copious downpours to the windward slopes, and in New South Wales even anticyclonic winds which rise over the range from seaward are rainy.

Oceanic conditions. The north and east coasts are washed by the warm waters brought across the South Pacific Ocean by the south equatorial current. Part of the current makes its way westward, filling the shallow seas and straits north of Australia, where the highest mean annual sea-temperature of the globe is found; part branches southward and flows past Queensland and New South Wales as the warm East Australian current. The west coasts of South Africa and South America in the latitudes of Western Australia are remarkable for the cold water which in part is brought by the Antarctic Drift, in part wells up from the depths under the influence of the trade winds sweeping away the surface water. No doubt there is a tendency to the same conditions in the south-east trade wind drift off west Australia, but, perhaps owing to the less length of north–south coastline and to its convex shape, the current is weak and variable and there seems to be no up-welling; the shore water is even warmer than the water out at sea, though it is cooler than the sea off south-east Africa on the opposite side of the Indian Ocean, especially in summer in the neighbourhood of the tropic. The striking contrasts in temperature between the east and west coasts of the other southern continents are not found in Australia; indeed Perth is somewhat warmer than Sydney during most of the year. And as regards rainfall, which largely depends on the temperature of the sea-water, hardly any of the west coast of Australia is true desert, while hundreds of miles of the west coasts of the other continents are almost rainless. The cool Antarctic Drift keeps well to the south of Australia but surrounds Tasmania. There is much warmer water inshore along the Australian Bight.

CHAPTER XLIII

AUSTRALIA: TEMPERATURE

In summer the warmest region is the Pilbarra district in the north-west, where the sun is overhead and there is little cloud; a considerable area is enclosed by the 90° isotherm in December. Almost all the continent north of the tropic has a mean temperature above 80°. The interior is warmer than the coasts, and the west coast is considerably warmer than the east. It becomes cooler towards the south, the isotherms having a general east–west direction, but tending to run parallel to the south coast, and making a bend northward as they approach the east coast of the continent; there is a similar but much weaker bend towards the north in the neighbourhood of the west coast. The 65° isotherm skirts the coast of Victoria.

The 90° isotherm (Fig. 142) continues to encircle the Pilbarra district in February and March. The east coast of the continent is cooler than the west in all these months, and the mean temperature on the Queensland coast is as high as 80° only in January. In April there is a marked drop in temperature everywhere; the 80° isotherm encloses Pilbarra, and the 55° isotherm is appearing over Victoria. July is the coolest month; the north-west coast is the warmest part of the continent with a mean temperature just over 75°, Victoria and the south of New South Wales coolest, with a temperature below 50°; the west coast of the continent is warmer than the east, as in summer.

Not only the highest mean temperatures but also the highest midday readings are recorded in the west and centre of the continent, a short distance inside the tropic, as in Africa. According to official statistics the maximum shade temperature has been known to exceed 100° over a wide area on 64 consecutive days. Marble Bar, Pilbarra, appears to have the most persistent heat, and here a maximum of 90° or over has been recorded on 151 consecutive days (Fig. 143); the absolute maximum temperature is 121°, the mean maximum for January 107°, the mean minimum for January 79°. The heat is evidently not much less than in the hottest parts of the

Sahara. Exceedingly high temperatures occur everywhere in the interior near the tropic, where the cloudless sky and dry air give free passage to the sun's rays, which are most powerful during the southern summer when the earth is nearest to the sun. Stuart recorded 131°, and says the sand was so hot that matches burst into flame when dropped on to it. Alice Springs, situated almost on the tropic, 2,000 feet above the

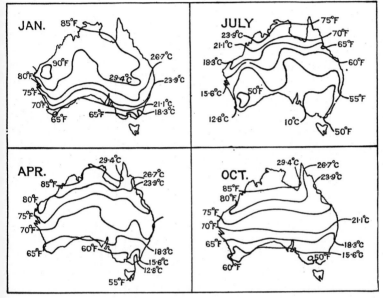

Fig. 142. Mean temperature.

sea, records 115° in most years. Intense heat is sometimes experienced as far south as the south coast; the thermometer at Bourke has touched 121°, at Adelaide 116°, at Melbourne 111°, at Sydney 108°; even the dryness of the air cannot render this extreme heat comfortable, and the smoke and heat from bush fires sometimes intensify the stifling conditions. In the north of the continent the heavy rain and thick clouds of the summer monsoon preclude such high temperatures as are experienced much farther from the Equator. The warmest month at Darwin is November with a mean temperature of 86°, and the highest temperature recorded in most years does not much exceed 100°. But in winter these lower latitudes are much warmer than the rest of the continent, the July mean at Darwin being 77° and the temperature rarely falling below 60°.

Australia labours under many disabilities owing to her arid climate, but in one respect at any rate the dry air is an advantage, inasmuch as it tempers the summer heat by promoting rapid evaporation, and so lowering the 'physiological' tem-

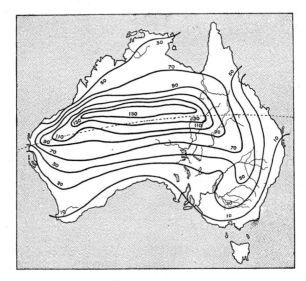

Fig. 143. Lines showing the number of consecutive days on which the air temperature has exceeded 90°.

perature, that is to say, the actual heat felt by man. It has often been pointed out that the wet-bulb thermometer is a better indication of the physiological conditions than the ordinary dry-bulb. The average wet-bulb readings at Pilbarra are some 20° lower than the dry-bulb, the mean for the summer months being only about 75°. Along the tropic the mean summer wet-bulb temperature is about 70°. At Melbourne the wet-bulb very rarely exceeds 75° even on the hottest days.

The relative humidity of the air is much lower in most parts of the continent in summer than in winter, although summer is the rainy season. In the extreme north, however, the air is much drier in winter, since the effect of the higher temperature in summer is more than neutralized by the moist air of the monsoon.

The temperature may fall below freezing-point on winter nights everywhere south of the tropic except on the west coast, which is free from frost nearly to Perth, where frost is rare, and on the east coast to Sydney where the absolute minimum is 35°; the clear dry air, which is so transparent

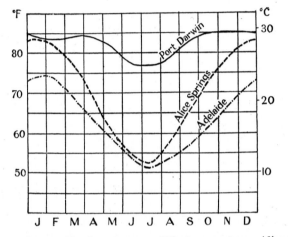

Fig. 144. Curves showing mean monthly temperature. Alice Springs (lat. 24°) is as warm as Darwin (lat. 12°) in summer, but much colder in winter. Adelaide (lat. 35°) has almost the same mean as Alice Springs in winter, but is cooler in summer.

to the rays of the sun by day, is but a feeble protection against loss of heat by radiation at night. Even in summer the nights are cold in the desert, and in most winters the thermometer falls as low as 25° at Alice Springs. The winters in the interior are pleasant, and travellers naturally choose that season for journeys if possible, since the strong dry south-east wind makes even the hottest hours of the day bearable. It is often mentioned in journals of travel that water-bottles which had been left outside the tent all night were found frozen solid on winter mornings. On the south coast, though the mean temperature is lower, the nights are less cold owing to the influence of the sea. At Adelaide the thermometer has fallen to freezing-point, but not below it; at Melbourne to

27°. Kiandra, 4,640 feet above the sea, in the Australian Alps, has recorded −8°.

From these facts it follows that the range of temperature depends as much on distance from the sea as on latitude. The mean annual range at Darwin is only 8°, since the town is on the sea coast and in a low latitude, but at Adelaide it is 23°, and at Alice Springs 31° (Fig. 144). The daily range is greater than might be expected, owing probably to the dryness of the air, and it is, of course, greatest in the arid interior:

MEAN DAILY RANGE OF TEMPERATURE

	Month with greatest range.	*Month with least range.*
Darwin . . .	20 (July)	13 (Feb.)
Melbourne . . .	21 (Jan.)	13 (June)
Adelaide . . .	25 ,,	14 ,,
Brisbane . . .	21 (Aug.)	16 (Feb.)
Alice Springs . .	31 (Sept.)	26 (June)

Comparing Australia with Europe in respect of temperature, we find that Melbourne resembles Oporto fairly closely. Perth, which is representative of the Mediterranean climate region of Australia, has summers not unlike those of the Riviera, but much warmer winters. Hobart is similar to Penzance.

The hot waves and cold waves, which are an important feature of the south and east of Australia, are described on p. 427.

CHAPTER XLIV

AUSTRALIA: PRESSURE AND WINDS

THE central feature in the meteorology of Australia is the high-pressure ridge, part of the subtropical high-pressure belt of the southern hemisphere, which appears on the mean isobar map of every month of the year. Its significance can be best appreciated from the point of view of the daily weather. The high-pressure system shown by the mean isobars really represents an almost constant procession of anticyclones, moving from west to east at an average speed of about 17 miles an hour. The anticyclones usually enter Australia as more or less circular systems, but their north–south axis widens as they advance, till the system may cover half the continent; this widening is seen in the mean isobars which enclose the high-pressure area. An anticyclone is, speaking generally, a system of slowly descending air, and as the air descends it becomes compressed and tends to be warmer and drier, with the result that there can be little cloud and rain, so that a country which is mainly under anticyclonic conditions must have an arid climate. The winds blow out, and are deflected to the left hand like all other free movements in the southern hemisphere of the rotating earth, to appear as south-east winds (trade winds) on the equator-ward side; and here they have the usual trade-wind characteristic of dryness, caused both by their origin and by the fact that they are reaching warmer latitudes, and their vapour-capacity is increasing. On the poleward side the out-blowing winds are north-westerly, and they also are dry as long as they are within the anticyclonic influence, but they are ready to provide rain when they enter the cyclonic belt of the Roaring Forties.

Between each pair of anticyclones there must be some arrangement of lower pressure, just as there are higher pressures between the successive depressions of North-west Europe. But there is rarely a fully developed cyclone between the anticyclones of Australia. The lower pressures are usually merely in the form of a 'col'; that is to say, there is a continuous ridge of high pressure, on which the separate anticyclones form isolated 'summits' of still higher pressure

(Fig. 145). Rain in any quantity is rare in a col, and it is to be noted that, since the high-pressure ridge persists even in the col, the north and south of the continent are meteorologically isolated from each other, and the winds which start in the high pressures in the centre of the land mass can contain little moisture. But sometimes the ridge is completely broken down between two anticyclones, which are separated by a pronounced depression connecting the low pressures over the north and the south of the continent (Fig. 145). The word

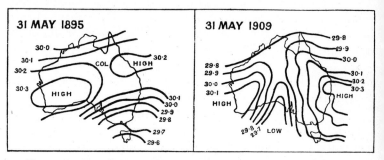

FIG. 145. Showing a 'col' on 31 May 1895, and a 'trough' on 31 May 1909.

'trough' is applied to this formation by the Commonwealth meteorologists, who lay great stress on the essential difference between it and the col, both as definite pressure formations, and in their controls of the rainfall of much of the continent. They compare the 'col' to the mountain feature of that name, that is a saddle in a ridge between the massifs on each side, while a 'trough' is a river valley cutting through the ridge and so effecting a complete separation of the massifs. The col is essentially an anticyclonic formation, preventing any passage of air from north to south through the baric ridge. But, just as a valley permits the passage of the river from one side of a ridge to the other, so a trough allows air currents to sweep right across the continent, and it is during the passage of a trough that the interior of Australia, a region of scant and uncertain precipitation, sometimes receives good and general rains, the rain falling in the north–south belt in the front of the trough.

The next point to be considered is the seasonal migration

of the high-pressure belt, that is to say, of the path of the procession of anticyclones. The mean isobars (Fig. 146) show that the belt is farthest north during the southern winter, owing partly to the northward swing of the pressure belts with the sun, partly to the intensification of the high pressures in the dry cool air over the land mass. In the July map the 30·1-inch isobar encloses most of the continent south of the tropic, the highest pressures being along lat. 30° S. To the north there is a steady and uniform decrease of pressure,

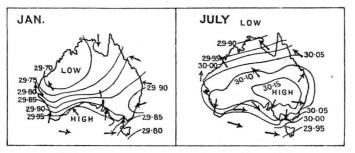

FIG. 146. Mean pressure and prevailing winds.

and the prevailing winds are the south-east trades. This is the dry season over the whole continent north of the tropic, and, except in the east, the sky is almost cloudless. The trades are rarely interrupted by disturbances, since the centre of low pressure is far away, over north India, where the summer monsoon is blowing. On the south side of the baric ridge the gradient is southward and the prevailing winds are north-west (west on the coast of New South Wales), but the conditions are much more disturbed and irregular from day to day than in the north. The southward gradient leads to the low pressures of the Roaring Forties, where cyclone follows cyclone throughout the year and the weather is stormy, rainy, and mild. These Antarctic depressions control the weather of the south-west of Western Australia, the south of South Australia, all Victoria and Tasmania, and the south of New South Wales. As a rule, the main depressions pass from west to east, well out to sea, giving the wild weather for which the Bight is famous, and only the extreme south of the continent derives some benefit from the rainy northern sectors. But often secondary V-shaped extensions, with the point towards the north, project from the primary depression even beyond the tropic, between anticyclones of the high-pressure belt. When a depression makes its way farther north than usual, so that its centre passes over Victoria, the weather there is unusually boisterous and wet, and the south coast is swept by cold polar winds.

In summer pressure is lower everywhere. The high-pressure belt is much diminished in width and intensity and, having swung south with the sun, lies over and south of the south coast. The Antarctic depressions are kept well to the south and rarely extend so far north as to give Australia any rain, but Tasmania is still well within their influence; Victoria, being farthest south, is most liable to be affected, but even here the rainfall is much less than in winter. The rest of the south coast enjoys rainless and very sunny weather. The north of Australia is having its rainy season, for just as the hot land-surface of Asia develops a deep low-pressure system in July, so in January a closed depression lies over the north-west of Australia; Pilbarra, the hottest region, has the lowest pressure and is the scene of numerous shallow, slowly-moving, depressions. The wind, usually light in force, blows in from all sides, and there is heavy rain, especially in the north and east of the continent, where the air is saturated with vapour after crossing the hot seas between Asia and Australia. But on the west side of the low-pressure system the winds are south-east, and as they have come over the land from the high pressures on the south they are dry and give little rain. The New South Wales coast has north-east, Melbourne south and south-west winds. The general winds are masked on the coasts by land and sea breezes. The afternoon sea breeze is notably regular in the Perth district, and it is valuable in tempering the heat of summer days.

CHAPTER XLV

AUSTRALIA: RAINFALL

AUSTRALIA falls naturally into three main rainfall provinces, the north, the south, and the interior, determined directly by the distribution of pressure. The north receives its rain in summer, when the high pressures have retreated far to the south, leaving the way open for the monsoon (Figs. 147 and 148). The south has rain in winter, when the high-pressure belt is over the interior, and Antarctic cyclones reach the coast (Fig. 149). The interior is dry in all seasons, since neither the monsoon rains of summer nor the cyclonic rains of winter reach it in strength; this arid tract, with less than 10 inches of rain a year, is of vast extent, no less than 1,045,000 square miles, including more than one-third of the whole continent. The rainfall is both scanty and very unreliable, the sky is almost cloudless and the sun glares down pitilessly on the bare rocks and sand dunes; the air is very dry, especially in summer. The boundaries of the summer and winter rainfall provinces are shown in Fig. 150; the region between them is arid in the west and centre, and in the east gets some rain in all seasons (Fig. 151). A fourth rainfall province (Fig. 152), which includes the east coast and the adjacent highlands and owes its existence to the relief, may be marked off; parts of it have the heaviest rainfall of the continent. On the Queensland coast, east and south-east winds, which are for the most part true trade winds, prevail all the year. The trades are, by their nature, dry winds, but here they blow from a warm sea, and in rising over the Eastern Highlands they are cooled below dew-point and give copious rain. The coast of New South Wales has variable winds, since it lies in the track of the anticyclones which pass over it in all seasons as they leave the continent; much of the rainfall may perhaps be described as anticyclonic, since it results from the ascent of east winds blowing out from anticyclones over the Tasman Sea, but saturated with moisture by their passage over the warm water. The west coast of Australia is not so favourably situated. Numerous anticyclones cross it as they do the east coast, but the south-west winds in front of them come from a cool sea

E e

to a warm land, and there is no elevation sufficient to cause much precipitation, and the north-east winds in rear of anticyclones which have crossed the coast are even more ineffective, since they blow from the land. It might seem likely that the west coast about the tropic would derive considerable rain in summer from the monsoonal low-pressure systems of the north of the continent, but unfortunately the prevailing winds here are the dry south-east trades. In winter the rainy influence of the Antarctic depressions is appreciable almost to Shark Bay, but between here and the tropic there is very little rain in any season, and the arid tract, with less than 10 inches of rain, which covers so much of the interior, reaches the coast.

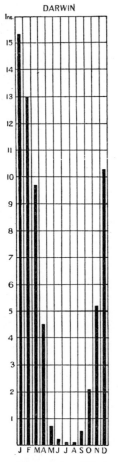

Fig. 147. Mean rainfall at Darwin, typical of the region with a pronounced summer maximum.

The rainy area of Australia in the different seasons (Fig. 153) has been aptly likened by the authors of *Climate and Weather of Australia* to a crescent, which lies over the north-west, north, and east coasts in summer, the north-east, east, and south-east in April, the south-east, south, and south-west in July, and in October has swung back so that it covers the east coast with its tips over the south and north. Thus it covers the east coast all the year, the north coast mainly in summer, and the south coast mainly in winter; but the west is never within its influence. The rainfall of Australia is essentially peripheral.

The summer-rain region has two well-marked seasons, the wet and the dry. The dry season continues almost rainless till the end of September, when as the heat increases, the south-east trades become less constant. Thunderstorms begin early in October, and they become more frequent and violent till, in November, the monsoon sets in more and more steadily from north-west; at Darwin there are 86 days in the year with thunder, most during the hot weather with weak and variable winds at the beginning and end of the rainy season. In December–March the sky is overcast with heavy clouds and rain falls almost every day. The air is saturated with vapour, and therefore the heat, though less intense than just before the monsoon, is much more uncomfortable. The rains continue till the end of April, when the south-east winds return, with clear skies and cool nights. The rainfall is greatest, over 60 inches, on the north coast round Darwin, and it

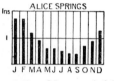

Fig. 148. Mean rainfall at Alice Springs. The summer maximum is clearly marked, but the total rainfall is scanty.

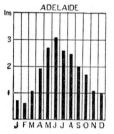

Fig. 149. Mean rainfall at Adelaide, typical of the region with a pronounced winter maximum.

decreases southward, the 10-inch isohyet passing near Alice Springs.

The Queensland coast is the rainiest part of Australia, and has rain all the year, most in summer and autumn, least in spring. The rainfall is heaviest, over 140 inches, on the seaward slopes of the Atherton Plateau. In spite of the low latitude, 17° S., there are permanent white settlers in the coastal belt, and white labour, mostly British, works the plantations of tropical products even where the mean air temperature ranges from 70° in July to 82° in January, and the mean monthly wet-bulb temperature exceeds 70°, the figure which is often taken as separating 'comfortable' and 'uncomfortable' conditions for British settlers, for 7 months. The mean annual rainfall here much exceeds 100 inches; the summer months have over 16 inches each, and even the driest months, July to October, have almost 2 inches each. But the region north of Cairns, including the Cape York peninsula, has a pronounced dry season covering the six winter months, the rainfall being monsoonal as in the Darwin district; the range of temperature is small. There is a rapid decrease towards the west, to only 30 inches south-east of the Gulf of Carpentaria. New South Wales also has heavy coastal rains, well distributed over the year; at Sydney there is most rain

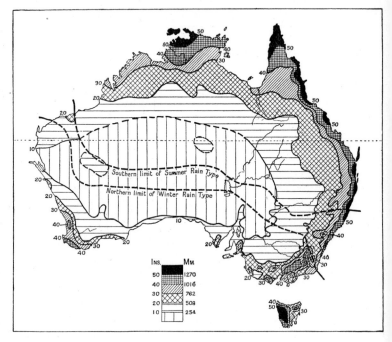

Fig. 150. Mean annual rainfall.

in autumn. All the east coast of Australia is liable to exceedingly heavy downpours; at Harvey Creek 255 inches is the maximum, 80 inches the minimum, recorded in a year; many stations both on the coast and on the hills have recorded more than 20 inches in a day. The hills overlooking Brisbane have had 105 inches in 12 days. At such times rivers have been known to rise in flood 80 feet above the ordinary level. Sydney has recorded 9 inches in a day in summer.

In Victoria the heaviest rainfall is not on the coast but on the hills. The annual amount exceeds 50 inches both on the highlands of the interior, and on the hills which rise on both sides of Port Philip and bound the Great Valley on the south. The Great Valley itself has less than 25 inches at its east end. In Victoria, as in New South Wales, the rain is well distributed over the year, with a winter maximum.

The rainfall decreases rapidly on the continental side of the Eastern Highlands, and the 30-inch isohyet follows the 2,000 feet contour line in much of New South Wales and Victoria.

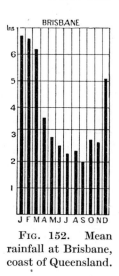

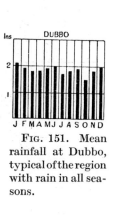

Fig. 151. Mean rainfall at Dubbo, typical of the region with rain in all seasons.

Fig. 152. Mean rainfall at Brisbane, coast of Queensland.

The Darling Downs have a pleasantly dry and cool climate, with from 20 to 30 inches of rain. The great sheep lands of the lower Darling have a mean rainfall of 10 to 20 inches uniformly distributed over the year. But evaporation is very vigorous, the evaporimeter at Broken Hill giving an annual mean of about 90 inches (January 12 inches, July 3 inches). The excessive evaporation on the hot and almost cloudless summer days (121 °F. has been recorded at Wilcannia) and the uncertainty of the rainfall are the great disadvantages of the region. It is an important fact that only a little more than 40 per cent. of Queensland and Victoria has more than 20 inches of rain, and about 17 per cent. has less than 10 inches. Unfortunately the rainfall is not only scanty but also uncertain, and serious droughts are only too common everywhere inside the Highlands. Victoria is the only state which has a mean rainfall of more than 10 inches everywhere, the 10-inch isohyet passing just outside its north-west corner. But northern Victoria often shares the long droughts of the Riverina.

In South Australia the mountains have a good rainfall, and

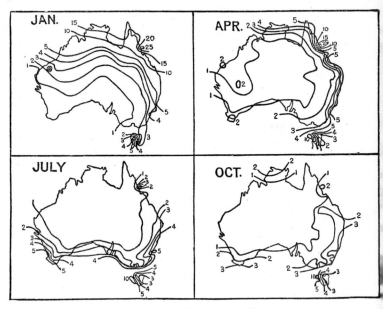

FIG. 153. Mean rainfall.

the 10-inch isohyet is thrust far north by the Flinders Range. The seaward end of the range near Adelaide has over 40 inches, Adelaide itself 21 inches a year, nearly all in winter. South Australia has a smaller proportion of its area with adequate rainfall than any other state, only 16 per cent. receiving more than 10 inches. The region round Lake Eyre, with less than 5 inches, is the driest part of the continent. The lowest annual means recorded, about 4 inches, are from the forbidding desert south of Lake Eyre.

The shores of the Bight are arid desert, the 10-inch isohyet skirting the coast, but in the south-west of Western Australia the conditions are much better. The Darling Range and other elevated parts of the edge of the plateau face the cyclonic winds of winter, and a considerable area has more than 20 inches of rain. There is more than 40 inches round Cape Leeuwin; Perth has 33 inches. The rainy season is sharply defined and lasts from May till October; the rainiest months are June and July, each with 6 inches in the Perth district. The rain is of the greater agricultural value as it falls in the cool season when evaporation is not excessive, and there is the further advantage that the rain is fairly reliable, in con-trast to the very serious variability from year to year in most of Australia (Fig. 154).

The Spencer Gulf district and the south-west corner of Western Australia form Australia's 'Mediterranean' climate province. Probably owing to the dry air and bright sunshine wheat flourishes remarkably well, and commands the highest prices in the world's markets. The olive and other character-istic trees of the south of Europe have been introduced with success.

Tasmania has very heavy rain, more than 110 inches on the windward slopes of the mountains. Winter and spring are the rainiest seasons, but no month can be called dry. The rainfall is the heaviest in the Commonwealth, except on the Queensland coast. But the east of Tasmania, in the lee of the mountains, has less than 20 inches, the contrast between the wet west and dry east being very sharp.

The uncertainty of the rainfall in Australia and the danger of droughts is most serious in those regions where the mean annual amount is between 10 and 30 inches, especially in western New South Wales and northern Victoria, for settlers have established large farms which flourish in years of good or average rain, but fail in bad years, and general ruin results. The variability is greatest, however, in the almost uninhabited arid interior where the mean annual rainfall is less than 10 inches. Even in normal years much of the rain falls in short heavy thunderstorms, and, as evaporation is very rapid, a large proportion is wasted. It is estimated that only 1·5 per cent. of the rainwater of the basin of the River Darling above Bourke flows past that town. Most of the rivers dry up, or become merely a string of water holes, long before they can reach the sea or Lake Eyre. Lake Eyre itself is usually a great plain of salt, and only occasionally contains water. A station on the Darling once recorded no appreciable rainfall for thirty months. The Finke River in the middle of the continent may remain dry for several consecutive years and then be swollen by sudden rains till it is 200 feet wide. Sometimes a single drought year is preceded and followed by years of plenty. At other times there is a series of years of deficient rainfall ending with an especially dry year, and the consequences are exceedingly disastrous. Droughts are almost always accompanied by abnormally high barometric pressure; in other words, rain is scanty when the anticyclones are extensive and separated merely by slight cols, not by deep troughs, so that there is a continuous high-pressure ridge fending off the Antarctic cyclones, and also preventing the monsoonal rains of the north of the continent from extending south. The summer rain fails more often than the winter. The rainfall statistics for Monkira, south-west Queensland, are suggestive; the mean annual rainfall is 9 inches, but one year had 29 inches, another only 2 inches, and 11 inches once fell in a single day. The variation at the state capitals is as follows:

ANNUAL RAINFALL

	Mean.	Highest on record.	Lowest on record.
	Inches.	Inches.	Inches.
Perth . . .	33	47	20
Adelaide . . .	21	31	11
Melbourne . .	25	37	16
Sydney . . .	48	83	21
Brisbane . . .	47	88	16
Hobart . . .	23	41	13

The rain is most reliable in the extreme south-east, along the south coast, in the Perth district, and in the north in Arnhem Land and the Cape York peninsula (Fig. 154).

Evaporation is hardly less important in determining the available water-supply than is the rainfall, with which it tends to vary inversely. In the arid interior the mean annual evaporation from a water surface exceeds 100 inches. It is much less in the rainier regions, 66 inches at Perth, 39 inches at Melbourne, 38 inches at Sydney. It is far greater in the hot than the cool months.

Most of Australia never sees snow, and Sydney is said to have had only one snowfall within living memory. But snow

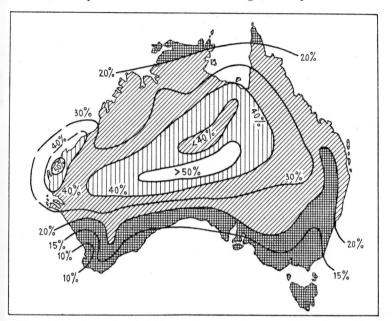

Fig. 154. Annual rainfall: mean percentage variation from the normal. (G. Taylor.)

often lies deep on the higher parts of the Eastern Highlands in New South Wales and Victoria and even in Queensland; on the Kosciusko plateau winter sports are available down to 5,000 feet in most winters, and there are patches of perennial snow.

CHAPTER XLVI

AUSTRALIA: TROPICAL CYCLONES; HOT WINDS AND COLD WINDS

Tropical Cyclones. Both the north-west and the north-east coasts are sometimes visited by destructive hurricanes of the same kind as, for example, those of the West Indies (Fig. 155). These revolving storms are called willy-willies on the north-west coast. They originate over the hot Timor Sea, and travel

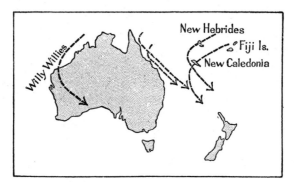

Fig. 155. Typical paths of tropical cyclones.

first to the south-west off the coast, the sequence of wind and weather on land indicating their proximity. The pearl fishers at sea often suffer severe losses, but usually it is only after the storms recurve to the south-east that the coast suffers. They strike inland generally between Condon and Fortescue, and work all the havoc for which tropical cyclones are noted. Thence they continue in the same direction over the interior of Western Australia towards the Great Australian Bight, but, as is usual with tropical cyclones, their violence is exhausted when they leave the sea, and they are rather welcomed in the interior for the rain they give. If they continue as far as the Southern Ocean they assume the form there of extra-tropical depressions of the ordinary type. They occur during summer and autumn, usually one or more each year. Very heavy downpours of rain may fall on the north-west coast during their passage; places with a mean annual rainfall of 12 inches have received more than 20 inches from a single storm. Neither South Africa nor South America have tropical cyclones in the corresponding localities, and their occurrence in the north-west of Australia is no doubt due to the very warm seas round the north and north-west of the continent, and the absence of a cool current off the west coast.

It is not surprising to find tropical cyclones off the northeast of Queensland, since this region corresponds in position to the China Sea in the northern hemisphere. The cyclones spring up in the neighbourhood of the Fiji Islands, where they do great damage. Some reach the Queensland coast near Cairns, and then recurve towards the south-east on the usual parabolic course, but occasionally they continue westward to the Gulf of Carpentaria. They work great havoc on the Queensland coast, and sometimes give phenomenal falls of rain. Fortunately most cyclones recurve before the coast feels their full violence. They very rarely reach New South Wales.

Hot winds and Cold winds. The south of Australia is sometimes visited by very hot, dry, and dusty winds from the deserts of the interior. The temperature has been known to rise to 120° in the north of Victoria. Melbourne has recorded a maximum of over 100° on six consecutive days, when the pressure distribution was such as to cause a steady flow of air from the north.

'In Victoria the hot winds are known as "Brick Fielders", a name originally applied to the "Southerly Bursters" in Sydney because of the dust they raised from the brickfields to the south of the city. When the gold fields were discovered in Victoria the miners hailing from Sydney gave the name to the dusty winds from the opposite quarter' (*Australia Year Book*).

On the east coast of the continent hot winds are not so prominent a feature as cold winds from the south, known as Southerly Bursters, really a closely related phenomenon. A pair of anticyclones moving eastward are often separated by a trough of low pressure projecting in the form of an inverted V from an Antarctic depression. When the trough extends, as is sometimes the case, almost from the south to the north of the continent, the temperature falls sharply as the line of lowest pressure passes any point, since in front of it there is a warm wind from a northerly direction, and in rear a cold south wind. The longer the trough the greater the distance the air currents travel, and, therefore, the greater the temperature excess of the north wind and deficit of the south wind. The north winds are the hot winds of South Australia and Victoria, the heat being the greater owing to the proximity of the hot deserts; but on the coast of New South Wales, especially near Sydney, the cold winds in rear of the trough are more prominent. After a day or more of hot sultry weather with a northerly wind there is a short lull, and then very suddenly, when the line of lowest pressure has passed, a strong, often violent, wind sets in from the south. A striking roll of cumulus cloud may accompany the Burster, and there is usually heavy rain. Temperature drops suddenly, generally as much as 20°. The phenomenon is most frequent in spring and summer. Its intensification on the coast of New South Wales is attributed by the local meteorologists largely to the topography, one important suggestion being that the Eastern Highlands impede the advance of the second of the pair of anticyclones; the southerly winds do not start till the barometric gradient has become steep enough to overcome the resistance of the barrier, when they set in with gale force.

CHAPTER XLVII

NEW ZEALAND

THE main climatic features of the Dominion are readily understood from a consideration of its position and relief. The
islands lie within the variable westerlies of the south hemisphere all the year, and the prevailing winds blow strongly
from north-west, west, and south-west; Cook Strait in particular is noted for its strong and persistent north-west winds.
The meteorological situation corresponds to that of the British
Isles. In summer, when the climatic belts have swung south,
easterly winds are frequent on the northern peninsula of the
North Island. The rest of the North Island is then on the
border of the westerlies, and enjoys much less windy and rainy
weather than in winter.

The temperature is equable for the latitude. The annual
range is least on the west coast, 16° at Hokitika, while at
Christchurch on the east coast it is 19°. The small range is,
of course, due to the vast surrounding ocean. The winters
are very mild, the summers cool. New Zealand is in the same
latitudes as Italy, part of it indeed is nearer the Equator, but
the mean summer temperature is more than 10° lower, and
the extremes of heat are very much less; at Auckland in the
north 85° is not often exceeded. The winters are slightly
warmer in New Zealand than in Italy. Dunedin has very
similar temperatures to those of Falmouth, which is 400 miles
nearer the Pole; Auckland is comparable with Lisbon. Frost
does not occur in most winters near the coasts of the North
Island and is rarely severe enough to do agricultural damage,
but in the South Island frosty nights are frequent in calm
weather even near the sea. The west coast is a little warmer
than the east in winter owing partly to the warmer sea-water
brought by the East Australian current (the east coast has
cool Antarctic water), partly to the damper air and cloudier
sky. In summer the east coast is the warmer, being to leeward of the heated interior. Thus the interior and the east
coast have slightly more extreme temperatures.

The Dominion has more sunshine than might be expected
in a moist oceanic climate. In the east of the islands there is

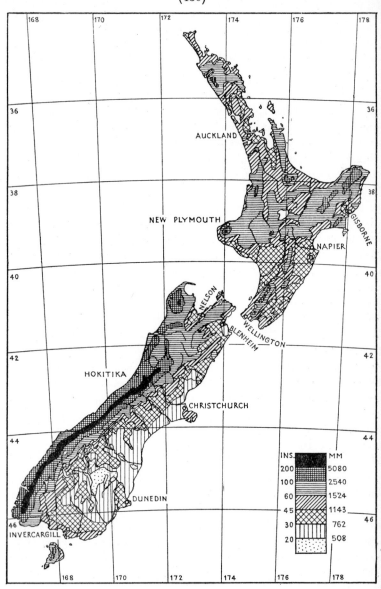

Fig. 156. Mean annual rainfall. (Kidson.)

almost as much as in Italy, considerably more than in the British Isles. Napier has the highest record with an annual average of 2,550 hours, and most of New Zealand has over 2,000 hours. Rome has 2,360 hours, the south of England only about 1,700 hours.

The rainfall (Fig. 156) is reminiscent of that of the British Isles both in amount and distribution. The relief is similar in the two regions, the land rising rapidly from the west coast and forming a high mountain barrier on the windward side. But in the South Island of New Zealand the mountains are higher and more continuous, rising to over 10,000 feet, and the area with excessive rainfall is greater. There is a wide strip, including the west coast and the mountains, which receives more than 100 inches of rain a year, and much of the higher land has 200, and probably parts of it 300, inches. Much of the precipitation falls as snow on the mountains, and there are vast snowfields which are drained by large glaciers. The snow-line is about 7,000 feet, but the Franz Josef glacier, in a valley on the west of South Island in the latitude of Florence, descends within 700 feet of sea-level. East of the mountains the rainfall decreases very rapidly. In most of the eastern half of the South Island there is less than 40 inches, in part of eastern Otago less than 20 inches, the lowest mean annual total registered in the Dominion being 14 inches at Clyde, which is situated in the interior of the South Island just east of the mountains. The Canterbury Plains have from 20 to 30 inches. In this drier region irrigation is available from the rivers from the southern Alps. Most of the North Island has over 40 inches.

There is an important connexion between the rainfall and temperature under certain weather conditions in South Island. As everywhere in the zone of the westerlies, the weather is controlled by a procession of depressions, which move usually from south-west to north-east in the neighbourhood of New Zealand, and pass either south of the islands or over the extreme south of the South Island. Their approach will, therefore, be indicated in most of the Dominion by north winds, veering north-west. The excessive rainfall of the west coasts and mountains is due to the ascent of these vapour-laden winds. The condensation liberates latent heat, and as the winds descend the eastern slopes they are dry and abnormally warm, in fact föhn winds. No doubt the effect is often intensified in New Zealand by the westerly winds being derived from the hot interior of Australia. They are then very warm owing to their origin, and are able to pick up the more water vapour as they cross the sea, so that much latent heat is liberated on condensation. These north-west winds are very hot and enervating on the Canterbury Plains. As the depression passes on towards the north-east, the wind veers to south-west, and being derived from a polar quarter it is very cool and damp, but refreshing after the previous heat.

No part of the North Island has so much rain as the west of the South Island, no part so little as the east, since the mountains are not nearly so continuous. Most of the higher mountains have more than 75 inches a year, Egmont more than 100 inches. Ruapehu is the only peak in the North Island which has any glaciers, and they are very small.

The rain is evenly distributed over the year. The cyclonic activity of the westerlies appears to be almost as great in summer as in winter. The periodicity of the rainfall is greatest in the northern peninsula of the North Island, which in summer is, to a certain extent, free from the influence of the stormy westerlies. Winter is the rainiest season, June the rainiest month; January is the least rainy month, with about half as much rain as June. But there is no real dry season; the rainfall periodicity is not nearly so pronounced as in the Mediterranean region of Europe, with which the north of New Zealand has some affinity in climate. Another important difference is the comparatively cool summer, but in the neighbourhood of Auckland oranges, lemons, and grapes can be grown, as well as apples, pears, and the other fruits of north-west Europe which flourish in both the North and the South Islands. In the western half of the South Island (illustrated by Hokitika, p. 437) there is little seasonal difference; October–December is the rainiest period, and October the rainiest month, February the least rainy. This régime is probably associated with the mean force of the wind, which is greatest in spring and especially in October, for the rainfall is largely orographical.

The drier part of the eastern half of the South Island also

has its rain very evenly distributed over the year, with a slight summer maximum due to convection. But at and north of Christchurch winter is a little more rainy than summer.

The even rainfall combined with the equable temperature produces the evergreen vegetation which is characteristic of New Zealand. New Zealand enjoys a great advantage over Australia in respect of the amount, the duration, and the reliability of the rain.

STATISTICS

MEAN TEMPERATURE (°F.)

AUSTRALIA

Queensland

Station.	Alt. Feet.	Jan.	Feb.	Mar.	Apr.	May.	June.	July.	Aug.	Sept.	Oct.	Nov.	Dec.	Year.	Range.
C. York	69	80·4	80·6	80·2	80·1	80·1	77·5	76·6	76·1	77·0	79·7	81·1	81·7	79·3	5·6
Brisbane	137	77·2	76·5	74·3	70·3	64·5	60·2	58·5	60·4	65·3	69·8	73·6	76·4	68·9	18·7
Cloncurry	696	86·9	84·8	83·0	77·6	70·9	64·1	61·3	66·9	72·4	82·5	85·2	88·0	76·9	26·7
Charleville	975	82·8	80·2	75·8	68·8	60·2	53·5	51·0	56·5	62·8	71·6	77·4	80·2	68·4	31·8

New South Wales

Station.	Alt. Feet.	Jan.	Feb.	Mar.	Apr.	May.	June.	July.	Aug.	Sept.	Oct.	Nov.	Dec.	Year.	Range.
Port Macquarie	49	73·0	73·0	70·5	65·8	60·6	55·8	54·5	56·8	60·3	63·9	67·8	71·2	64·4	18·5
Sydney	146	71·6	71·0	69·2	64·5	58·6	54·3	52·3	54·8	58·8	63·4	67·0	70·0	63·0	19·3
Bourke	460	84·2	82·6	77·5	68·5	58·5	54·1	51·4	55·9	62·8	70·0	75·7	82·2	68·5	32·8
Broken Hill	1,000	78·6	78·2	72·0	64·0	56·6	51·1	49·2	52·6	58·4	65·9	72·9	76·6	64·7	29·4
Wilcannia	267	81·4	79·9	74·0	65·4	57·7	52·3	50·0	53·9	60·2	68·2	74·8	79·4	66·4	31·4
Dubbo	870	78·7	77·3	70·9	64·1	55·2	49·4	47·4	50·5	56·1	63·4	70·7	76·3	63·3	31·3
Kiandra	4,640	56·3	56·8	51·6	45·5	38·1	35·2	31·6	34·3	39·7	44·1	51·8	55·6	45·0	25·2

Victoria and Tasmania

Station.	Alt. Feet.	Jan.	Feb.	Mar.	Apr.	May.	June.	July.	Aug.	Sept.	Oct.	Nov.	Dec.	Year.	Range.
Sale	30	65·8	66·5	63·1	58·4	53·2	49·1	47·5	49·9	52·4	56·0	61·4	64·0	57·3	19·0
Melbourne	115	67·5	67·2	64·7	59·6	54·1	50·3	48·5	51·0	53·9	57·5	61·3	64·5	58·3	19·0
Hobart	160	62·0	62·2	59·4	55·4	50·6	47·1	45·7	48·1	50·8	54·0	57·3	59·8	54·3	16·5

AUSTRALIA (continued)

Western Australia

Station.	Alt. Feet.	Jan.	Feb.	Mar.	Apr.	May.	June.	July.	Aug.	Sept.	Oct.	Nov.	Dec.	Year.	Range.
Wyndham	23	88.0	88.0	88.2	86.7	81.9	77.5	75.7	79.2	84.9	89.2	90.1	90.0	84.9	14.4
Broome	63	85.9	85.4	85.4	83.1	76.4	71.2	70.3	72.4	77.0	81.0	84.6	85.9	79.8	15.6
Onslow	13	85.3	85.3	84.0	79.7	70.9	64.9	63.7	65.7	69.3	74.1	79.0	83.1	75.4	21.6
Carnarvon	15	79.8	80.6	73.4	74.7	67.9	62.7	60.6	62.6	65.6	69.0	73.0	76.9	71.1	20.0
Geraldton	13	74.1	75.0	73.4	68.7	63.7	60.1	58.6	59.4	61.0	63.7	68.4	72.1	66.5	16.4
Perth .	197	73.5	74.1	71.1	66.4	60.4	56.2	55.0	55.9	58.0	60.9	65.4	70.6	64.0	19.1
Eucla .	30	70.8	71.1	69.3	66.1	60.8	55.9	54.3	56.2	59.2	62.7	65.9	69.2	63.5	16.8
Nullagine	1,265	89.8	88.6	84.2	77.3	68.5	61.1	59.3	63.9	71.0	78.2	85.8	88.8	76.4	30.5
Coolgardie	1,389	77.3	75.5	71.3	65.4	57.5	52.3	50.8	53.3	58.2	63.5	71.0	76.0	64.4	26.5

Northern Territory

Station.	Alt. Feet.	Jan.	Feb.	Mar.	Apr.	May.	June.	July.	Aug.	Sept.	Oct.	Nov.	Dec.	Year.	Range.
Darwin	97	83.8	83.4	84.0	84.1	81.8	78.9	77.4	79.4	82.6	85.3	85.8	85.1	82.6	8.4
Daly Waters	700	86.8	85.5	83.8	80.4	74.7	70.4	68.6	72.8	79.8	86.1	88.3	88.1	80.4	19.7
Alice Springs	2,000	83.3	82.0	76.6	68.1	59.7	54.4	52.6	58.2	65.5	73.3	79.0	82.3	69.6	30.7

South Australia

Station.	Alt. Feet.	Jan.	Feb.	Mar.	Apr.	May.	June.	July.	Aug.	Sept.	Oct.	Nov.	Dec.	Year.	Range.
Adelaide	140	74.2	74.0	69.9	64.0	57.7	53.4	51.5	53.8	57.0	61.9	67.0	71.1	62.9	22.7
William Creek	250	82.7	82.5	76.1	67.2	59.2	53.9	52.2	56.2	62.4	70.3	77.1	81.4	68.4	30.5

NEW ZEALAND

Station.	Alt. Feet.	Jan.	Feb.	Mar.	Apr.	May.	June.	July.	Aug.	Sept.	Oct.	Nov.	Dec.	Year.	Range.
Auckland	260	66.5	67.0	64.9	61.1	56.7	53.5	51.7	52.2	54.6	57.2	60.2	63.9	59.1	15.3
Napier	7	66.1	65.5	62.9	58.6	53.8	50.1	49.0	49.9	53.6	57.5	60.7	64.2	57.6	17.1
New Plymouth	43	64.0	64.6	63.3	60.1	55.4	52.3	50.2	50.7	53.2	55.2	58.3	61.9	57.4	14.4
Wellington .	142	62.4	62.2	61.0	57.4	52.9	49.6	47.5	48.6	51.1	54.0	56.8	60.8	55.2	14.9
Christchurch	20	61.7	60.8	58.5	53.1	48.4	45.0	42.4	43.9	48.6	52.7	56.3	60.8	52.5	19.3
Dunedin	500	57.7	57.4	55.4	51.4	47.3	44.1	42.4	44.1	46.8	50.7	53.2	56.3	50.5	15.3

MEAN RAINFALL (inches)

AUSTRALIA

Queensland

Station	Alt. Feet	Jan.	Feb.	Mar.	Apr.	May.	June.	July.	Aug.	Sept.	Oct.	Nov.	Dec.	Year.
C. York	69	22·9	18·6	16·9	8·1	3·7	0·5	0·6	0·4	0·1	0·1	2·0	8·2	82·0
Harvey Creek	coast	30·9	22·2	32·2	22·2	13·2	8·0	4·2	5·4	3·7	3·8	8·1	11·7	165·6
Brisbane	137	6·3	6·2	5·6	3·6	2·8	2·6	2·3	2·1	2·1	2·6	3·7	4·8	44·7
Cloncurry	696	5·1	4·9	2·7	0·9	0·4	0·3	0·5	0·1	0·5	0·5	1·1	3·0	20·0
Charleville	975	2·6	3·3	3·3	1·5	1·5	1·2	0·8	0·6	0·8	1·3	1·4	2·3	20·6

New South Wales

Station	Alt. Feet	Jan.	Feb.	Mar.	Apr.	May.	June.	July.	Aug.	Sept.	Oct.	Nov.	Dec.	Year.
Port Macquarie	coast	5·9	7·5	6·5	5·9	5·6	4·6	4·5	3·8	3·9	3·2	4·1	5·9	61·5
Sydney	146	3·7	4·2	4·8	5·6	5·1	4·8	4·8	3·0	2·9	3·2	2·8	2·9	47·9
Bourke	456	2·0	1·9	1·6	1·4	1·1	1·0	0·9	0·9	1·0	1·1	1·3	1·1	15·2
Broken Hill	1,000	0·7	0·7	0·7	0·8	0·9	1·2	0·6	1·0	0·7	0·8	0·6	0·6	9·3
Wilcannia	267	1·0	0·8	1·1	0·7	1·0	1·1	0·6	0·8	0·7	0·9	0·7	0·8	10·2
Dubbo	870	2·0	1·9	1·8	1·9	1·9	2·0	1·5	1·9	1·9	1·6	1·8	2·0	22·3
Kiandra	4,640	4·1	3·2	4·0	4·4	5·3	8·7	6·6	5·9	6·9	6·6	4·9	3·9	64·5

Victoria and Tasmania

Station	Alt. Feet	Jan.	Feb.	Mar.	Apr.	May.	June.	July.	Aug.	Sept.	Oct.	Nov.	Dec.	Year.
Sale	30	2·1	1·5	2·0	1·9	1·8	2·3	1·9	2·0	2·3	2·2	2·1	2·1	24·2
Melbourne	115	1·9	1·8	2·2	2·3	2·2	2·1	1·9	1·8	2·4	2·7	2·2	2·3	25·6
Hobart	160	1·8	1·5	1·6	1·8	1·9	2·2	2·1	1·8	2·1	2·2	2·5	1·9	23·6

AUSTRALIA (continued)

Western Australia

Station	Alt. Feet	Jan.	Feb.	Mar.	Apr.	May.	June.	July.	Aug.	Sept.	Oct.	Nov.	Dec.	Year.
Wyndham	23	9·7	5·9	4·3	1·0	0·4	0·1	0	0	0·1	0·5	2·2	4·2	28·4
Broome	63	5·0	6·4	3·8	1·4	0·4	1·2	0·3	0·5	0·1	0	0·9	3·5	23·0
Onslow	13	0·5	0·7	0·8	0·3	1·6	1·8	0·9	0	0	0	0	0·2	7·2
Carnarvon	15	0·3	0·7	0·5	0·5	1·3	2·8	1·9	0·6	0·3	0·1	0	0·1	9·1
Geraldton	13	0·2	0·2	0·4	1·1	2·6	4·6	3·6	2·9	1·1	0·7	0·3	0·1	17·8
Perth .	197	0·3	0·3	0·7	1·7	4·9	6·6	6·4	5·6	3·3	2·1	0·8	0·6	33·3
Albany	39	0·6	0·9	1·3	2·6	4·6	5·3	4·8	5·0	3·7	2·8	1·3	1·0	33·7
Eucla .	30	0·7	0·5	0·9	1·2	1·2	1·1	0·9	1·0	0·8	0·7	0·7	0·4	10·1
Nullagine	1,265	2·7	2·0	2·6	1·0	0·5	1·1	0·7	0·5	0	0	0·4	1·2	12·7
Coolgardie	1,389	0·4	0·7	0·6	0·6	1·3	1·2	0·9	0·9	0·6	0·7	0·5	0·6	9·2

Northern Territory

Station	Alt. Feet	Jan.	Feb.	Mar.	Apr.	May.	June.	July.	Aug.	Sept.	Oct.	Nov.	Dec.	Year.
Darwin	97	15·9	13·0	10·1	4·1	0·7	0·1	0·1	0·1	0·5	2·2	4·8	10·3	61·8
Daly Waters	700	6·1	6·7	5·0	1·0	0·2	0·3	0·1	0·1	0·3	0·8	2·2	4·1	26·9
Alice Springs	2,000	1·8	1·7	1·2	1·0	0·7	0·6	0·4	0·4	0·4	0·7	1·0	1·6	11·1

South Australia

Station	Alt. Feet	Jan.	Feb.	Mar.	Apr.	May.	June.	July.	Aug.	Sept.	Oct.	Nov.	Dec.	Year.
Adelaide	140	0·7	0·7	1·0	1·8	2·8	3·1	2·7	2·5	2·0	1·7	1·2	1·0	21·2
William Creek	250	0·5	0·4	0·8	0·4	0·4	0·7	0·3	0·3	0·4	0·3	0·4	0·3	5·4

NEW ZEALAND

Station	Alt. Feet	Jan.	Feb.	Mar.	Apr.	May.	June.	July.	Aug.	Sept.	Oct.	Nov.	Dec.	Year.
Auckland	260	2·7	3·0	3·0	3·4	4·4	4·9	5·0	4·2	3·6	3·6	2·9	2·9	43·9
Wellington	142	2·8	2·7	3·1	3·5	4·0	4·2	4·7	3·8	3·1	3·4	2·9	2·8	41·1
Hokitika	13	9·9	7·2	9·7	9·3	9·8	9·7	9·1	9·4	9·1	11·9	10·7	10·6	116·5
Dunedin	500	2·2	1·8	2·1	2·0	2·6	2·6	2·8	1·8	1·8	1·6	2·0	2·0	25·2

PART VIII

ANTARCTICA

THOUGH many of the major topographical features, and almost all the minor features are still uncertain, we know enough of the Continent to appreciate the main facts of the climate and

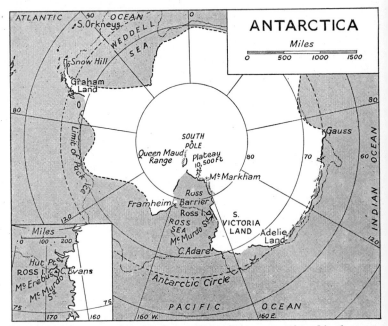

FIG. 157. Key map, showing the position of places mentioned in the text.

their causes. Antarctica is an unbroken expanse of snow and ice—the few exposures of bare rock around the coasts are negligible from our point of view—and almost certainly there is a continuous land surface below, though the possibility must be remembered that the ice sheet conceals channels of the sea dividing the land mass. The area may be estimated at 5 million square miles; Antarctica is much larger than Australia with its 3 million square miles. The coastline is very regular, and there are only two large indentations, the

Ross Sea south of New Zealand, and the Weddell Sea south of the Atlantic Ocean. It is known that a very large part, probably more than half, of the continent is a high plateau. Explorers who have had their base in the Ross Sea region have made us familiar with the plateau edge which forms the lofty wall, probably a line of fracture, some 7,000 feet high along the west side of the Ross Sea and the Ice Barrier, then turns to the south-east so as to include the South Pole, and continues towards the Weddell Sea. Probably most of the great tract on the Indian Ocean side of this line consists of an unbroken high plateau. The altitude of the South Pole itself is 10,000 feet, and the highest level crossed by Amundsen on his journey from Framheim on the east of the Barrier to the Pole was 11,000 feet. The edge of the plateau overlooks the Ross Sea from an altitude of between 7,000 and 8,000 feet, and behind the edge isolated peaks rise to considerable elevations above the general level, Mount Markham exceeding 15,000 feet above the sea. From the Indian Ocean the land rises steeply some thousands of feet to a plateau, and presumably the plateau block is continuous at an unknown altitude which may be estimated at 3,000 to 10,000 feet as far as the faulted edge just mentioned.

We have hardly any knowledge of the interior of that half of Antarctica which faces the Pacific. There can be little doubt that the surface is snow or ice, and there are reasons for supposing that it is of considerably less altitude than the rest of the continent, but Graham Land has a peak of 8,000 feet. The mean altitude of the whole of Antarctica has been estimated at 6,600 feet. It is the largest area of high plateau on the globe, a fact which is of the more importance meteorologically since the plateau includes and lies symmetrically about the Pole. The lengths of the summer days and winter nights, each six months at the Pole, are in themselves outstanding facts and fundamental controls of the climate.

A glance at a map shows the vast expanse of unbroken ocean surrounding Antarctica; the oceans of the northern hemisphere are small by comparison. The climate over the southern ocean is remarkably uniform, for there are none of those sharp contrasts between very warm and very cold currents which bring about such large climatic variations in similar latitudes in the northern oceans. The temperature is low, and pack-ice often extends hundreds of miles from the Antarctic coasts, the extent varying greatly from year to year; the northern limit was 60° S. and 72° S. in consecutive years in the Weddell Sea area. The ocean helps to prevent very intense winter cold on the coasts, but it is also an important factor in the very cold summers. The Weddell Sea and Ross Sea indentations carry the oceanic conditions far south. The Ross Sea penetrates as far as about 78° S. lat., where it meets the ice cliffs of the Barrier, a snow-covered plain, probably floating ice, which continues the Ross Sea southwards to lat. 85°; its altitude is about 170 feet. The dry powdery snow forms a very effective insulator from the heat of the sea. The Ross Sea itself is open water in summer, and the middle of it is open even during most of the winter.

There is perhaps sometimes a tendency to attribute more uniformity than really exists to the climate of Antarctica. Though the general features are very similar everywhere there must be considerable local differences such as were demonstrated along the south of the Ross Sea by the simultaneous records of Amundsen's and Scott's parties in 1911. The topography of that region favours large differences of climate, but considerable local peculiarities are also to be expected elsewhere.

The exhaustive examinations and discussions of the data available compensate to some extent for their scantiness. Special mention must be made of the work by Sir G. C. Simpson on the results of the British Antarctic Expedition 1910–13.

Pressure and Winds.

It has long been known that the atmospheric pressure decreases towards the south from the subtropical high-pressure belt of the southern hemisphere. Owing to the almost unbroken ocean which surrounds the earth in these latitudes, and the uniformity of the temperature distribution, the mean isobars are remarkably parallel in the belt of the Roaring Forties and higher latitudes, and it was formerly believed that the pressure went on decreasing as far as the Pole, the low pressure being caused by the strong centrifugal force in the polar whirl of westerly winds. It has, however, now been proved highly probable if not certain that Antarctica is covered by an anticyclone.

The low pressures of the Roaring Forties continue to decrease as far as the neighbourhood of the Antarctic circle, that is, almost to the shores of Antarctica. But there a change takes place, and pressure begins to increase towards the Pole, for the dynamical effect of the circumpolar whirl is more than counterbalanced by the thermal effect of the intense cold of the snow-covered continent, which tends to produce high atmospheric pressure. The belt of lowest pressure is between 60° S. lat. and the Antarctic circle, but its position is variable and appears to be determined by the extent of the pack-ice round Antarctica, the high pressures of the continent being continued to the edge of the pack-ice, which may change very much from year to year.

The low-pressure belt has prevailing westerly winds controlled by a procession of depressions, the mean path of which is the trough of mean lowest pressure. In general character they are similar to those of the westerlies of the northern hemisphere, but they are deeper, and the winds stronger. It is a wild tract of open ocean, where gale follows gale with little interruption.

A proof that the zone of lowest pressure has been passed when ships make their way to the far south is the change in the prevailing winds from westerly to easterly, and this change has been reported by every expedition. The records have been remarkably consistent. The South Orkney Islands (lat. 61° S.) are just on the north side of the lowest pressures, and during her stay there in 1902–4 the *Scotia* found 71 per cent. of the winds westerly, only 2 per cent. easterly; but at Snow Hill, Graham Land (lat. 64° S.) south and south-south-east winds prevailed in the winter and spring of 1903. The *Gauss* expedition (lat. 66° S., long. 89½° E.) experienced easterly winds almost without interruption in 1902–3. There are longer records from the Ross Sea region. On Ross Island the *Discovery* expedition at Hut Point had prevailing ENE. winds in 1903, the British Antarctic Expedition at Cape Evans almost constant E., ESE., or SE. winds in 1911–13, these

directions making 84 per cent. of the observations. At Framheim, on the east of the Great Barrier, Amundsen found E.
winds in 1911, and SE. was the prevailing direction at Cape
Adare also in 1911. During Mawson's journey on the plateau
of Adelie Land in 1913 the terrific gales which blew almost
continuously were from a southerly point. On the polar
plateau itself Shackleton found SSE. to SSW. winds in the
summer of 1908–9, Scott almost constant (73 per cent.) S.,
SSE., and SSW. winds on his last journey to the South Pole
in 1911, and Amundsen prevailing winds from the same directions (54 per cent.) on his march to the Pole in the same
summer.

These records show that not only is the mean distribution
of pressure over Antarctica anticyclonic, but also the anticyclone is very constant in position. Direct observations of
pressure, which show the increase towards the Pole, are also
available, but as they are not synchronous the conclusions to
be drawn are probable rather than certain. The mean annual
pressure in the zone of lowest pressure is probably under
29·1 inches; at Cape Adare it was 29·19, at Cape Evans 29·26.
In the heart of the continent the very few records that have
been made are quite insufficient for comparison with mean
values, and further uncertainties are introduced by the fact
that the exact altitude of the plateau is unknown, and even
if the altitude were known the reduction of the barometer
readings for comparison with the sea-level pressures would be
very difficult. All the records agree in showing considerably
higher pressures in summer than in winter.

The prevailing southerly to easterly winds are the natural
circulation round the anticyclone, but there is another factor.
On such snow-covered domes as Antarctica and Greenland
the air resting on the surface is so much chilled that its increased density makes it flow down the slopes more or less
radially from the highest parts; from whatever side the South
Pole is approached head winds are encountered. In some
places the descending winds are very strong owing to the
steep gradient and the slight friction on the smooth snow.
Possibly the blizzards of certain regions are produced in this
way, and probably the extraordinarily violent winds which
Mawson found to rage almost continually in Adelie Land

with a mean speed of 50 miles an hour, have in part the same cause, acting in a specially favourable topography.

Many features of the weather which seem to be common to most of Antarctica are easily understood if the conditions are anticyclonic—the clear sky and hence very vigorous radiation of heat from the snow surface, the dry air, the scanty precipitation, the frequency of calms and light winds.

The anticyclone, being due to the intense cold of the snow surface, is essentially a shallow system not more than some few thousand feet deep, and above it the general polar cyclone must exist in an intensified form. The upper winds are best shown by the movements of the clouds and by the drift of the smoke from the volcanic Mount Erebus (13,000 feet). In the McMurdo Sound region the clouds between 10,000 and 13,000 feet and the smoke from Erebus indicated prevailing winds between west and north, the opposite of the surface direction on the Barrier, and associated presumably with the cyclonic circulation of the middle atmosphere (Fig. 158).

But though the weather is anticyclonic in its main features, cyclonic characteristics are not lacking. Boisterous weather, violent winds with driving snow, 'blizzards', have been reported by all explorers. The essential element in the blizzard is the strong wind, generally from the south, but in most cases an equally important feature is the thick whirling snow that fills the air so that it is impossible to see more than a few yards, and the traveller is bewildered and lost; how much of the snow is swept up from the ground, how much descends from the clouds it is impossible to say, but probably most of it is new snow from above. The blizzard usually springs up very quickly, a calm changing within a few hours to a wind blowing in furious gusts of 30 to 50 miles an hour (Fig. 159), and the storm may last for a few hours or even a few days. In winter the temperature rises suddenly when the storm begins, a rise of as much as 32° having been recorded, but in summer it generally falls.

In 1911–12 blizzards were raging during almost a quarter of the time at Cape Evans, but they were almost unknown at Framheim. Cape Adare had a remarkably high proportion of calms, the wind being under 5 miles an hour for over 70 per cent. of the period of observation, and yet hurricanes (not, however, the blizzard type) of over 70 miles an hour occurred each month. Evidently the wind is controlled largely by the topography round the station. On the coasts such storms might well seem, on first consideration, to be associated with passing depressions of the variable westerlies, the

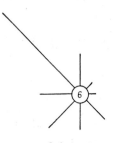

S. Orkneys

C. Evans

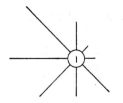

Mt. Erebus smoke

FIG. 158. Mean wind directions. The lines, read towards the centre, are proportional to the frequencies. The figures at the centres denote percentage of calms and variable winds.

southern sectors of which may sweep the edge of Antarctica. But it is difficult to apply this explanation to the blizzards which formed so prominent a feature of the weather on the west of the Barrier, far from the open ocean. The examination of his own records at Cape Evans, and those made simultaneously at Framheim and Cape Adare, has convinced Simpson that the disturbances in the Ross Sea region, at any rate, are quite unconnected with depressions of the westerlies, and are not even circular cyclonic systems, but pressure waves or surges which move outwards from the Pole.

The steep and lofty plateau edge which bounds the barrier on the west is thought by him to be the cause of the great frequency of blizzards there, owing to the obstacle it presents to the east winds. At any rate it would seem that the very frequent blizzards on the west of the Barrier, which were an important factor in the disaster to Scott's Polar party, are a local feature, for Amundsen, whose route led across the

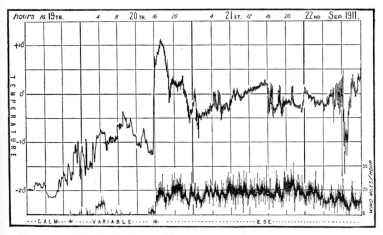

Fig. 159. Wind velocity and temperature, Cape Evans. The blizzard started at 16 h. on the 20th. (British Antarctic Expedition results: Simpson.)

Barrier much farther to the east, found comparatively light winds (Simpson, *Scott's Polar Journey and the Weather*).

At Framheim in 1911 42 per cent. of the observations were calms or very light winds of under 4 miles an hour, and only 2 per cent. winds over 30 miles an hour, but at Cape Evans (1911–12) only 22 per cent. were calms or light winds and 30 per cent. winds more than 30 miles an hour. The large percentage of calms shows dominant anticyclonic conditions at both stations; the frequency of high winds at Cape Evans is an expression of the curious frequency also of the opposite conditions, raging blizzards.

More than one theory of blizzards has been advanced. Simpson's, based on his experiences in the Ross Sea region, depends on the existence on the surface of a calm layer of very cold dense air already referred to, a layer so dense that even strong winds in the higher atmosphere can slide over it, while the calm persists below. But when the air movement aloft becomes still more vigorous eddy motion gradually extends downwards and in a short time the whole of the surface layer is churned up and mixed with the gale above. Thus the

MEAN MONTHLY TEMPERATURES (°F.)

	McMurdo Sound, 5 years (C. Evans and Hut Pt. records combined).	Framheim, 1911–12.	C. Adare (computed by Simpson).	'Gauss', lat. 65° S., 1902.	Snow Hill, Graham Land, lat. 64½° S., 1902–3.	S. Orkneys, 1903–4.
Jan.	23·7	14·5	(31·6)	30·6	30·0	31·4
Feb.	15·8	(4·2)	(27·0)	(25·9)	24·4	31·5
Mar.	4·4	(−6·7)	18·7	16·9	12·5	31·3
Apr.	−8·8	−17·7	9·4	3·9	6·5	22·8
May	−10·5	−31·7	−2·2	6·8	0·0	13·8
June	−11·9	−29·9	−14·5	0·5	−3·6	13·1
July	−14·6	−33·7	−11·9	−0·6	−6·0	11·8
Aug.	−14·6	−48·6	−13·6	−7·4	−2·9	15·7
Sept.	−11·7	−35·5	−7·5	0·1	2·8	16·9
Oct.	−2·1	−11·6	−0·6	8·6	14·0	22·7
Nov.	14·2	4·1	18·5	19·9	16·5	30·2
Dec.	24·9	19·9	29·5	30·0	28·1	30·1
Year	0·7	−14·4	7·0	11·3	9·4	22·6

blizzard is merely the extension to the surface of a very strong wind in the higher atmosphere, which is due to a temporary steepening of the barometric gradient. This theory goes far to explain the frequency both of calms and of high winds as compared with winds of moderate strength. It also explains the sudden rise in temperature that occurs at the beginning of a winter blizzard, the very cold surface air being removed and mixed with the warmer general air currents.

Temperature.

It was to be expected that the Antarctic winters would prove very cold. A more striking feature is the cold summers. So cold are they that land animals (except birds) and flowering plants are almost completely absent and there are no human settlements. The astronomical facts suggest warmer conditions, for in the southern summer the earth makes its nearest approach to the sun, and on December 21 more inso-

TEMPERATURE (°F.) AT McMURDO SOUND (CAPE EVANS, 2 YEARS, AND HUT POINT, 2 YEARS, RECORDS COMBINED)

| | | *Mean.* | | *Absolute.* | |
		Daily Maximum.	*Daily Minimum.*	*Maximum.*	*Minimum.*
January	.	28·9	16·9	39·9	4·0
February	.	20·0	8·7	33·1	—9·5
March	.	9·4	—2·2	27·5	—20·0
April	.	—2·0	—15·5	19·5	—42·0
May	.	—5·2	—20·7	17·0	—51·2
June	.	—4·9	—22·4	20·6	—47·0
July	.	—6·1	—23·6	15·9	—54·2
August	.	—6·5	—23·8	17·8	—53·2
September	.	—5·1	—22·7	15·9	—58·5
October	.	2·2	—12·1	24·1	—42·8
November	.	18·6	7·3	34·0	—6·5
December	.	28·6	18·3	42·0	4·2

lation is received from the sun in the 24 hours above the South Pole than at any other latitude on any day of the year. But the air temperature depends much more on the temperature of the surface of the earth with which the air is in contact than on the direct passage of the rays of the sun. The long oblique course through the atmosphere weakens the insolation so much before it reaches the earth that even when the sun is at its greatest altitude it is never powerful enough to melt the snow, the temperature of which, and consequently the air temperature also, remains well below freezing-point. There is little doubt that the mean temperature of the warmest month everywhere inside the Antarctic circle is below 32°. In this region the highest readings are not in the interior of the land mass, but on the coasts of the boisterous Southern Ocean, where the mean temperature in December and January is probably about 30°; at Cape Evans the mean temperature for these months is about 24°. The mean January temperature on the Barrier is estimated at 15°. At McMurdo Sound (see Table) the mean daily maximum temperature is below

32° in every month, but probably the temperature rises above 32° once or twice in December and January in most years; but it may also sink almost to zero.

For the Polar plateau we have the records made in December 1911 and January 1912 by Amundsen and Scott. The mean temperature observed in December was −8·6, in January −18·7. The lowest record was −19·3 in December and −29·7 in January; the highest maximum, 5·5 in December and −3·2 in January. From December 22 till February 6, the period during which he was on the Plateau, Scott did not once record a reading above zero. The great fall in temperature from December to January shows how rapidly the temperature responds to the changing attitude of the sun, a result of the good insulation of the dry snow.

In summer the sun is above the horizon all the 24 hours for at least one day everywhere in Antarctica. At the Pole its altitude is almost constant throughout the 24 hours of each day during the 6 months that it is above the horizon, though it rises slightly higher day by day from the horizon to a maximum altitude of $23\frac{1}{2}°$ on December 21, and presumably the mean diurnal range of temperature is very small; during the 4 days January 16–20 when Scott was at or within 30 miles of the South Pole, the highest reading was −19·1, the lowest −26·7. But the difference between the midday and midnight altitudes of the sun becomes greater and greater with decreasing latitude; thus at lat. 70° the altitude is $43\frac{1}{2}°$ at midday, only $3\frac{1}{2}°$ at midnight, on December 21. The consequent diurnal range in temperature is remarkably large; on the Barrier members of Scott's party recorded a mean amplitude of 20° during a spell of 6 calm clear days in November, and the mean amplitude during November, December, and January was 11°. But at McMurdo Sound the figures were far lower, the highest figure, that for January, being only 5°. The high range on the Barrier is explained by the presence of the thick layer of dry loose snow on its surface. This forms an excellent heat insulator, and consequently the varying intensity of insolation as the sun rises and sinks in the sky is reflected strongly in the curve of air temperature. The range is considerably higher in the early part of the summer when the snow is very dry and loose than towards the end of the season. It is probably for the same reason that the warmest month is December and not January, the decreasing altitude of the sun after the solstice having an almost immediate effect on the air temperature, which falls very rapidly; from May to September there is little change in the intense cold from month to month.

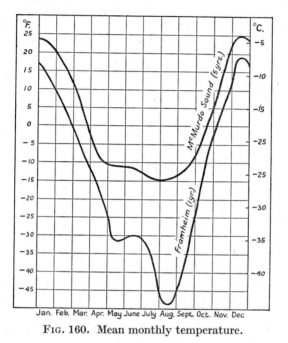

Fig. 160. Mean monthly temperature.

The winter temperatures on the Polar plateau have never been observed, but the mean for July is probably very low. On the Barrier it has been estimated at well below −35°. The lowest reading recorded was −76°, taken on the Barrier near Ross Island on 6 July 1911. Other low readings were −57° (Shackleton) and −67° on 15 September 1903, near the winter quarters of the *Discovery* on Ross Island. The mean temperature for August is −15° in McMurdo Sound, but it is very much lower at Framheim, −49° (Fig. 160); this difference is probably related to the absence of blizzards at Framheim, where the surface layer of supercooled air is not often churned up and dissipated, while at McMurdo Sound the frequent blizzards, though one of the greatest trials of life, bring higher temperatures. The winter temperatures are naturally much higher on the ocean coasts, but the means are probably everywhere below zero. The middle of the Ross Sea is warmer than its coasts, for the winter pack ice is thin and sometimes not continuous.

The very cold Antarctic winters are not surprising on a great snow-covered plateau lying round the Pole itself, much of it without any insolation for several months to replace the extremely rapid loss of heat by radiation. Possibly the centre of Antarctica has the coldest winters of the whole world, but no records exist to prove it; the winters of the Ross Sea region and the ocean coasts are by no means so cold as those of the interior of eastern Siberia.

Precipitation.

There are few, if any, reliable statistics of the amount of precipitation, but it is known to be scanty, equivalent probably to not more than 10 inches of rain; it all falls as snow, mostly fine crystals, dry and powdery. The difficulty in measuring it is due to the strong winds which almost always accompany it, for the snow is whirled about and cannot settle in a gauge. Moreover, it is impossible to say how much of the snow is newly fallen from the clouds, how much has been swept up from the ground.

A perplexing problem is the cause of the precipitation in view of the anticyclonic conditions which prevail. That precipitation exceeds evaporation—and evaporation is certainly considerable—seems to be proved by the great glaciers that move down from the plateau and by the calving from the edge of the ice sheet of the numerous icebergs that beset the surrounding ocean. There must be considerable precipitation in the interior to feed this dispersal from the long periphery. The depressions of the westerlies provide considerable snowfall on the coasts that come within their influence, but their influence does not appear to extend far inland.

Antarctica enjoys very clear skies and long sunshine in the summer months, the sunshine traces being sometimes continuous for the whole 24 hours. In December 1903 the *Discovery* station at McMurdo Sound recorded 490 hours, 66 per cent. of the possible duration, and in a year there were 1,725 hours, which is more than we have in the sunniest parts of England, though the sun in Antarctica was above the horizon for only 246 days. The totals recorded by Scott's party at Cape Evans were:

November 1911	378 hours.
December 1911	433 ,,
January 1912	412 ,,
November 1912	335 ,,
December 1912	334 ,,

EQUIVALENTS

INCHES AND MILLIMETRES

Inches.	Milli-metres.	Inches.	Milli-metres.	Inches.	Milli-metres.	Inches.	Milli-metres.	Inches.	Milli-metres.
0·05	1·3	3·3	83·8	6·6	167·6	9·9	251·5	30·3	769·6
0·1	2·5	3·4	86·4	6·7	170·2	10·0	254·0	30·4	772·2
0·2	5·1	3·5	88·9	6·8	172·7	11·0	279·4	30·5	774·7
0·3	7·6	3·6	91·4	6·9	175·3	12·0	304·8	31·0	787·4
0·4	10·2	3·7	94·0	7·0	177·8	13·0	330·2	32·0	812·8
0·5	12·7	3·8	96·5	7·1	180·3	14·0	355·6	33·0	838·2
0·6	15·2	3·9	99·1	7·2	182·9	15·0	381·0	34·0	863·6
0·7	17·8	4·0	101·6	7·3	185·4	16·0	406·4	35·0	889·0
0·8	20·3	4·1	104·1	7·4	188·0	17·0	431·8	36·0	914·4
0·9	22·9	4·2	106·7	7·5	190·5	18·0	457·2	37·0	939·8
1·0	25·4	4·3	109·2	7·6	193·0	19·0	482·6	38·0	965·2
1·1	27·9	4·4	111·8	7·7	195·6	20·0	508·0	39·0	990·6
1·2	30·5	4·5	114·3	7·8	198·1	21·0	533·4	40·0	1016·0
1·3	33·0	4·6	116·8	7·9	200·7	22·0	558·8	41·0	1041·4
1·4	35·6	4·7	119·4	8·0	203·2	23·0	584·2	42·0	1066·8
1·5	38·1	4·8	121·9	8·1	205·7	24·0	609·6	43·0	1092·2
1·6	40·6	4·9	124·5	8·2	208·3	25·0	635·0	44·0	1117·6
1·7	43·2	5·0	127·0	8·3	210·8	26·0	660·4	45·0	1143·0
1·8	45·7	5·1	129·5	8·4	213·4	27·0	685·8	46·0	1168·4
1·9	48·3	5·2	132·1	8·5	215·9	28·0	711·2	47·0	1193·8
2·0	50·8	5·3	134·6	8·6	218·4	29·0	736·6	48·0	1219·2
2·1	53·3	5·4	137·2	8·7	221·0	29·1	739·1	49·0	1244·6
2·2	55·9	5·5	139·7	8·8	223·5	29·2	741·7	50·0	1270·0
2·3	58·4	5·6	142·2	8·9	226·1	29·3	744·2	51·0	1295·4
2·4	61·0	5·7	144·8	9·0	228·6	29·4	746·8	52·0	1320·8
2·5	63·5	5·8	147·3	9·1	231·1	29·5	749·3	53·0	1346·2
2·6	66·0	5·9	149·9	9·2	233·7	29·6	751·8	54·0	1371·6
2·7	68·6	6·0	152·4	9·3	236·2	29·7	754·4	55·0	1397·0
2·8	71·1	6·1	154·9	9·4	238·8	29·8	756·9	56·0	1422·4
2·9	73·7	6·2	157·5	9·5	241·3	29·9	759·5	57·0	1447·8
3·0	76·2	6·3	160·0	9·6	243·8	30·0	762·0	58·0	1473·2
3·1	78·7	6·4	162·6	9·7	246·4	30·1	764·5	59·0	1498·6
3·2	81·3	6·5	165·1	9·8	248·9	30·2	767·1	60·0	1524·0

Fahr.	Cent.	Fahr.	Cent.	Fahr.	Cent.	Fahr.	Cent.	Fahr.	Cent.
−20·0	−28·9	+10·0	−12·2	+40·0	+ 4·4	+70·0	+21·1	+100·0	+37·8
19·5	28·6	10·5	11·9	40·5	4·7	70·5	21·4	100·5	38·1
19·0	28·3	11·0	11·7	41·0	5·0	71·0	21·7	101·0	38·3
18·5	28·1	11·5	11·4	41·5	5·3	71·5	21·9	101·5	38·6
18·0	27·8	12·0	11·1	42·0	5·6	72·0	22·2	102·0	38·9
17·5	27·5	12·5	10·8	42·5	5·8	72·5	22·5	102·5	39·2
17·0	27·2	13·0	10·6	43·0	6·1	73·0	22·8	103·0	39·4
16·5	26·9	13·5	10·3	43·5	6·4	73·5	23·1	103·5	39·7
16·0	26·7	14·0	10·0	44·0	6·7	74·0	23·3	104·0	40·0
15·5	26·4	14·5	9·7	44·5	6·9	74·5	23·6	104·5	40·3
15·0	26·1	15·0	9·4	45·0	7·2	75·0	23·9	105·0	40·6
14·5	25·8	15·5	9·2	45·5	7·5	75·5	24·2	105·5	40·8
14·0	25·6	16·0	8·9	46·0	7·8	76·0	24·4	106·0	41·1
13·5	25·3	16·5	8·6	46·5	8·1	76·5	24·7	106·5	41·4
13·0	25·0	17·0	8·3	47·0	8·3	77·0	25·0	107·0	41·7
12·5	24·7	17·5	8·1	47·5	8·6	77·5	25·3	107·5	41·9
12·0	24·4	18·0	7·8	48·0	8·9	78·0	25·6	108·0	42·2
11·5	24·2	18·5	7·5	48·5	9·2	78·5	25·8	108·5	42·5
11·0	23·9	19·0	7·2	49·0	9·4	79·0	26·1	109·0	42·8
10·5	23·6	19·5	6·9	49·5	9·7	79·5	26·4	109·5	43·1
10·0	23·3	20·0	6·7	50·0	10·0	80·0	26·7	110·0	43·3
9·5	23·1	20·5	6·4	50·5	10·3	80·5	26·9	110·5	43·6
9·0	22·8	21·0	6·1	51·0	10·6	81·0	27·2	111·0	43·9
8·5	22·5	21·5	5·8	51·5	10·8	81·5	27·5	111·5	44·2
8·0	22·2	22·0	5·6	52·0	11·1	82·0	27·8	112·0	44·4
7·5	21·9	22·5	5·3	52·5	11·4	82·5	28·1	112·5	44·7
7·0	21·7	23·0	5·0	53·0	11·7	83·0	28·3	113·0	45·0
6·5	21·4	23·5	4·7	53·5	11·9	83·5	28·6	113·5	45·3
6·0	21·1	24·0	4·4	54·0	12·2	84·0	28·9	114·0	45·6
5·5	20·8	24·5	4·2	54·5	12·5	84·5	29·2	114·5	45·8
5·0	20·6	25·0	3·9	55·0	12·8	85·0	29·4	115·0	46·1
4·5	20·3	25·5	3·6	55·5	13·1	85·5	29·7	115·5	46·4
4·0	20·0	26·0	3·3	56·0	13·3	86·0	30·0	116·0	46·7
3·5	19·7	26·5	3·1	56·5	13·6	86·5	30·3	116·5	46·9
3·0	19·4	27·0	2·8	57·0	13·9	87·0	30·6	117·0	47·2
2·5	19·2	27·5	2·5	57·5	14·2	87·5	30·8	117·5	47·5
2·0	18·9	28·0	2·2	58·0	14·4	88·0	31·1	118·0	47·8
1·5	18·6	28·5	1·9	58·5	14·7	88·5	31·4	118·5	48·1
1·0	18·3	29·0	1·7	59·0	15·0	89·0	31·7	119·0	48·3
− 0·5	18·1	29·5	1·4	59·5	15·3	89·5	31·9	119·5	48·6
0·0	17·8	30·0	1·1	60·0	15·6	90·0	32·2	120·0	48·9
+ 0·5	17·5	30·5	0·8	60·5	15·8	90·5	32·5	120·5	49·2
1·0	17·2	31·0	0·6	61·0	16·1	91·0	32·8	121·0	49·4
1·5	16·9	31·5	− 0·3	61·5	16·4	91·5	33·1	121·5	49·7
2·0	16·7	32·0	0·0	62·0	16·7	92·0	33·3	122·0	50·0
2·5	16·4	32·5	+ 0·3	62·5	16·9	92·5	33·6	122·5	50·3
3·0	16·1	33·0	0·6	63·0	17·2	93·0	33·9	123·0	50·6
3·5	15·8	33·5	0·8	63·5	17·5	93·5	34·2	123·5	50·8
4·0	15·6	34·0	1·1	64·0	17·8	94·0	34·4	124·0	51·1
4·5	15·3	34·5	1·4	64·5	18·1	94·5	34·7	124·5	51·4
5·0	15·0	35·0	1·7	65·0	18·3	95·0	35·0	125·0	51·7
5·5	14·7	35·5	1·9	65·5	18·6	95·5	35·3	125·5	51·9
6·0	14·4	36·0	2·2	66·0	18·9	96·0	35·6	126·0	52·2
6·5	14·2	36·5	2·5	66·5	19·2	96·5	35·8	126·5	52·5
7·0	13·9	37·0	2·8	67·0	19·4	97·0	36·1	127·0	52·8
7·5	13·6	37·5	3·1	67·5	19·7	97·5	36·4	127·5	53·1
8·0	13·3	38·0	3·3	68·0	20·0	98·0	36·7	128·0	53·3
8·5	13·1	38·5	3·6	68·5	20·3	98·5	36·9	128·5	53·6
9·0	12·8	39·0	3·9	69·0	20·6	99·0	37·2	129·0	53·9
9·5	12·5	39·5	4·2	69·5	20·8	99·5	37·5	129·5	54·2

BIBLIOGRAPHY

GENERAL

WOEIKOF, A. *Die Klimate der Erde.* Jena, 1887.

HANN, J. *Handbuch der Klimatologie.* Stuttgart, 1908.

(And many papers by same author in *Met. Zeit.*)

HETTNER, A. *Die Klimate der Erde. Geogr. Zeit.* XVII.

BUCHAN, A. 'Reports on Atmospheric Circulation', *Challenger Reports,* Edinburgh, 1889.

HANN, J. *Atlas der Meteorologie* (Berghaus.) Gotha, 1887.

BARTHOLOMEW. *Atlas of Meteorology.* Westminster, 1899.

HERBERTSON, A. J. *The Distribution of Rainfall over the Lands.*

Oxford Survey of the British Empire. Oxford, 1914. (Articles on climate by various authors.)

DE MARTONNE, E. *Traité de géographie physique,* i. Paris, 1925.

SHAW, N. *Manual of Meteorology,* vol. ii. Cambridge, 1936.

KÖPPEN, W., u. GEIGER, R. *Handbuch der Klimatologie.* Berlin, 1930–. (Contains comprehensive bibliographies.)

World Weather Records. Smithsonian Institution, Washington, 1929, 1934.

BROOKS, C. E. P. *Climate.* London, 1929.

MILLER. *Climatology.* London, 1931.

Deutsche Seewarte. *Atlantischer Ozean.* Hamburg, 1902.

—— *Stiller Ozean.* Hamburg, 1896.

—— *Indischer Ozean.* Hamburg, 1891.

SCHOTT, G. *Geographie des Atlantischen Ozeans.* Hamburg, 1926.

—— *Geographie des Indischen und Stillen Ozeans.* Hamburg, 1935.

AFRICA

KNOX, A. *The Climate of the Continent of Africa.* Cambridge, 1911.

SCHIRMER, H. *Le Sahara.* Paris, 1893.

LASSERRE. 'Aperçu météorologique' in *Les Territoires du sud de l'Algérie,* i. Alger, 1930.

BROOKS, C. E. P. 'Le Climat du Sahara et de l'Arabie', in Hachisuka, *Le Sahara.* Paris, 1932.

PERRET. 'Le Climat du Sahara.' *Ann. de Géogr.,* 1935.

BROOKS, C. E. P. 'Notes on the Climatology of the British Empire— Sierra Leone.' *Quart. Journ. Roy. Met. Soc.,* xlviii. London, 1922.

—— 'The Rainfall of Nigeria and the Gold Coast.' *Quart. Journ. Roy. Met. Soc.,* xlii. London, 1916.

(And many other papers by same author in same journal.)

CHANNEY. *The Climatology of the Gold Coast.* Accra, Dept. of Agriculture.

CHUDEAU, R. 'Le Climat de l'Afrique occidentale et équatoriale.' *Ann. de Géogr.,* 1910, pp. 429 et seq.

HUBERT, H. *Le Service météorologique de l'Afrique occidentale française en 1922.* Paris, 1923.

HUBERT, H. *Nouvelles Études sur la météorologie de l'Afrique occidentale française*. Paris, 1926.

LYONS, H. G. *Physiography of the Nile Basin*. Cairo, 1906.

CRAIG, J. J. *The Rains of the Nile Basin*. Cairo, 1913.

Climatological Normals for Egypt and the Sudan, Candia, Cyprus and Abyssinia. Physical Dept., Cairo, 1922.

Atlas of Egypt. Survey Dept., Cairo, 1928.

HURST, H. E., and PHILLIPS, P. *The Nile Basin*, vol. i. Govt. Press, Cairo, 1931.

British East African Meteor. Service. (Monthly and annual publications.)

Official Yearbook of the Union of South Africa. Pretoria, annual.

ASIA

BLANFORD, H. F. *The Climates and Weather of India, Ceylon, and Burma*. London, 1889.

ELIOT, J. *Handbook of Cyclonic Storms in the Bay of Bengal*, Calcutta 1900.
—— *Climatological Atlas of India*. Bartholomew, 1906.

Imperial Gazetteer of India ('Meteorology', Chap. III, vol. i). Oxford, 1909.

NEWNHAM, E. V. *Hurricanes and Tropical Revolving Storms*. Stationery Office, London, 1922.

SIMPSON, G. C. 'The South-West Monsoon.' *Quart. Journ. Roy. Met. Soc.*, July 1921.

VERYARD and ROY. *Meteorological Conditions Affecting Aviation over the North-West Frontier*. India Met. Dept., 1934.

Indian Meteorological Dept.—Memoirs, various.

GAUTHIER, H. *La Température en Chine*. Shanghai, 1918.

GHERZI, E. *Étude sur la pluie en Chine*. Shanghai, 1928.

KENDREW, W. G. 'Climate of China', in *China*, Buxton. Oxford, 1929.

Climatological Atlas of Japan.

OKADA. *The Climate of Japan*.

SANDERS, E. M. 'The Climate of Japan and Formosa.' *Monthly Weather Review*, 1920.

BRAAK, C. *The Climate of the Netherland Indies*. K. Mag. Met. Observ., Batavia, 1921–9.

CORONAS, J. *The Climate and Weather of the Philippines*. Weather Bureau, Manila, 1920.

EXNER, F. M. *Zum Klima von Palästina*. Leipzig, 1910.

Climate and Weather of Iraq. Weather Bureau, Baghdad, 1919.

WEICKMANN, L. *Zum Klima der Türkei*. München, 1922.

ELLSWORTH HUNTINGTON. *The Pulse of Asia*. London, 1907.

WOEIKOF, A. 'Le Climat de la Sibérie orientale.' *Ann. de Géogr.* Paris, 1897–8.
—— Article on the Climate of Russia in Kirchhoff, *Länderkunde von Europa*, III. Teil. Vienna, 1907.

Atlas de Finlande. 1910.

Klima der Union der Sozial. Sowjet-Republiken. Geophysikalisches Zentral-Observatorium, with Atlases. Leningrad, 1926–.

EUROPE

HELLMANN, G. *Untersuchungen über die jährliche Periode der Niederschläge in Europa.* Preussische Akad. der Wissensch. 1924.

GLASSPOOL, J. 'The Distribution of Average Seasonal Rainfall over Europe.' *Quart. Journ. Roy. Met. Soc.*, London, 1929.

Atlas de Climat de Norwège. Graarud and Irgens. Oslo, 1922.

The Book of Normals of Meteorological Elements for the British Isles. Stationery Office, London, 1919.

Rainfall Atlas of the British Isles. Royal Meteorological Society, London, 1926.

ANGOT, A. 'Études sur le climat de la France.' *Ann. du Bur. central météor.*, 1897, 1900, 1902, 1903.

—— 'Régime des pluies de l'Europe occidentale.' *Ann. du Bur. central météor.*, 1895.

Klima Atlas von Deutschland. Kön. Preussisch. Met. Inst., Berlin, 1921.

WALLÉN, A. *Climate of Sweden.* Stockholm, 1930.

Klimatographie von Oesterreich. Zentralanstalt für Meteor. u. Geodyn., Wien, 1919.

MAURER, BILLWILLER, and HESS. *Das Klima der Schweiz.* Frauenfeld, 1909.

PHILIPPSON, A. *Das Mittelmeergebiet.* Leipzig, 1922.

FISCHER, T. 'Studien über das Klima der Mittelmeerländer.' *Petermann's Mitteilungen*, Ergänzungsheft No. 58. Gotha, 1879.

Monthly Meteorological Charts of the Mediterranean Sea. Stationery Office, London, 1919.

Notes on the Climates of the Eastern Mediterranean and Adjacent Countries. Stationery Office, London, 1916.

MARIOLOPOULOS, E. G. *Étude sur le climat de la Grèce.* Paris, 1925.

—— and LIVATHENOS. *Atlas climatique de la Grèce.* Athens, 1935.

ANGOT, A. 'Régime des pluies de la Péninsule Ibérique', *Ann. du. Bur. central météor.* Paris, 1893.

EREDIA, F. 'Il temperatura in Italia.' *Ann. Uff. centr. meteor.* Rome, 1909.

—— *Le Precipitazioni atmospheriche in Italia, 1880–1905.* Rome, 1908.

NORTH AMERICA

CONNOR, A. J. *The Temperature and Precipitation of Alberta, Saskatchewan and Manitoba.* Ottawa, 1915.

—— *The Temperature and Precipitation of British Columbia.* Ottawa, 1920.

DENISON, F. N. 'The Climate of British Columbia.' *Monthly Weather Review*, 1925.

KOEPPE, C. E. *The Canadian Climate.* Bloomington, Ill., 1931.

The Geography and Geology of Alaska. Section on Climate by Cleveland Abbe. Washington, 1906.

WARD, R. DE C. *The Climates of the United States.* New York, 1925.

Summary of the Climatological Data for the United States, by various authors. U.S. Dept. of Agriculture, Weather Bureau, 1926.

Bulletins (various) on the Climates of the United States, U.S. Dept. of Agriculture, Weather Bureau.

Atlas of American Agriculture. U.S. Dept. of Agriculture. Washington, 1928.

SOUTH AND CENTRAL AMERICA, THE WEST INDIES

Voss, E. L. 'Die Niederschlagsverhältnisse von Südamerika.' *Petermann's Mitteilungen*, Ergänzungsheft No. 157. Gotha, 1907.

Mossman, R. C. 'The Climate of Chile.' *Journ. of the Scot. Met. Soc.*, 1911.

Jefferson, M. 'The Rainfall of Chile.' *American Geogr. Soc. Research Series*, No. 7.

Davis, W. G. *Climate of the Argentine Republic*. Buenos Aires, 1910.

Carvalho, C. de. *Météorologie du Brésil*. London, 1917.

Morize, H. *Contribuição ao Estudo do Clima do Brasil*. Rio de Janeiro, 1922.

Reed, W. W. 'Climatological Data for Central America.' *Monthly Weather Review, 51*. 1923.

Hall, M. *The Rainfall of Jamaica*. Kingston, 1923.

AUSTRALIA AND NEW ZEALAND

Hunt, Quayle, and Taylor. *The Climate and Weather of Australia*. Melbourne, 1913.

Griffith Taylor. *Australian Meteorology*. Oxford, 1920.

The New Zealand Year Book. Wellington, annual.

ANTARCTICA

National Antarctic Expedition, 1901–4; *Meteorology*. London, 1908.

Simpson, G. C. *British Antarctic Expedition: Meteorology*. Calcutta, 1919.

INDEX

H h

PRINTED IN
GREAT BRITAIN
AT THE
UNIVERSITY PRESS
OXFORD
BY
JOHN JOHNSON
PRINTER
TO THE
UNIVERSITY